D0305794

THE AUTHOR

Wilfred Kaplan received the A.B., A.M., and Ph.D. degrees from Harvard University, where he was also a Rogers traveling fellow during 1936 and 1937. His previous academic positions include that of teaching fellow, Rice Institute, instructor at the College of William and Mary, and research associate at Brown University. Since 1940 he has been at the University of Michigan, and is now Professor of Mathematics.

During World War II, Dr. Kaplan was with the Office of Scientific Research and Development, and did consulting and research work for the U.S. Army and Navy. While holder of a Guggenheim Foundation Fellowship (1949–50), Professor Kaplan studied at the Federal Institute of Technology in Switzerland. During 1953–54 he was recipient of a grant for research on complex variables from the National Science Foundation. He is a member of the American Physical Society, the American Mathematical Society and the Mathematical Association of America, the Swiss Mathematical Society, and the Société Mathematique de France. His special fields of interest are nonlinear differential equations, dynamics, Riemann surfaces, and statistical mechanics.

Elements of ORDINARY DIFFERENTIAL EQUATIONS

This book is in the

ADDISON-WESLEY SERIES IN MATHEMATICS

Elements of ORDINARY DIFFERENTIAL EQUATIONS

by

WILFRED KAPLAN
Department of Mathematics
University of Michigan

ADDISON-WESLEY PUBLISHING COMPANY, INC.
READING, MASSACHUSETTS · PALO ALTO · LONDON

Printed in the United States of America

Library of Congress Catalog Card No. 64-20098

Since the discovery of the calculus, the problem of integration of differential equations has been of major interest for mathematicians. For almost all problems of applied mathematics, and many of pure mathematics, lead to differential equations satisfied by a function to be determined. But the history of mathematics has shown that the formulation of the problem of solution of a differential equation had to go through a long series of stages of development, until it became fully clear to what extent a function was known when one had set up a differential equation which the function was known to satisfy.

LUDWIG SCHLESINGER

PREFACE

This book is intended to serve as a text for a first course on differential equations. It provides more than enough material for a one-semester course.

The book is a much shortened version of the author's *Ordinary Differential Equations* (525 pp., Addison-Wesley Publishing Company 1958). The principal differences are as follows: the section on matrices and the chapters on exact differential equations of higher order, phase plane analysis, and fundamental theory (proofs of existence theorems) are omitted; the treatment of linear equations from the point of view of the systems designer (input-output analysis) is considerably abbreviated; the material is regrouped in 10 short chapters.

With all these changes, the present volume still retains the principal aspects of the longer work: the emphasis on gaining insight and understanding as opposed to pure manipulative skill; the use of physical examples both as illustrations of the mathematical methods and as aids to understanding these methods.

SUMMARY. Chapter 1 presents the important concepts and the main problems. By a study of simple numerical methods, an understanding of the existence theorem is gained. Chapter 2, devoted to equations of first order and first degree, gives some special procedures for solving problems in explicit form but also emphasizes understanding the processes. Chapter 3 gives a number of applications of first order equations; for the linear equations, some discussion of the systems point of view is given. Chapter 4 considers linear equations of arbitrary order, presents the main theorems, and methods for equations with constant coefficients; additional methods, based on differential operators and Laplace transforms, are given in Chapter 5. Chapter 6 treats applications of linear equations, including such topics as stability, transients, response to sinusoidal forcing functions, with illustrations in mechanics and circuit theory. Chapter 7 is devoted to simultaneous linear equations, with emphasis on the method of exponential substitution; operational methods are also introduced; applications are treated briefly. Chapter 8 discusses equations not of first degree and introduces the concept of singular solution. Chapter 9 covers power series solutions, and includes solution of linear equations at regular singular points. The final chapter is a brief treatment of numerical methods.

The mathematical exposition is rigorous throughout. However, the more difficult proofs are omitted, with references given in each case. In particular, frequent reference is made to the author's *Ordinary Differential Equations*, abbreviated as ODE.

Suggested course schedule. The following is a sample outline for a one-semester course meeting three hours a week: 1–1 to 1–3; 1–4; 1–5 to 1–6; 1–7 to 1–10; 2–1 to 2–2; 2–3 to 2–4; 2–5 to 2–6; 2–7 to 2–8; 2–9; 3–1; 3–2; 3–3; 3–4; 4–1 to 4–3; 4–4 to 4–5; *4–6 to *4–7; 4–8; 4–9; 5–1 to 5–2; 5–3; 5–4; *5–5; 6–1 to 6–3; 6–4; *6–5; 6–6; 6–7; 6–9; 7–1; 7–2 to 7–3; 7–5 to 7–6; *7–7, *7–8 and *7–9; 8–1; 8–2 to 8–3; 8–4 to 8–5; 9–1; 9–2; 9–3; *9–4; *9–5; 10–1 to 10–4; 10–5 to 10–8. The starred sections can be omitted.

A similar course has been offered at the University of Michigan. To enhance the course a film has been prepared entitled "The Analogue Computer and its Application to Ordinary Differential Equations." This can be obtained for a nominal rental or purchased from the Audio-Visual Education Center of the University of Michigan.

March 1964
Ann Arbor, Michigan W. K.

CONTENTS

CHAPTER 1

BASIC IDEAS

1–1 Significance of differential equations. By an *ordinary differential equation* is meant a relation between x, an unspecified function y of x, and certain of the derivatives y', y'', ..., $y^{(n)}$ of y with respect to x. For example,

$$y' = 1 + y, \tag{1–1}$$

$$y'' + 9y = 8 \sin x, \tag{1–2}$$

$$y'^2 - 2y' + y - 3x = 0 \tag{1–3}$$

are ordinary differential equations.

In the calculus we learn how to find the successive derivatives of a given function y of x. For example, if $y = e^x - 1$, then

$$y' = e^x = y + 1; \tag{1–4}$$

thus for this function the relation (1–1) is satisfied. We say that $y = e^x - 1$ is a *solution* of Eq. (1–1). However, this is not the only solution, for $y = 2e^x - 1$ also satisfies Eq. (1–1):

$$y' = 2e^x = y + 1.$$

One fundamental problem to be studied is that of *determining all solutions of a given differential equation.* This problem can be considered as a generalization of that of solving an equation such as

$$x^2 - x + 2 = 0 \tag{1–5}$$

in algebra. The solutions of Eq. (1–5) are *numbers;* the solutions of a differential equation are *functions.*

There is a second problem, more fundamental than the first. It will be seen that for many differential equations it is very difficult to obtain explicit formulas for all the solutions. However, a general "existence theorem" guarantees that there are solutions; in fact, infinitely many. The problem is *to determine properties of the solutions,* or of some of the solutions, from the differential equation itself. It will be seen that many properties can be found *without explicit formulas for the solutions;* we can, in fact, obtain numerical values for solutions to any accuracy desired. Accordingly, we are led to regard a differential equation itself as a sort of explicit formula describing a certain collection of functions. For example, we can show that all solutions of Eq. (1–2) are given by

$$y = \sin x + c_1 \cos 3x + c_2 \sin 3x, \tag{1–6}$$

where c_1 and c_2 are "arbitrary constants." Equation (1–2) itself, $y'' + 9y = 8 \sin x$, is another way of describing all these functions.

The fact that a single differential equation can describe many functions makes it a remarkably concise form of expression. It is not surprising, therefore, that most laws of physics have been stated in the form of differential equations. An outstanding example is Newton's second law:

$$\text{Force} = \text{mass} \times \text{acceleration}.$$

For a particle of mass m moving on a line, this equation corresponds to the differential equation

$$m \frac{d^2x}{dt^2} = F\left(t, x, \frac{dx}{dt}\right) \tag{1–7}$$

describing the position x at time t in terms of the force F, which may depend on time t, position x, and velocity dx/dt.

Throughout this book we shall be concerned with both of the problems referred to above. We shall try to obtain explicit expressions for the solutions where feasible; it will be found that the expressions may take a variety of forms, including infinite series. We shall also try to deduce properties of the solutions, such as numerical values, graphs, asymptotes, etc., directly from the differential equations. Experience has shown that, except for a few special types of equations, the problems are difficult. It is fortunate indeed that among the special types are the *linear equations*, for which most questions can be answered satisfactorily, and that these equations are sufficient for the majority of applications in the sciences. Linear equations will receive a large share of attention in this book.

1–2 Basic definitions. An *ordinary differential equation* of *order* n is an equation of form

$$F(x, y, y', \ldots, y^{(n)}) = 0, \tag{1–8}$$

which expresses a relation between x, an unspecified function $y(x)$, and its derivatives through the nth order. Thus

$$xy'' + 2y' + 3y - 6e^x = 0, \tag{1–9}$$

$$(y''')^2 - 2y'y''' + (y'')^3 = 0 \tag{1–10}$$

are ordinary differential equations of orders 2 and 3, respectively.

Equation (1–10) is a quadratic equation in the highest derivative y'''; we say that the equation is of *degree* 2, whereas Eq. (1–9) is of degree 1. In general, if a differential equation has the form of an algebraic equation of degree k in the highest derivative, then we say that the differential equation is of *degree* k. Most equations to be studied in this book are of *first degree* and are expressible in the form

$$y^{(n)} = G(x, y, \ldots, y^{(n-1)}). \tag{1–11}$$

An ordinary differential equation is said to be *linear* if it has the form

$$a_0(x)y^{(n)} + a_1(x)y^{(n-1)} + \cdots + a_{n-1}(x)y' + a_n(x)y = Q(x). \tag{1–12}$$

Thus the equation is linear in y and its derivatives. An example is provided by Eq. (1–9) above, in which

$$a_0(x) \equiv x, \qquad a_1(x) \equiv 2, \qquad a_2(x) \equiv 3, \qquad Q(x) \equiv 6e^x. \tag{1–13}$$

A linear differential equation is always of first degree, but not conversely; thus

$$y' = 1 + xy^2 \tag{1–14}$$

is of first degree but is nonlinear.

The word "ordinary" is used to emphasize that no partial derivatives appear, since there is just one independent variable. An equation such as

$$\frac{\partial^2 z}{\partial x^2} + \frac{\partial^2 z}{\partial y^2} = 0 \tag{1–15}$$

is called a *partial differential equation.* Throughout this book, with very few exceptions, only ordinary differential equations are considered and, this being understood, the word "ordinary" will generally be omitted.

1–3 Solutions. By a *solution* (or *particular solution*) of a differential equation

$$F(x, y, y', \ldots, y^{(n)}) = 0 \tag{1–16}$$

is meant a function $y = f(x)$, defined in some interval $a < x < b$ (perhaps infinite), having derivatives up to the nth order throughout the interval, and such that Eq. (1–16) becomes an identity when y and its derivatives are replaced by $f(x)$ and its derivatives. For example, $y = e^{2x}$ is a solution of the equation

$$y'' - 4y = 0, \tag{1–17}$$

since $y'' = 4e^{2x}$, so that

$$y'' - 4y = 4e^{2x} - 4e^{2x} \equiv 0.$$

For many of the differential equations to be considered, it will be found that all solutions can be included in one formula:

$$y = f(x, c_1, \ldots, c_n), \tag{1–18}$$

where $c_1, \ldots, c_n$ are arbitrary constants. Thus for each special assignment of values to the c's, (1–18) gives a solution of Eq. (1–16) and all solutions can be so obtained. (The range of the c's and of x may have to be restricted in some cases to avoid imaginary expressions or other degeneracies.) For example, all solutions of Eq. (1–17) are given by

$$y = c_1e^{2x} + c_2e^{-2x}; \tag{1–19}$$

the solution $y = e^{2x}$ is obtained when $c_1 = 1$, $c_2 = 0$. When a function (1–18) is obtained, providing *all* solutions, it is called the *general solution.* In general, the number of arbitrary constants will equal the order n, as will be explained in Section 1–7.

The definitions can be illustrated by the simplest type of differential equation of first order:

$$y' = F(x), \tag{1–20}$$

where $F(x)$ is defined and continuous for $a < x < b$. All solutions of Eq. (1–20) are obtained by integrating:

$$y = \int F(x)\,dx + C, \qquad a < x < b. \tag{1–21}$$

Here the arbitrary constant appears as the familiar one associated with the indefinite integral. This can be generalized to equations of higher order, as the following example shows:

$$y'' = 20x^3. \tag{1–22}$$

Since y'' is the derivative of y', we find by integrating twice in succession that

$$y' = 5x^4 + c_1, \qquad y = x^5 + c_1x + c_2. \tag{1–23}$$

Note that there are *two* arbitrary constants, c_1, c_2, and that Eq. (1–22) has order *two*.

PROBLEMS

1. For each of the following differential equations state the order and degree and whether or not the equation is linear:

(a) $y' = x^2 - y$, (b) $y'' - (y')^2 + xy = 0$,
(c) $(y')^2 + xy' - y^2 = 0$, (d) $x^3y'' - xy' + 5y = 2x$,
(e) $y^{(\text{vi})} - y'' = 0$, (f) $\sin(y'') + e^{y'} = 1$.

2. Find the general solution of each of the following differential equations:

(a) $y' = e^{2x} - x$, (b) $y'' = 0$,
(c) $y''' = x$, (d) $y^{(n)} = 0$,
(e) $y^{(n)} = 1$, (f) $y' = 1/x$.

3. Verify that the following are solutions of the differential equations given:

(a) $y = \sin x$, for $y'' + y = 0$;
(b) $y = e^{2x}$, for $y''' - 4y' = 0$;
(c) $y = c_1 \cos x + c_2 \sin x$ (c_1 and c_2 any constants), for $y'' + y = 0$;
(d) $y = c_1e^{2x} + c_2e^{-2x}$, for $y'' - 4y = 0$.

4. Given the differential equation $y' = 2x$,

(a) show that $y = x^2 + c$ is the general solution;
(b) choose c so that the solution passes through the point (1, 4);
(c) choose c so that the solution is tangent to the line $y = 2x + 3$;
(d) choose c so that the solution satisfies the condition $\int_0^1 y\,dx = 2$.

5. Given the differential equation $y'' = x^2 - 1$,

(a) find the general solution;
(b) find a solution $y(x)$ such that $y(0) = 1$, $y'(0) = 2$;
(c) find a solution passing through the points (1, 2) and (3, 5);
(d) find a solution $y(x)$ such that $y(1) = 2$, and $y'(2) = 1$.

6. Find the general solution of the following equations:

(a) $xy' + y = \sin x$ [*Hint:* $xy' + y = (d/dx)(xy)$],
(b) $x^2y' + 2xy = e^x$,
(c) $2xyy' + y^2 = 3x^2$,
(d) $x^2y'' + 4xy' + 2y = e^x$.

ANSWERS

1. Orders: (a) 1, (b) 2, (c) 1, (d) 2, (e) 6, (f) 2; degrees: (a) 1, (b) 1, (c) 2, (d) 1, (e) 1, (f) undefined; (a), (d), (e) are linear.

2. (a) $\frac{1}{2}(e^{2x} - x^2) + c$, (b) $c_1x + c_2$, (c) $\frac{1}{24}x^4 + c_1x^2 + c_2x + c_3$, (d) $c_1x^{n-1} + c_2x^{n-2} + \cdots + c_{n-1}x + c_n$, (e) $(x^n/n!) + c_1x^{n-1} + \cdots + c_n$, (f) $\log|x| + c$ $(x \neq 0)$.

4. (b) $c = 3$, (c) $c = 4$, (d) $c = \frac{5}{3}$.

5. (a) $y = \frac{1}{12}(x^4 - 6x^2 + 12c_1x + 12c_2)$, (b) $y = \frac{1}{12}(x^4 - 6x^2 + 24x + 12)$, (c) $y = \frac{1}{12}(x^4 - 6x^2 + 2x + 27)$, (d) $y = \frac{1}{12}(x^4 - 6x^2 + 4x + 25)$.

6. (a) $y = (c - \cos x)/x$, $x \neq 0$; (b) $y = (e^x + c)x^{-2}$, $x \neq 0$; (c) $y = \pm[(x^3 + c)/x]^{1/2}$, $x \neq 0$; (d) $y = (e^x + c_1x + c_2)x^{-2}$, $x \neq 0$.

1–4 Geometric interpretation of the first order differential equation. Graphical solution. An equation of first order and first degree can be written in the form

$$y' = F(x, y). \tag{1–24}$$

The solutions sought are functions of form $y = f(x)$. Equation (1–24) prescribes the slope of the *tangent* to the solution at each point (x, y). Accordingly, it is possible to construct the tangent to a solution $y = f(x)$ through a specified point, even though the function itself is not known.

We can systematically plot many short tangent line segments through scattered points in the xy-plane, and thereby obtain a "field of line elements." This is shown in Fig. 1–1 for the differential equation

$$y' = -\frac{x}{y}. \tag{1–25}$$

For example, at (1, 1) the slope is -1; we draw a short line segment of slope -1 and midpoint (1, 1). At (3, 2) the slope is $-3/2$ and we draw

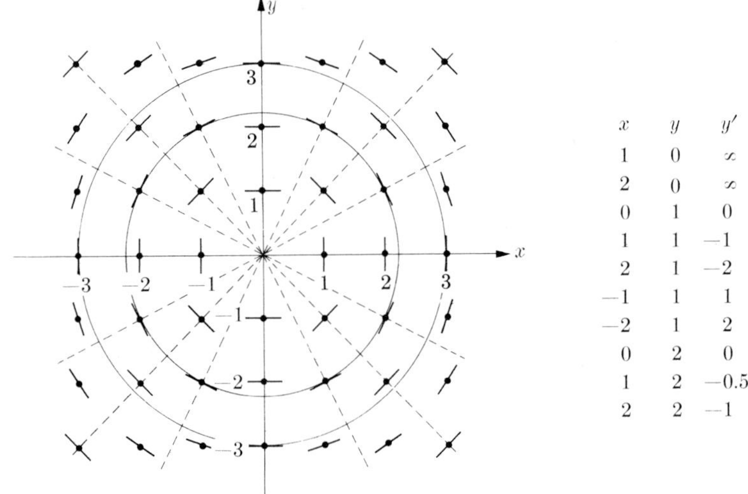

x	y	y'
1	0	∞
2	0	∞
0	1	0
1	1	−1
2	1	−2
−1	1	1
−2	1	2
0	2	0
1	2	−0.5
2	2	−1

FIG. 1–1. Line elements for the equation $y' = -x/y$.

the corresponding segment. The numerical work can be summarized in tabular form, as shown in Fig. 1–1.

If many judiciously spaced line elements are drawn, the figure begins to suggest a family of curves whose tangents are the line elements; in Fig. 1–1 the curves suggested are the circles

$$x^2 + y^2 = c^2, \tag{1–26}$$

for different values of the constant c. For each circle (1–26) the slope of the tangent at the point (x, y) is precisely $-(x/y)$; that is, each circle in (1–26) represents a solution of Eq. (1–25). It is plausible that these are the only solutions; a proof is easily given (Prob. 3 below).

The principles just discussed and illustrated suggest some basic conclusions about the general equation (1–24): *the solutions of Eq.* (1–24) *form a family of curves in the xy-plane; through each point* (x, y) *there is precisely one solution curve.* These conclusions can be fully justified, provided reasonable assumptions are made about the continuity of $F(x, y)$. (A full discussion is given in Section 1–7.) That some condition on $F(x, y)$ is needed is suggested by the example (1–25), for which $F(x, y)$ is discontinuous when $y = 0$. Actually, this causes no serious trouble for $x \neq 0$, since the slope is infinite; however, at $(0, 0)$ there is no solution in any sense.

We can apply the graphical procedure of the above example to any given first order equation. We simply plot line elements until the solutions begin to take shape; at the proper stage, the drawing of smooth curves with the line elements as tangents completes the analysis.

The above procedure is open to several criticisms. It gives us solution curves but no formulas. The curves, being graphically obtained, are only approximations to the solutions and we know nothing of their accuracy. The method is also time-consuming. In answer to these criticisms it should be noted that in many cases no explicit formulas (in terms of elementary functions) are available for the solutions. As remarked in Section 1–1, the differential equation itself can be considered as a sort of formula describing the solutions, and there may be no other simple way of describing them. Solutions by the graphical method can be obtained to any desired accuracy, as will be shown in the following section.

The speed with which solutions are obtained depends considerably on the skill of the investigator. It is possible to significantly accelerate the process by means of curves called *isoclines.* These are the loci along which the slope prescribed has a constant value m; that is, for Eq. (1–24) they are the curves

$$F(x, y) = m, \tag{1–27}$$

for different choices of the constant m. Once the curves (1–27) have been sketched, it is usually a simple matter to draw, for each m, a series of parallel line segments of slope m, all having their midpoints on the curve $F(x, y) = m$. For Eq. (1–25) the isoclines are the curves

$$-\frac{x}{y} = m; \tag{1–28}$$

they are straight lines through (0, 0) with slope $-1/m$. Thus, in this case, the line elements are perpendicular to the isoclines; the isoclines are shown as broken lines in Fig. 1–1.

It is to be stressed that *the isoclines are not the solutions sought,* although it will occasionally happen that an isocline is a solution curve; in such a case, the isocline must be a straight line of slope m.

EXAMPLES. For the differential equation

$$y' = 1 - \frac{1}{x + y}, \tag{1–29}$$

the isoclines are the lines

$$x + y = \frac{1}{1 - m},$$

as shown in Fig. 1–2. The values of m are indicated on the corresponding lines.

For the differential equations

$$y' = \cos x - y, \tag{1–30}$$

$$y' = x^2 + y^2, \tag{1–31}$$

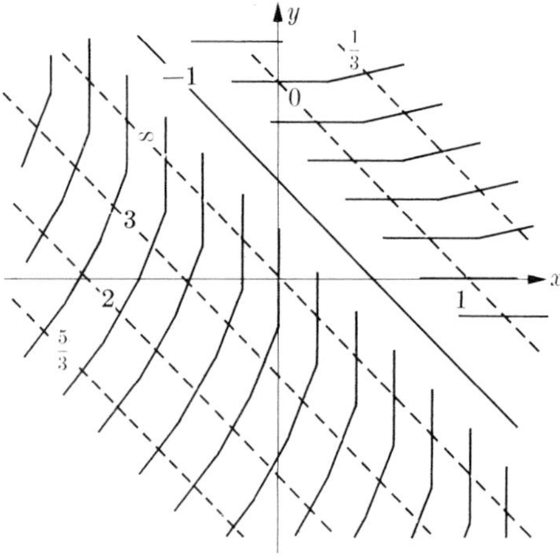

FIG. 1–2. Isoclines for the equation $y' = 1 - 1/(x + y)$.

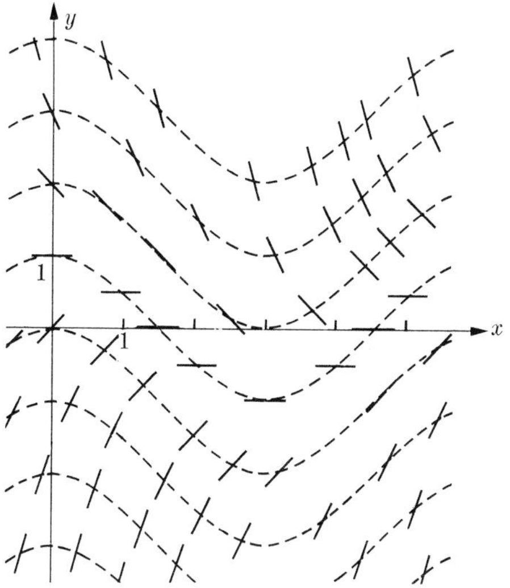

FIG. 1–3. $y' = \cos x - y$.

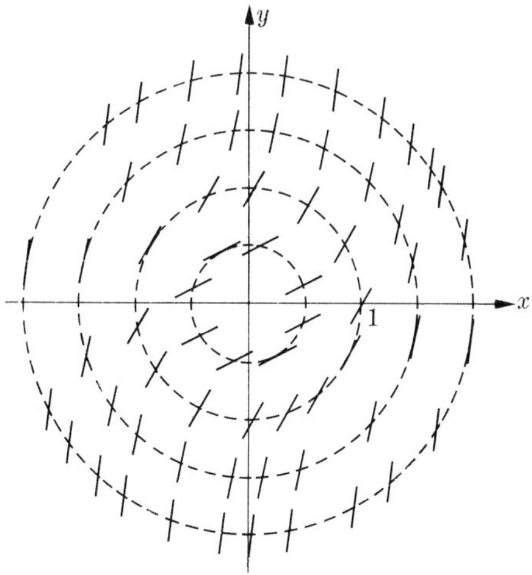

FIG. 1–4. $y' = x^2 + y^2$.

$$y' = \frac{x + y}{x - y}, \tag{1-32}$$

$$y' = \frac{(1 - x^2)y - x}{y}, \tag{1-33}$$

the solutions and isoclines are shown in Figs. 1–3, 1–4, 1–5, and 1–6. The

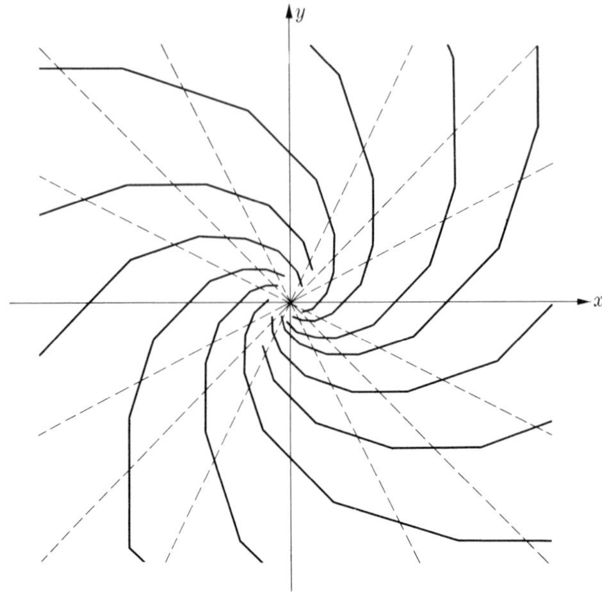

FIG. 1–5. $y' = (x + y)/(x - y)$.

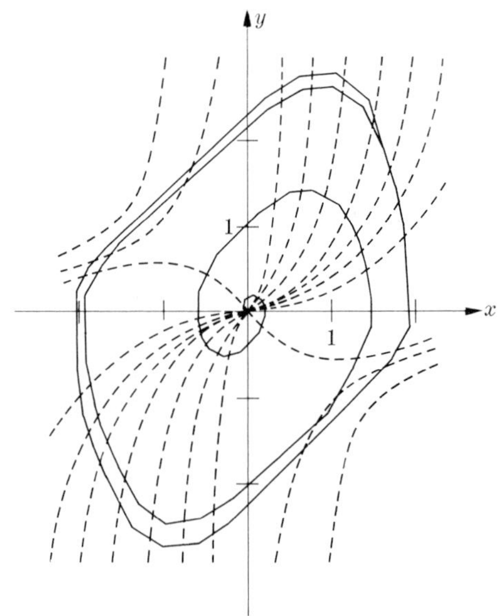

FIG. 1–6. $y' = [(1 - x^2)y - x]/y$.

verification of the graphs is left as an exercise (Prob. 4 below). The figures illustrate the great variety of configurations which can arise.

Equations of higher degree. An equation of first order and *second* degree has the form

$$Py'^2 + Qy' + R = 0, \tag{1-34}$$

where P, Q, and R depend on x and y. We can solve Eq. (1-34) for y' by the quadratic formula

$$y' = \frac{-Q \pm \sqrt{Q^2 - 4PR}}{2P}. \tag{1-35}$$

Thus Eq. (1-34) is really equivalent to *two* first degree equations:

$$\begin{aligned} y' &= \frac{-Q + \sqrt{Q^2 - 4PR}}{2P} = F_1(x, y), \\ y' &= \frac{-Q - \sqrt{Q^2 - 4PR}}{2P} = F_2(x, y), \end{aligned} \tag{1-36}$$

both of which can be solved graphically. The solutions form two families of curves which are, in general, unrelated, although they may fit together smoothly along a borderline curve. If the two families are analyzed on the same graph, we will find two line elements through each point at which $Q^2 - 4PR > 0$, one where $Q^2 - 4PR = 0$, and none where $Q^2 - 4PR < 0$. The locus $Q^2 - 4PR = 0$ may happen to contain a solution curve, which then serves as a borderline curve.

Example. For the differential equation

$$y'^2 + xy' - y = 0, \tag{1-37}$$

we find

$$y' = \frac{-x \pm \sqrt{x^2 + 4y}}{2}.$$

Hence $Q^2 - 4PR = x^2 + 4y$ and we have

$$\begin{aligned} &\text{for } x^2 + 4y > 0, \quad \text{2 elements;} \\ &\text{for } x^2 + 4y = 0, \quad \text{1 element;} \\ &\text{for } x^2 + 4y < 0, \quad \text{no element.} \end{aligned}$$

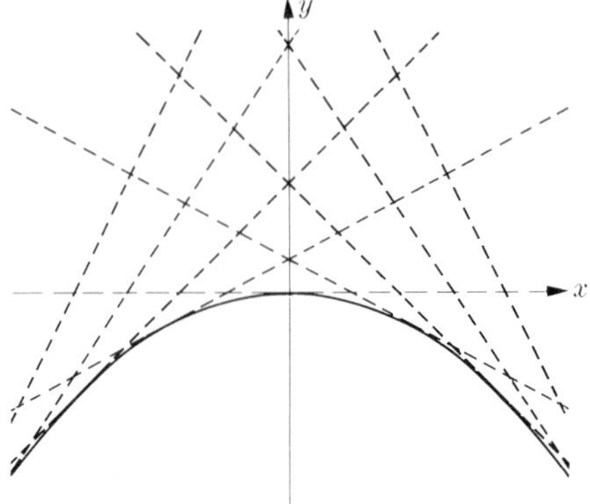

FIG. 1–7. $y'^2 + xy' - y = 0$.

The locus $x^2 + 4y = 0$ serves as a borderline curve common to the two families, for it is a solution curve (Prob. 5 below). The graphical analysis is shown in Fig. 1–7.

PROBLEMS

1. Plot line elements for each of the following differential equations and then plot the exact solution curves:

(a) $y' = 2x$, (b) $y' = 1/x$,
(c) $y' = \cos x$, (d) $y' = e^x$.

2. Obtain solutions graphically, with the aid of isoclines, for each of the following differential equations and compare the results with the general solutions given:

(a) $y' = 2y$, general solution $y = ce^{2x}$;
(b) $y' = x + y$, general solution $y = ce^x - x - 1$;
(c) $y' = -y/x$, general solution $xy = c$.

3. Write Eq. (1–25) in the form $(d/dx)(y^2) = -2x$, to show that all solutions are given by (1–26). [For each c, Eq. (1–26) defines two functions, $y = \pm\sqrt{c^2 - x^2}$, $-c < x < c$, each of which is a solution.]

4. Obtain graphical solutions for the following, with the aid of isoclines, and compare with the corresponding figures in the text:

(a) Eq. (1–30), Fig. 1–3, (b) Eq. (1–31), Fig. 1–4,
(c) Eq. (1–32), Fig. 1–5, (d) Eq. (1–33), Fig. 1–6.

5. (a) Obtain solutions of Eq. (1–37) graphically and compare with Fig. 1–7.
(b) Show that $y = -\frac{1}{4}x^2$ is a solution of Eq. (1–37).

6. For a particle moving on the x-axis with velocity $v = dx/dt$, the acceleration is

$$\frac{d^2x}{dt^2} = \frac{dv}{dt} = \frac{dv}{dx}\frac{dx}{dt} = v\frac{dv}{dx}.$$

Hence if the particle is subject to a force F which depends only on x and v, Newton's law, Eq. (1–7), gives

$$mv\frac{dv}{dx} = F(x, v).$$

This is a *first* order equation relating x and v. Its solutions can be studied graphically in the xv-plane, often called the *phase plane* (see Chapter 11 of ODE*). Reduce the following equations to the x, v form and analyze the solutions graphically in the xv-plane:

(a) $d^2x/dt^2 = 32$ (falling body),
(b) $d^2x/dt^2 = -x$ (undamped oscillations of a spring),
(c) $d^2x/dt^2 = -x - v$ (damped oscillations of a spring).

7. Show that the van der Pol equation

$$\frac{d^2x}{dt^2} + (x^2 - 1)\frac{dx}{dt} + x = 0,$$

in x, v form (Prob. 6), is the same as Eq. (1–33) (Fig. 1–6), with y replaced by v. This differential equation occurs in the theory of electric circuits which contain vacuum tubes. The solution by isoclines still remains one of the best methods for obtaining the solutions, for which no simple explicit formulas are known. [See Section 11–14 of ODE and pp. 250–252 of Reference 1 at the end of this chapter.]

ANSWERS

6. (a) $v(dv/dx) = 32$, curves are parabolas $v^2 = 64x + c$; (b) $v(dv/dx) = -x$, curves are circles $x^2 + v^2 = c$; (c) $v(dv/dx) = -x - v$, curves are spirals winding about (0, 0).

1–5 Method of step-by-step integration.

Given the first order differential equation

$$y' = F(x, y), \tag{1–38}$$

we may require one particular solution through a given point (x_0, y_0), rather than the family of all solutions, as in the preceding section. Finding this solution is the *initial value problem*. (The term "initial value" arose in mechanics, where it referred to specification of the values of positions and velocities at an initial time t_0.)

---

* ODE is an abbreviation for the author's text, *Ordinary Differential Equations* (Reading, Mass.: Addison-Wesley, 1958).

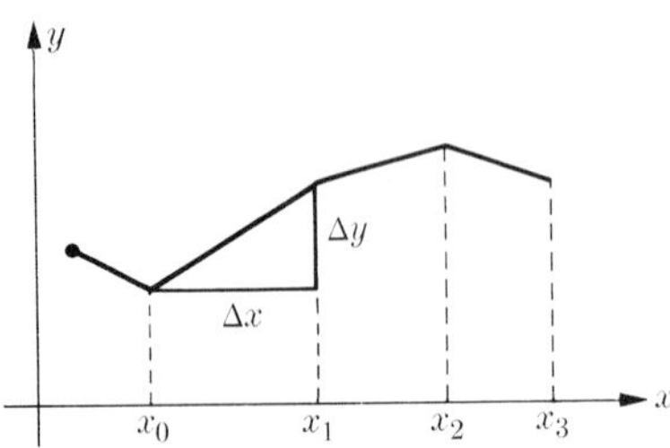

FIG. 1–8. Solution obtained by step-by-step integration.

We can obtain such a solution graphically with the aid of line elements, but we need not draw a whole field of such elements. We can simply draw a short segment through (x_0, y_0), with slope $F(x_0, y_0)$, and follow this to a nearby point (x_1, y_1), with $x_1 > x_0$. At this point we evaluate the slope $F(x_1, y_1)$ and draw a line with that slope from (x_1, y_1) to a nearby point (x_2, y_2), with $x_2 > x_1$. By repeating the process many times, we obtain a broken line which is an approximation to the solution sought; see Fig. 1–8. It is clear that the shorter the segments used, the more accurate the solution will be. By proceeding to the left from x_0, rather than to the right, we can extend the graphical solution to values of x less than x_0.

The procedure described is known as *step-by-step integration*. Actually, we need not use the graph at all, for the steps are purely numerical. The work can be recorded in tabular form in four columns, listing the values of x, y, $F(x, y)$, and Δy, as in Table 1–1. The increment Δx is chosen at discretion, while Δy is computed by the formula

$$\Delta y = F(x, y)\, \Delta x. \tag{1–39}$$

Thus Δy is really being computed by the use of the approximation $dy = \Delta y$. The increment Δx can be varied from step to step, although it is simpler to keep it constant, as is done in Table 1–1.

TABLE 1–1

x	y	$F(x, y)$	Δy
x_0	y_0	$F(x_0, y_0)$	$F(x_0, y_0)\,\Delta x$
$x_0 + \Delta x$	$y_0 + \Delta y$	$F(x_0 + \Delta x, y_0 + \Delta y)$	$\cdots$
$x_0 + 2\,\Delta x$	$\cdots$	$\cdots$	$\cdots$

The example

$$y' = x^2 - y^2, \tag{1–40}$$

with $x_0 = 1$, $y_0 = 1$, $\Delta x = 0.1$, is worked out in Table 1–2. The third and fourth columns are introduced to simplify the work.

TABLE 1–2

x	y	x^2	y^2	$x^2 - y^2$	$\Delta y = (x^2 - y^2)\,\Delta x$
1	1	1	1	0	0
1.1	1	1.21	1	0.21	0.021
1.2	1.021	1.44	1.042	0.398	0.040
1.3	1.061	...	...	...	...

1–6 The equation $y' = F(x)$. Let $F(x)$ be continuous for $a < x < b$. Then the general solution of the differential equation

$$y' = F(x) \tag{1–41}$$

is obtained by integration:

$$y = \int F(x)\,dx + C, \qquad a < x < b, \tag{1–42}$$

where $\int F(x)\,dx$ is an indefinite integral of $F(x)$. This can also be written as follows:

$$y = \int_{x_0}^{x} F(u)\,du + C, \qquad a < x < b, \tag{1–43}$$

where $a < x_0 < b$. Thus the indefinite integral has been replaced by a definite integral from x_0 to x, with u as a "dummy variable" of integration. It is a standard theorem of calculus that

$$\frac{d}{dx}\int_{x_0}^{x} F(u)\,du = F(x), \tag{1–44}$$

so that the integral on the right of Eq. (1–43) is indeed an indefinite integral of $F(x)$ (Prob. 5 below).

We now seek the solution of Eq. (1–41) such that $y = y_0$ when $x = x_0$. This forces us to choose C appropriately in Eq. (1–43):

$$y_0 = \int_{x_0}^{x_0} F(u)\,du + C = 0 + C.$$

Hence $y_0 = C$ and the solution sought is

$$y = \int_{x_0}^{x} F(u)\,du + y_0. \tag{1–45}$$

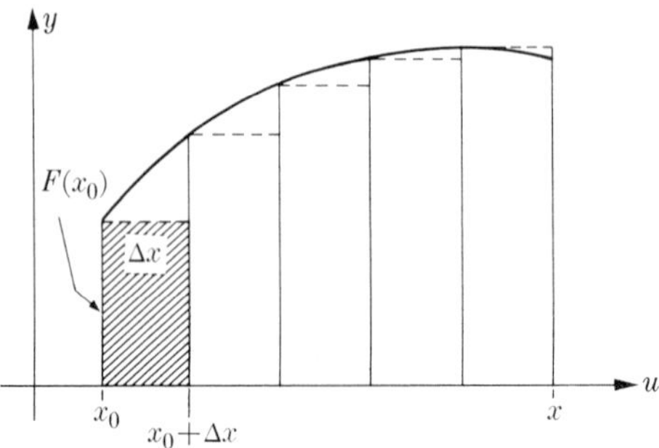

FIG. 1–9. Integration and step-by-step integration.

Explicit evaluation of the integral would provide a satisfactory solution of the problem; however, it often happens that explicit evaluation in terms of elementary functions is not possible. Equation (1–45) then still provides a significant solution and means for computing the value of y for each x. For when x is fixed the definite integral can be evaluated approximately by any one of the standard procedures: the trapezoidal rule, Simpson's rule, etc. In particular, it can be evaluated by "rectangular sums" as follows. Fix x and divide the interval from x_0 to x into n equal parts Δx, so that $x = x_0 + n\,\Delta x$. Then, approximately,

$$y = y_0 + \int_{x_0}^{x} F(u)\,du = y_0 + F(x_0)\,\Delta x + F(x_0 + \Delta x)\,\Delta x + \cdots + F[x_0 + (n-1)\,\Delta x]\,\Delta x, \tag{1–46}$$

as suggested in Fig. 1–9.

Equation (1–46) provides the same value of y at x as that given by step-by-step integration. The successive values of y for $x = x_0, x_0 + \Delta x, \ldots, x_0 + n\,\Delta x$ are

$$\begin{aligned}
&y_0,\\
&y_0 + \Delta y = y_0 + F(x_0)\,\Delta x,\\
&y_0 + F(x_0)\,\Delta x + F(x_0 + \Delta x)\,\Delta x,\\
&\vdots\\
&y_0 + F(x_0)\,\Delta x + \cdots + F[x_0 + (n-1)\,\Delta x]\,\Delta x.
\end{aligned}$$

In other words, step-by-step integration is in this case simply one method for approximate evaluation of a definite integral.

This example suggests the reason for the word "integration" in connection with the step-by-step procedure. In general, solution of a differential equation should be thought of as a kind of generalized process of integration. Certain mechanical and electrical devices exist for solving differential equations which are composed of "integrators"; these devices carry out the step-by-step process continuously; that is, effectively they proceed to the limit corresponding to $\Delta x \to 0$.

PROBLEMS

1. Using step-by-step integration, with $\Delta x = 0.1$, find the value of y for $x = 1.5$ on the solution of $y' = x - y^2$ such that $y = 1$ when $x = 1$. Plot the solution as a broken line.

2. (a) Using step-by-step integration, with $\Delta x = 0.1$, find the value of y at $x = 0.5$ on the solution of $y' = \sqrt{1 - y^2}$ such that $y = 0$ for $x = 0$. Compare the result with the exact solution, which is $y = \sin x$.

(b) Proceed as in part (a), with $\Delta x = 0.05$, and compare again with the exact solution.

3. Show that the value of y when $x = 1$ on the solution of $y' = xe^x$ through $(0, 1)$ is given by $1 + \int_0^1 xe^x\,dx$. Obtain the value numerically by step-by-step integration with $\Delta x = 0.2$. Compare with the exact value. Also show how the steps correspond to rectangles whose total area approximates the integral.

4. Find the value of y for $x = 0.6$ on the solution of $y' = e^{-x^2}$ through $(0, 2)$

(a) by step-by-step integration with $\Delta x = 0.2$;

(b) by the trapezoidal rule, using subdivision points at $x = 0, 0.2, 0.4, 0.6$;

(c) by Simpson's rule, using subdivision points at $x = 0, 0.1, 0.2, 0.3, 0.4, 0.5, 0.6$;

(d) by employing tables of the error function.

5. Carry out the indicated steps to prove the rule (1–44). Let $G(x) = \int_{x_0}^{x} F(u)\,du$.

(a) Show that $G(x + \Delta x) - G(x) = \int_x^{x+\Delta x} F(u)\,du$.

(b) Apply the law of the mean to show that

$$G(x + \Delta x) - G(x) = F(x_1) \int_x^{x+\Delta x} du = F(x_1)\,\Delta x,$$

where x_1 is between x and $x + \Delta x$.

(c) Conclude that $G'(x) = \lim_{\Delta x \to 0} \dfrac{G(x + \Delta x) - G(x)}{\Delta x} = F(x)$.

6. A pair of simultaneous equations

$$\frac{dy}{dx} = F(x, y, z), \qquad \frac{dz}{dx} = G(x, y, z) \tag{a}$$

is called a *system of two first order differential equations*. A *solution* of such a system is a pair of functions $y = f(x)$, $z = g(x)$, defined in some interval, which satisfy (a) identically. Show that $y = 5e^{5x}$, $z = -e^{5x}$ is a solution of the system

$$\frac{dy}{dx} = 4y - 5z, \qquad \frac{dz}{dx} = -y.$$

7. The method of step-by-step integration can be extended to the simultaneous equations of Prob. 6, the corresponding incremental equations being

$$\Delta y = F(x, y, z)\,\Delta x, \qquad \Delta z = G(x, y, z)\,\Delta x. \tag{b}$$

If values of y and z are given for some $x = x_0$, Eqs. (b) successively determine y, z for $x = x_0 + \Delta x$, $x = x_0 + 2\,\Delta x, \ldots$ Apply the procedure described to find the values of y, z for $x = 4$ on the solution of

$$\frac{dy}{dx} = y - z, \qquad \frac{dz}{dx} = 2y - 3z$$

such that $y = 2$, $z = 3$ for $x = 1$. Use $\Delta x = 1$.

8. A second order equation $y'' = G(x, y, y')$ is equivalent to the pair of simultaneous equations

$$\frac{dy}{dx} = z, \qquad \frac{dz}{dx} = G(x, y, z). \tag{c}$$

For elimination of z in Eqs. (c) yields the given equation. Let the equation $y'' = yy' + x$ be given.

(a) Replace the equation by a pair of simultaneous equations.

(b) Apply the method of Prob. 7 to find the solution such that $y = 1$, $y' = 0$ for $x = 0$. Use $\Delta x = 0.5$ and make 4 steps.

9. Generalize the discussion of Probs. 6, 7, 8 to systems of n first order equations. In particular, show that the nth order equation is equivalent to a system of n first order equations. Such a system is said to have order n.

ANSWERS

1. 1.082. 2. (a) 0.4850, exact value 0.47943; (b) 0.4822. 3. Step-by-step: 1.7429, exact value 2. 4. (a) 2.56259, (b) 2.53235, (c) 2.53516, (d) 2.53515.

7. For $x = 1, 2, 3, 4$, $y = 2, 1, 4, 2$, $z = 3, -2, 6, -4$.

8. (a) $y' = z$, $z' = yz + x$; (b) for $x = 0, 0.5, \ldots$, $y = 1, 1, 1, 1.125, 1.563$.

1–7 Existence theorem. Initial value problem and boundary value problem. The analysis in the previous sections has strongly indicated that for the differential equation

$$\frac{dy}{dx} = F(x, y) \tag{1-47}$$

there is a unique solution $y = f(x)$ which passes through a *given initial point* (x_0, y_0). Under appropriate assumptions concerning the function $F(x, y)$, existence of such a solution can indeed be guaranteed. For the equation of nth order,

$$y^{(n)} = F(x, y, y', \ldots, y^{(n-1)}), \tag{1-48}$$

we expect that there will be a unique solution satisfying *initial conditions:*

$$\text{when } x = x_0, \qquad \text{then } y = y_0, \quad y' = y'_0, \quad \ldots, \quad \text{and } y^{(n-1)} = y_0^{(n-1)}, \tag{1-49}$$

where $x_0, y_0, \ldots, y_0^{(n-1)}$ are given numbers. The following fundamental theorem justifies these expectations.

Existence theorem. *Let $F(x, y, y', \ldots, y^{(n-1)})$ be a function of the variables $x, y, y', \ldots, y^{(n-1)}$, defined and continuous when*

$$|x - x_0| < h, \qquad |y - y_0| < h, \qquad \ldots, \qquad |y^{(n-1)} - y_0^{(n-1)}| < h,$$

and having continuous first partial derivatives with respect to $y, y', \ldots, y^{(n-1)}$. Then there exists a solution $y = f(x)$ of the differential equation (1–48), *defined in some interval $|x - x_0| < h_1$, and satisfying the initial conditions* (1–49). *Furthermore, the solution is unique; that is, if $y = g(x)$ is a second solution satisfying* (1–49), *then $f(x) \equiv g(x)$ wherever both functions are defined.*

A proof of this theorem is given in Chapter 12 of ODE. One method of proof is to show that, as the increment Δx tends to zero, the broken-line solution obtained by step-by-step integration approaches as limit precisely the solution $y = f(x)$ sought. A second method, described in Chapter 12 of ODE, is based on the Picard procedure of "successive approximation."

Example. For the differential equation

$$y'' = \sin x, \tag{1-50}$$

the general solution is found by integrating twice:

$$y' = -\cos x + c_1, \qquad y = -\sin x + c_1 x + c_2. \tag{1-51}$$

If the given initial conditions are

$$\text{for } x = 0: \qquad y = y_0, \qquad y' = y_0', \tag{1–52}$$

then we obtain equations for c_1 and c_2:

$$y_0 = c_2, \qquad y_0' = -1 + c_1. \tag{1–53}$$

Accordingly, $c_1 = y_0' + 1$, $c_2 = y_0$, and the solution sought is

$$y = -\sin x + (y_0' + 1)x + y_0. \tag{1–54}$$

This example shows why it is natural that the general solution (when obtainable) of an nth order equation should depend on n arbitrary constants. For the initial conditions (1–49) lead to n equations in the arbitrary constants, and n equations in n unknowns have "in general" one solution.

With this in mind, we can consider ways of determining the values of the arbitrary constants other than by initial conditions (1–49). The most common alternative is to require that certain *boundary conditions* be satisfied at the ends of an interval $a \leqq x \leqq b$ in which the solution is sought. For example, for Eq. (1–50) we could impose the conditions

$$y = y_1 \quad \text{for} \quad x = 0, \qquad y = y_2 \quad \text{for} \quad x = \pi. \tag{1–55}$$

From the second part of (1–51), we then obtain the equations

$$y_1 = c_2, \qquad y_2 = c_1\pi + c_2; \tag{1–56}$$

accordingly, $c_1 = (y_2 - y_1)/\pi$, $c_2 = y_1$, and the solution sought is

$$y = -\sin x + \frac{y_2 - y_1}{\pi}x + y_1. \tag{1–57}$$

This particular example gave no difficulty, but it is not true that we can always find a solution which satisfies such boundary conditions or, if one does exist, that there is only one (see Prob. 4 in Section 1–10). There are existence theorems for such boundary value problems, but they involve complicated hypotheses and we attempt no formulation here.

An existence theorem analogous to the one stated above holds for systems of n first order equations (see Probs. 6, 9 following Section 1–6):

$$\frac{dy}{dx} = F(x, y, z, \ldots), \qquad \frac{dz}{dx} = G(x, y, z, \ldots), \qquad \ldots \tag{1–58}$$

in the n unknown functions $y, z, \ldots$ of x. For simplicity we state the theorem for the case of three unknowns, y, z, w:

$$\frac{dy}{dx} = F(x, y, z, w), \qquad \frac{dz}{dx} = G(x, y, z, w), \qquad \frac{dw}{dx} = H(x, y, z, w). \tag{1-59}$$

If the functions F, G, H are continuous and have continuous first partial derivatives with respect to y, z, w for $|x - x_0| < h$, $|y - y_0| < h$, $|z - z_0| < h$, $|w - w_0| < h$, then there is a unique solution

$$y = f(x), \qquad z = g(x), \qquad w = p(x), \qquad |x - x_0| < h_1, \tag{1-60}$$

which passes through the initial point (x_0, y_0, z_0, w_0). A proof is given in Chapter 12 of ODE.

This theorem includes the previous one as a special case, since Eq. (1-48) can always be replaced by an equivalent system (1-58) (see Probs. 8, 9 following Section 1-6). For the same reason, it also includes the case of a system such as the following:

$$\frac{d^2x}{dt^2} = F\left(t, x, y, \frac{dx}{dt}, \frac{dy}{dt}\right), \qquad \frac{d^2y}{dt^2} = G\left(t, x, y, \frac{dx}{dt}, \frac{dy}{dt}\right). \tag{1-61}$$

Newton's law (force = mass × acceleration), when applied to systems of particles, leads to systems of second order equations such as (1-61). The existence theorem ensures that there is a unique solution for (1-61) which satisfies given initial conditions:

$$\text{for } t = t_0: \qquad x = x_0, \qquad y = y_0, \qquad \frac{dx}{dt} = \left(\frac{dx}{dt}\right)_0, \qquad \frac{dy}{dt} = \left(\frac{dy}{dt}\right)_0; \tag{1-62}$$

that is, in the mechanical case the motion of the system is completely determined by the positions and velocities of all the particles at one instant of time. Similar laws apply to electric circuits.

1-8 Verification of a general solution. One important application of the existence theorem is to establish that a formula gives the general solution (*all solutions*) of a differential equation.

EXAMPLE. For the differential equation

$$y'' - 4y = 0, \tag{1-63}$$

the function

$$y = c_1 e^{2x} + c_2 e^{-2x}, \tag{1-64}$$

which depends on two arbitrary constants c_1, c_2, gives the general solution.

For

$$y'' = 4c_1e^{2x} + 4c_2e^{-2x} = 4y,$$

so that, no matter what values are assigned to c_1, c_2, (1–64) defines a solution of (1–63). Furthermore, for each set of initial conditions:

$$\text{for } x = x_0: \quad y = y_0, \quad y' = y'_0, \tag{1–65}$$

there is a choice of c_1, c_2 such that (1–64) satisfies these conditions:

$$y_0 = c_1e^{2x_0} + c_2e^{-2x_0}, \qquad y'_0 = 2c_1e^{2x_0} - 2c_2e^{-2x_0},$$

so that

$$c_1 = \tfrac{1}{4}e^{-2x_0}(2y_0 + y'_0), \qquad c_2 = \tfrac{1}{4}e^{2x_0}(2y_0 - y'_0).$$

Hence (1–64) gives *all* solutions and must be the general solution of (1–63).

In general, for an equation of second order

$$y'' = F(x, y, y'),$$

verification of a general solution, $y = f(x, c_1, c_2)$, consists of two steps: first, substitution of $y = f(x, c_1, c_2)$ in the differential equation and determining that, for all allowed choices of c_1, c_2, the equation is an identity in x; second, showing that the equations

$$y_0 = f(x_0, c_1, c_2), \qquad y'_0 = f_x(x_0, c_1, c_2)$$

can be solved for c_1, c_2 for every choice of x_0, y_0, y'_0 for which F has continuous first partial derivatives. Similar remarks apply to equations of higher order and to systems of equations.

It should be stressed that the existence theorem is applicable only when the continuity conditions are satisfied. For the equation

$$y' = F(x, y) \equiv 3y^{2/3}, \tag{1–66}$$

the function $F(x, y)$ has a partial derivative $F_y = 2y^{-1/3}$ which is discontinuous when $y = 0$. The points for which $y = 0$ must be considered as *singular points*, and solutions passing through these points (if there are any) require special investigation. Methods given in Chapter 2 lead us to the expression

$$y = (x - c)^3 \tag{1–67}$$

for the general solution of (1–66). We can verify at once that Eq. (1–67) does provide one and only one solution through every point (x_0, y_0) for which $y_0 \neq 0$. In fact, Eq. (1–67) also provides a unique solution through each singular point $(x_0, 0)$. There is, however, more than one solution through each singular point, for the function $y \equiv 0$ is a solution of Eq. (1–66); it passes through all the singular points, and is not included in Eq. (1–67).

Other examples can be given in which there are no solutions through singular points or in which there is just one solution through each singular point. A full discussion is given in Chapter 8.

1–9 Finding differential equation from primitive. At times a function $f(x, c_1, c_2, \ldots)$ which depends on x and several arbitrary constants is given, and we are asked to determine a differential equation of which the function f is the general solution. We call f a *primitive* of the differential equation.

For example, let the primitive be

$$y = c_1x^2 + c_2x^3. \tag{1–68}$$

To find the differential equation, we consider the equations for y, y', y'':

$$\begin{aligned} y &= c_1x^2 + c_2x^3, \\ y' &= 2c_1x + 3c_2x^2, \\ y'' &= 2c_1 + 6c_2x. \end{aligned} \tag{1–69}$$

Here we can eliminate c_1, c_2 by solving the first two equations for c_1, c_2 and substituting in the third equation:

$$c_1 = \frac{3y - xy'}{x^2}, \qquad c_2 = \frac{xy' - 2y}{x^3},$$

$$y'' = 2c_1 + 6c_2x = \frac{4xy' - 6y}{x^2}.$$

This last equation provides the differential equation sought, of form $y'' = F(x, y, y')$; note that F is discontinuous when $x = 0$ (locus of singular points). To complete the solution of the problem, we should then verify that $y = c_1x^2 + c_2x^3$ is the general solution of

$$y'' = \frac{4xy' - 6y}{x^2} \qquad (x \neq 0). \tag{1–70}$$

Because of the special form of equations (1–69), c_1 and c_2 can also be eliminated by employing a theorem of algebra: $n+1$ linear equations in n unknowns are consistent only if the determinant formed of the coefficients of the unknowns and the "constant" terms is 0. In (1-69), c_1, c_2 are regarded as unknowns and y, y', y'' as "constants." Hence

$$\begin{vmatrix} y & x^2 & x^3 \\ y' & 2x & 3x^2 \\ y'' & 2 & 6x \end{vmatrix} = 0,$$

$$x^4y'' - 4x^3y' + 6x^2y = 0. \tag{1–71}$$

For $x \neq 0$, this is the same as (1–70); for $x = 0$, (1–68) is found to satisfy (1–71), even though the existence theorem gives no information for $x = 0$.

In general, if the primitive is $y = f(x; c_1, c_2, \ldots, c_n)$, then the differential equation is obtained by differentiating n times with respect to x and eliminating $c_1, \ldots, c_n$ from these n equations and the equation $y = f(x; c_1, \ldots)$. There are various pitfalls here. For instance, the function $f(x; c_1, \ldots, c_n)$ may be expressible in terms of fewer than n constants. For example,

$$y = x^2 + c_1^2 - c_2^2$$

depends effectively on only one constant, $c = c_1^2 - c_2^2$. In such cases, fewer equations are needed to eliminate the c's and a differential equation of order less than n should be obtained. In general, elimination of the c's may be difficult and may yield only a complicated implicit relation between $x, y, y', \ldots, y^{(n-1)}$.

The primitive itself may be given as an implicit equation

$$F(x, y; c_1, \ldots, c_n) = 0. \tag{1–72}$$

A similar procedure can be followed here. For example,

$$(x - c_1)^2 + (y - c_2)^2 = 1, \tag{1–73}$$

differentiated twice, yields

$$2(x - c_1) + 2(y - c_2)y' = 0,$$

$$2 + 2(y - c_2)y'' + 2y'^2 = 0.$$

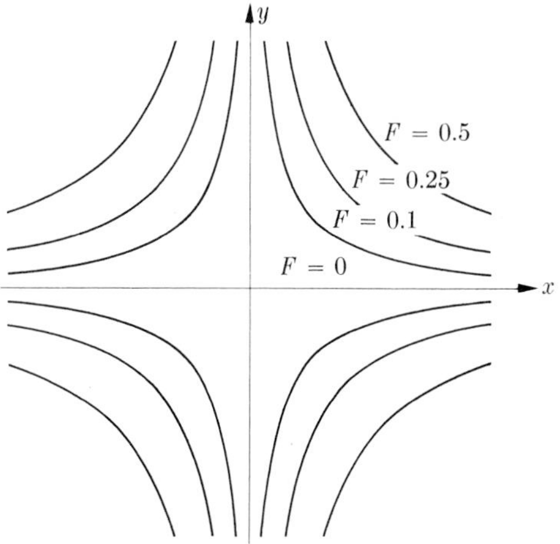

FIG. 1–10. Level curves of the function xy.

Elimination of c_1, c_2 gives

$$y''^2 = (1 + y'^2)^3. \tag{1–74}$$

This second degree equation is equivalent to two first degree equations:

$$y'' = \pm(1 + y'^2)^{3/2}. \tag{1–75}$$

It can be verified that Eq. (1–73) provides the general solution of (1–75) (Prob. 6 below).

An important special case is the equation

$$F(x, y) = c, \tag{1–76}$$

which describes the *level curves* of the function F. For example,

$$xy = c \tag{1–77}$$

describes the level curves of $F \equiv xy$ (Fig. 1–10). Differentiation gives

$$xy' + y = 0, \qquad y' = -\frac{y}{x} \qquad (x \neq 0).$$

On each level curve, y can be considered as a function of x: $y = c/x$, $(x \neq 0)$, and the functions so defined do give the general solution of the differential equation $y' = -y/x$, $(x \neq 0)$. We can treat the variables symmetrically by taking *differentials* rather than derivatives; from (1–77),

$$y\,dx + x\,dy = 0.$$

Here we think of y as a function of x or of x as a function of y, whichever is convenient. When $x = 0$, we think of x as a function of y, and the equation reads

$$y\frac{dx}{dy} + x = 0;$$

this is satisfied if $x \equiv 0$. Similarly, $y \equiv 0$ is a solution when we consider y as a function of x; hence there are two solution curves through the origin.

In general, we shall agree to consider an equation

$$P(x, y)\,dx + Q(x, y)\,dy = 0 \tag{1–78}$$

as a differential equation of first order. A solution is either a function $y = f(x)$ or a function $x = g(y)$ which satisfies the corresponding differential equation of standard type:

$$Q(x, y)\frac{dy}{dx} + P(x, y) = 0 \quad \text{or} \quad P(x, y)\frac{dx}{dy} + Q(x, y) = 0. \tag{1–79}$$

Thus (1–78) really describes two differential equations; however, except where P or $Q = 0$, the solution curves are the same. A point at which $Q(x, y) = 0$ appears as a singular point in the first form of Eq. (1–79), but if $P(x, y) \neq 0$ at that point, the point will generally not appear as a singular point in the second form of the equation. At such a point we have $dy/dx = \infty$ and $dx/dy = 0$. A point at which both $P(x, y)$ and $Q(x, y)$ are 0 is a singular point for both forms of Eq. (1–79).

1–10 General remarks. This chapter is in a sense introductory, but the importance of the ideas presented must not be underestimated. The existence theorem answers the crucial question of the conditions under which solutions can be found. The method of step-by-step integration tells how to find these solutions; the accuracy obtained can be made as great as desired by employing sufficiently short steps. Accordingly, one could very well stop at this point and consider himself adequately educated on the subject of differential equations.

There are, however, several justifications for going further. We shall find that for certain important differential equations which are widely used there are especially simple methods for obtaining the solutions in explicit form. For a larger class, the solutions may be more difficult to obtain, but from the form of the equation important conclusions can be reached as to the nature of the solutions. Also we shall discover that for the general equation there are several worthy alternatives to the method of step-by-step integration.

PROBLEMS

1. For each of the following differential equations find a solution satisfying the given initial conditions:

(a) $y' = \sin x$; $y = 1$ for $x = 0$;
(b) $y'' = e^x$; $y = 1$ and $y' = 0$ for $x = 1$;
(c) $y' = y$; $y = 1$ for $x = 0$.

2. Find a solution of the differential equation satisfying the given boundary conditions:

(a) $y'' = 1$; $y = 1$ for $x = 0$; $y = 2$ for $x = 1$;
(b) $y^{(\text{iv})} = 0$; $y = 1$ for $x = -1$ and $x = 1$; $y' = 0$ for $x = -1$ and $x = 1$.

3. Prove that $y = c_1 \cos x + c_2 \sin x$ gives the general solution of the differential equation $y'' + y = 0$.

4. Find (if possible) a solution of the differential equation of Prob. 3 which satisfies the following boundary conditions:

(a) $y = 1$ for $x = 0$; $y = -1$ for $x = \frac{1}{2}\pi$;
(b) $y = 1$ for $x = 0$; $y = 1$ for $x = \pi$;
(c) $y = 0$ for $x = 0$; $y = 0$ for $x = \pi$;
(d) $y = 0$ for $x = 0$; $y = 1$ for $x = \pi$.

5. Determine, on the basis of the existence theorem, the points (x_0, y_0) through which there is a unique solution of each of the following differential equations:

(a) $y' = \dfrac{x}{x^2 + y^2}$, (b) $y' = \dfrac{y}{x}$,

(c) $y' = x \log x$, (d) $y' = \dfrac{x + y - 1}{x + 2y}$.

6. (a) Verify that for each choice of c_1, c_2, Eq. (1–73) defines two functions y of x, both having derivatives for $c_1 - 1 < x < c_1 + 1$. Show that both of these functions satisfy (1–74) or (1–75). Show, on the basis of the existence theorem, that the functions (1–73) provide all solutions of (1–74).

(b) Show that every solution of (1–75) has constant curvature, equal to 1, and hence has form (1–73).

7. Obtain the differential equation having the given primitive:

(a) $y = c_1x + c_2$, (b) $y = cx + c^2$,
(c) $y = c_1x + c_2e^x$, (d) $y = c_1e^x + c_2e^{2x} + c_3e^{3x}$,
(e) $x^2 - xy = c$, (f) $(x - c_1)^2 + y^2 = c_2^2$.

ANSWERS

1. (a) $2 - \cos x$, (b) $e^x - ex + 1$, (c) e^x. 2. (a) $\frac{1}{2}(x^2 + x) + 1$, (b) 1. 4. (a) $\cos x - \sin x$, (b) impossible, (c) $c_2 \sin x$, (d) impossible. 5. (a) all except (0, 0), (b) $x_0 \neq 0$, (c) $x_0 > 0$, (d) all except the points of the line $x + 2y = 0$. 7. (a) $y'' = 0$, (b) $y'^2 + xy' = y$, (c) $(x - 1)y'' - xy' + y = 0$, (d) $y''' - 6y'' + 11y' - 6y = 0$, (e) $(2x - y)\,dx - x\,dy = 0$, (f) $yy'' + y'^2 + 1 = 0$.

SUGGESTED REFERENCES

1. ANDRONOW, A., and CHAIKIN, C. E., *Theory of Oscillations.* Princeton: Princeton University Press, 1949.

2. MARTIN, W. T., and REISSNER, E., *Elementary Differential Equations.* Reading, Mass.: Addison-Wesley, 1956.

3. MILNE, WILLIAM E., *Numerical Solution of Differential Equations.* New York: John Wiley and Sons, Inc., 1953.

4. VON KÁRMÁN, T., and BIOT, M. A., *Mathematical Methods in Engineering,* Chap. 1. New York: McGraw-Hill, 1940.

CHAPTER 2

EQUATIONS OF FIRST ORDER AND FIRST DEGREE

2–1 Different forms of the equation. By definition, a differential equation of first order and first degree has the form

$$Q(x, y)y' + P(x, y) = 0. \tag{2–1}$$

Where $Q(x, y) \neq 0$, this is equivalent to

$$y' = F(x, y), \qquad F = -\frac{P}{Q}. \tag{2–2}$$

In every portion of the xy-plane in which F and $\partial F/\partial y$ are continuous, the existence theorem (Section 1–7) guarantees existence of a unique solution of Eq. (2–2) through each point. The points at which $Q(x, y) = 0$ are singular points and must be investigated separately.

As remarked in Section 1–9, there are advantages in multiplying Eq. (2–1) by dx to obtain the equation

$$P(x, y)\,dx + Q(x, y)\,dy = 0, \tag{2–3}$$

which treats both variables on the same basis. Where $Q(x, y) \neq 0$, Eq. (2–3) can be divided by $Q(x, y)\,dx$, to yield Eq. (2–2). Where $P(x, y) \neq 0$, it can be divided by $P(x, y)\,dy$ to yield the equation

$$\frac{dx}{dy} + \frac{Q(x, y)}{P(x, y)} = 0, \tag{2–4}$$

for x as a function of y. We shall allow as a solution of Eq. (2–3) either a function $y(x)$ or a function $x(y)$ which satisfies (2–3) identically. At points (x, y) for which both P and Q are 0, both Eqs. (2–2) and (2–4) lose meaning. These are *singular points* for Eq. (2–3).

Concept of domain. By a *domain* or *open region* in the xy-plane is meant a portion of the xy-plane such that (a) each two points in the portion can be joined by a broken line within the portion, (b) for each point A in the portion there is a circle with center at A whose interior lies wholly in the portion. The following are examples of domains: all points inside a square; all points for which $x > 0$ (half-plane); all points except (1, 0) and (0, 1).

Throughout this chapter the emphasis will be on formal methods for finding explicit solutions. The functions that occur will be assumed continuous except for special points. Difficulties arising from discontinuities (usually caused by division by 0) will be illustrated by examples.

2–2 Exact differential equations. A differential equation of first order,

$$P(x, y)\, dx + Q(x, y)\, dy = 0, \tag{2–5}$$

is said to be *exact* if for some function $u(x, y)$

$$\frac{\partial u}{\partial x} = P, \qquad \frac{\partial u}{\partial y} = Q, \tag{2–6}$$

so that $du = P\, dx + Q\, dy$. More precisely, the equation (2–5) is exact in an open region D if (2–6) holds in D.

The solutions of an exact equation (2–5) are *level curves* of the function $u(x, y)$, that is, curves on which $u(x, y) \equiv \text{const}$ (Fig. 2–1). For example, if $y = f(x)$ is a solution of (2–5), then along the curve $y = f(x)$

$$\frac{du}{dx} = P + Q\frac{dy}{dx} = 0,$$

so that u is constant. In general, if a level curve of u is expressible in the form $y = f(x)$ [or $x = g(y)$], then $y = f(x)$ is a solution of (2–5). For if $y = f(x)$ satisfies

$$u(x, y) = c,$$

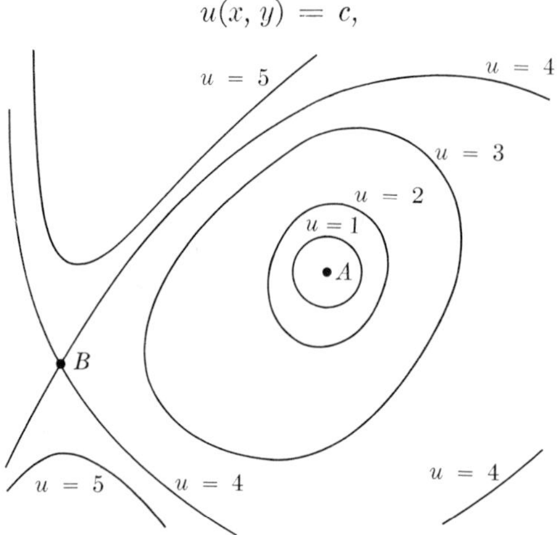

FIG. 2–1. Level curves of $u(x, y)$.

then from calculus

$$\frac{\partial u}{\partial x} \cdot 1 + \frac{\partial u}{\partial y}\frac{dy}{dx} = 0, \qquad P + Q\frac{dy}{dx} = 0.$$

We summarize the situation by saying: *the solutions of an exact differential equation are the level curves of the function u.* It can of course happen that a level curve is not expressible as a function $y = f(x)$ or $x = g(y)$, and exceptional points may arise on particular level curves. These are suggested in Fig. 2–1 (points A and B).

EXAMPLE 1. $x\,dx + y\,dy = 0$. Here clearly $u = \frac{1}{2}(x^2 + y^2)$,

$$du = \tfrac{1}{2}d(x^2 + y^2) = x\,dx + y\,dy.$$

Hence the solutions are the circles

$$x^2 + y^2 = c.$$

For $c = 0$, the level curve reduces to a point which is a singular point of the differential equation. For $c < 0$ the locus is imaginary.

EXAMPLE 2. $2xy\,dx + x^2\,dy = 0$. Here $u = x^2y$. The solutions are the curves $x^2y = c$ shown in Fig. 2–2. For $c = 0$ the level curve is formed

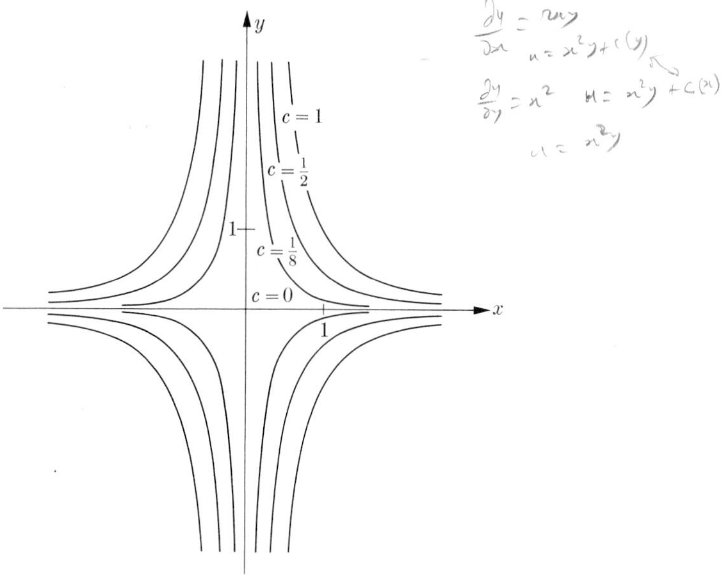

FIG. 2–2. Level curves of $u = x^2y$.

of the lines $x = 0$, $y = 0$. The point $(0, 0)$ is a singular point, through which *two* solutions pass.

PROBLEMS

1. Plot the level curves of each of the following functions $u(x, y)$:

(a) $u = 2x^2 + y^2$, (b) $u = 2x - 3y$,
(c) $u = y - 2x^2$, (d) $u = y^2e^{-x}$.

2. Find the differential equation for each of the families of level curves of Prob. 1. Indicate exceptional points for each.

3. Show that the following differential equations are exact, and find the general solution.

(a) $x\,dx + 3y^2\,dy = 0$, (b) $e^x\,dx - 2\,dy = 0$,

(c) $y^2\,dx + 2xy\,dy = 0$, (d) $\dfrac{x\,dy - y\,dx}{x^2} = 0$.

4. (a) A first order equation $P(x, y)\,dx + Q(x, y)\,dy = 0$ can be replaced by a system of *two* first order equations:

$$\frac{dx}{dt} = Q(x, y), \qquad \frac{dy}{dt} = -P(x, y) \tag{*}$$

in terms of a parameter t. For elimination of t from equations (*) gives $P\,dx + Q\,dy = 0$. Show in more detail that, if $x = \phi(t)$, $y = \psi(t)$ is a solution of (*), then solving $x = \phi(t)$ for t in terms of x (if possible) and substitution in $y = \psi(t)$ yields a function $y = f(x)$ which satisfies $P\,dx + Q\,dy = 0$.

(b) Carry out the process of part (a) for the equation $y\,dx + x\,dy = 0$. Verify that the general solution of the equations (*) is $x = c_1e^t$, $y = c_2e^{-t}$. Eliminate t to find the general solution of the equation in x and y.

ANSWERS

2. (a) $2x\,dx + y\,dy = 0$, $(0, 0)$ exceptional; (b) $2\,dx - 3\,dy = 0$; (c) $-4x\,dx + dy = 0$; (d) $-y^2e^{-x}\,dx + 2ye^{-x}\,dy = 0$, $y = 0$ exceptional.

3. (a) $x^2 + 2y^3 = c$, (x, y) not $(0, 0)$; (b) $e^x - 2y = c$; (c) $xy^2 = c$; (d) $y/x = c$ $(x \neq 0)$.

4. (b) $dx/dt = x$, $dy/dt = -y$, $xy = c$.

2–3 Equations with separable variables. If a differential equation of first order, after multiplication by a suitable factor, takes the form

$$X(x)\,dx + Y(y)\,dy = 0, \tag{2–7}$$

then the equation is said to have *separable variables*. For example, the equation

$$\frac{dy}{dx} = -\frac{x}{y}, \tag{2–8}$$

after multiplication by $y\,dx$, becomes

$$x\,dx + y\,dy = 0. \tag{2–9}$$

The equation is now exact, and we obtain the general solution as

$$x^2 + y^2 = c \qquad (c > 0). \tag{2–10}$$

An equation of form (2–7) is exact (except where X or Y is discontinuous), for we can choose

$$u = \int X\,dx + \int Y\,dy, \tag{2–11}$$

where the integrals are any indefinite integrals of the functions. Then

$$du = \frac{\partial u}{\partial x}\,dx + \frac{\partial u}{\partial y}\,dy = X\,dx + Y\,dy. \tag{2–12}$$

Hence the solutions of (2–7) are given by the level curves

$$\int X(x)\,dx + \int Y(y)\,dy = c. \tag{2–13}$$

An equation $y' = F(x, y)$ will have separable variables if F is expressible as a product of a function of x by a function of y:

$$y' = G(x)H(y). \tag{2–14}$$

For Eq. (2–14) can be written

$$G(x)\,dx - \frac{dy}{H(y)} = 0. \tag{2–15}$$

Equation (2–8) is of this type, with $G = x$, $H = -1/y$.

In converting an equation to form (2–7), we may introduce discontinuities (usually through division by 0) or extraneous solutions. Hence the general solution should be checked carefully against the original differential equation.

EXAMPLE 1. $$y\,dx - x\,dy = 0.$$

Solution. $$\frac{dy}{y} - \frac{dx}{x} = 0 \qquad (y \neq 0,\ x \neq 0),$$

$$\log y - \log x = c \qquad (x > 0, y > 0),$$

$$\log \frac{y}{x} = c,$$

$$\frac{y}{x} = c', \qquad y = c'x.$$

Hence $c' = e^c$ is a new arbitrary constant and $c' > 0$. However, the restrictions $x > 0$, $y > 0$, $c' > 0$ can be removed, since the solutions $y = c'x$ are valid for all x, y, c'. This is not quite the general solution, since the line $x = 0$ can also be considered as a solution. The restrictions to positive x, y could also have been avoided by noting that for $x \neq 0$, $y \neq 0$,

$$\int \frac{dx}{x} = \log |x| + \text{const}, \qquad \int \frac{dy}{y} = \log |y| + \text{const} \tag{2–16}$$

(all logarithms to base e).

EXAMPLE 2. $$\frac{dx}{y} + \frac{dy}{x} = 0.$$

Solution. $$x\,dx + y\,dy = 0,$$

$$x^2 + y^2 = c \qquad (c > 0).$$

(In the differential equation itself x and y are not allowed to be 0. Hence the points $x = 0$, $y = 0$ should be deleted from the solution obtained.)

EXAMPLE 3. $$y' = xe^{y^2}.$$

Solution. $$e^{-y^2}\,dy = x\,dx,$$

$$\int e^{-y^2}\,dy = \int x\,dx = \tfrac{1}{2}x^2 + c.$$

The integral on the left can remain as indicated. It cannot be expressed in terms of elementary functions, but we can express it in terms of an infinite series:

$$\int e^{-y^2}\,dy = \int \left(1 - y^2 + \frac{y^4}{2!} - \frac{y^6}{3!} + \cdots\right) dy$$

$$= y - \frac{y^3}{3} + \frac{y^5}{5 \cdot 2!} - \frac{y^7}{7 \cdot 3!} + \cdots + \text{const.}$$

We can also write

$$\int e^{-y^2}\,dy = \int_0^y e^{-t^2}\,dt + \text{const.}$$

For each fixed y the integral on the right is a definite integral which can be computed to the desired accuracy (see Section 1–6 above).

2–4 Homogeneous equations. If in the differential equation

$$y' = F(x, y) \tag{2–17}$$

the function $F(x, y)$ can be expressed in terms of the one variable

$$v = \frac{y}{x}, \tag{2–18}$$

then the equation is said to be a *homogeneous* first order equation. The following equations are of this type:

$$y' = \frac{y}{x},$$

$$y' = \frac{x^2 - y^2}{xy} = \frac{1 - v^2}{v},$$

$$y' = \sin\frac{y}{x} = \sin v.$$

A homogeneous equation can be reduced to exact form as follows: $y = xv$, so that $dy = x\,dv + v\,dx$ and

$$x\,dv + v\,dx = F(x, y)\,dx = G(v)\,dx.$$

Accordingly, the differential equation becomes

$$\frac{dv}{v - G(v)} + \frac{dx}{x} = 0 \quad \left(v = \frac{y}{x}\right). \tag{2–19}$$

In other words, the substitution $v = y/x$ and the elimination of y lead to a separation of variables.

EXAMPLE.
$$y' = \frac{x^2 + y^2}{xy}.$$

Solution.

$$y' = \frac{x}{y} + \frac{y}{x} = \frac{1}{v} + v,$$

$$x\,dv + v\,dx = dy = \left(\frac{1}{v} + v\right) dx,$$

$$v\,dv - \frac{dx}{x} = 0,$$

$$\tfrac{1}{2}v^2 - \log|x| = \tfrac{1}{2}c,$$

$$y^2 = x^2 \log x^2 + cx^2.$$

(The points $x = 0$, $y = 0$ are ruled out by the differential equation itself.)

Remarks. The most common case of a homogeneous equation is that in which $F(x, y)$ is the ratio of two homogeneous polynomials in x, y, of the same degree. When the equation is written in the form $P\,dx + Q\,dy = 0$, it appears as

$$(a_0x^n + a_1x^{n-1}y + \cdots + a_{n-1}xy^{n-1} + a_ny^n)\,dx$$
$$+ (b_0x^n + b_1x^{n-1}y + \cdots + b_ny^n)\,dy = 0. \quad (2\text{–}20)$$

In general, a function $P(x, y)$ is said to be homogeneous of degree n if

$$P(tx, ty) \equiv t^nP(x, y). \quad (2\text{–}21)$$

Since

$$(tx)^k(ty)^{n-k} = t^n(x^ky^{n-k}),$$

we see that the coefficients P, Q of Eq. (2–20) are homogeneous of degree n. Also

$$\sqrt{x^2 + y^2}, \qquad \sqrt{x^3 + x^2y + y^3}, \qquad xy \sin\frac{x + y}{x - y}$$

are homogeneous of degrees 1, 3/2, and 2, respectively. Whenever $P(x, y)$, $Q(x, y)$ are homogeneous of the same degree n, the differential equation $P\,dx + Q\,dy = 0$ is homogeneous. For then

$$\frac{dy}{dx} = F(x, y) = \frac{-P(x, y)}{Q(x, y)} = \frac{-P(x, vx)}{Q(x, vx)}$$

$$= \frac{-x^nP(1, v)}{x^nQ(1, v)} = \frac{-P(1, v)}{Q(1, v)} = G(v).$$

PROBLEMS

1. Find all solutions by separation of variables:

(a) $y' = e^{x+y}$, (b) $y' = 3y$,
(c) $y' = (y-1)(y-2)$, (d) $y' = x^3y^{-2}$,
(e) $\sin x \cos y\, dx + \tan y \cos x\, dy = 0$, (f) $y' = xy^2 + y^2 + xy + y$.

2. Verify that the following equations are homogeneous and find all solutions:

(a) $y' = \dfrac{x-y}{x+y}$, (b) $xy' - y = xe^{y/x}$,

(c) $(3x^2y + y^3)\, dx + (x^3 + 3xy^2)\, dy = 0$, (d) $y' = \dfrac{y}{x} + \sin \dfrac{y-x}{x}$.

3. (a) Show that the isoclines of a homogeneous equation of first order are straight lines through the origin.

(b) Show that the solutions of a homogeneous equation are *similar curves;* that is, if $y = f(x)$ is a solution, then so is $ky = f(kx)$ for each choice of the constant k.

(c) Solve Prob. 2(a) graphically, with the aid of isoclines.

4. Find the solution which satisfies the given initial conditions:

(a) $y^2\, dx + (x+1)\, dy = 0$; $x = 0$, $y = 1$;

(b) $\dfrac{dx}{dt} = \dfrac{xt}{x^2+t^2}$; $t = 0$, $x = 1$;

(c) $y' = \dfrac{x(y^2-1)}{(x-1)y^3}$; $x = 2$, $y = 1$;

(d) $y' = \dfrac{\sqrt{x^2+y^2}}{x+y}$; $x = 1$, $y = 3$.

ANSWERS

1. (a) $e^x + e^{-y} = c$; (b) $y = ce^{3x}$; (c) $y - 2 = ce^x(y-1)$, $y = 1$; (d) $4y^3 = 3x^4 + c, y \neq 0$; (e) $\cos x\, e^{-\sec y} = c, y \neq (2n+1)\pi/2$ $(n = 0, \pm 1, \ldots)$; (f) $\log |y/(y+1)| = \frac{1}{2}x^2 + x + c$, $y = 0$, $y = -1$.

2. (a) $x^2 - 2xy - y^2 = c$, $x + y \neq 0$; (b) $e^{-y/x} + \log |x| = c$, $x \neq 0$; (c) $x^3y + xy^3 = c$; (d) $\tan [(y-x)/(2x)] = cx$, $x \neq 0$.

4. (a) $y = 1/[1 + \log (x+1)]$; (b) $x = e^{t^2/(2x^2)}$; (c) $y = 1$;

(d) $$\int_3^v \frac{(1+u)\, du}{\sqrt{1+u^2} - u - u^2} = \log x, \qquad v = y/x.$$

2–5 The general exact equation. If the equation

$$P(x, y)\, dx + Q(x, y)\, dy = 0 \tag{2–22}$$

is exact, then for some function $u(x, y)$ we have

$$P(x, y)\,dx + Q(x, y)\,dy = du, \tag{2-23}$$

$$\frac{\partial u}{\partial x} = P(x, y), \qquad \frac{\partial u}{\partial y} = Q(x, y). \tag{2-24}$$

Therefore,

$$\frac{\partial^2 u}{\partial y\,\partial x} = \frac{\partial P}{\partial y}, \qquad \frac{\partial^2 u}{\partial x\,\partial y} = \frac{\partial Q}{\partial x}. \tag{2-25}$$

But from calculus

$$\frac{\partial^2 u}{\partial y\,\partial x} \equiv \frac{\partial^2 u}{\partial x\,\partial y}. \tag{2-26}$$

Therefore,

$$\frac{\partial P}{\partial y} \equiv \frac{\partial Q}{\partial x}. \tag{2-27}$$

Conversely, as will be shown below, if Eq. (2-27) holds, then the differential equation (2-22) is exact. *Hence Eq.* (2-27) *is a perfect test for exactness.* (We have tacitly assumed that P and Q have continuous derivatives in an open region of the xy-plane. Some further discussion of the regions concerned is required; see Section 2-6 of ODE.)

EXAMPLE 1. $(3x^2y + 2xy)\,dx + (x^3 + x^2 + 2y)\,dy = 0.$

Solution. Here $P = 3x^2y + 2xy,\quad Q = x^3 + x^2 + 2y$, and

$$\frac{\partial P}{\partial y} \equiv 3x^2 + 2x \equiv \frac{\partial Q}{\partial x}.$$

Therefore the differential equation is exact. We may be able to recognize by inspection the function u whose differential is $P\,dx + Q\,dy$. If this fails, we can proceed as follows. We write

$$\frac{\partial u}{\partial x} = 3x^2y + 2xy, \qquad \frac{\partial u}{\partial y} = x^3 + x^2 + 2y. \tag{2-28}$$

We now integrate one (but not both) of the equations (2-28). From the first equation we obtain, on integration with respect to x,

$$u = x^3y + x^2y + \text{const.} \tag{2-29}$$

But the constant could very well depend on y; it would still drop out when (2–29) is differentiated with respect to x. Hence we write

$$u = x^3y + x^2y + \phi(y), \tag{2–29a}$$

where $\phi(y)$ is a function to be determined. From (2–29a) we find

$$\frac{\partial u}{\partial y} = x^3 + x^2 + \phi'(y). \tag{2–30}$$

From this equation and the second of equations (2–28) we conclude that

$$x^3 + x^2 + \phi'(y) = x^3 + x^2 + 2y,$$

$$\phi'(y) = 2y,$$

$$\phi(y) = y^2 + c.$$

Accordingly,

$$u(x, y) = x^3y + x^2y + y^2 + c$$

is a function whose differential is $P\,dx + Q\,dy$. We can omit the c here, since we recover it in the general solution of the differential equation:

$$x^3y + x^2y + y^2 = c. \tag{2–31}$$

[It can be verified that the level curves in (2–31) are actual solution curves; the points (0, 0) and (−1, 0) are singular points through which two solutions pass: $y = 0$ and $y = -x^2 - x^3$.]

EXAMPLE 2. $y^2\,dx + 2xy\,dy = 0$. The equation is exact:

$$\frac{\partial P}{\partial y} \equiv 2y \equiv \frac{\partial Q}{\partial x}\cdot$$

By inspection, $y^2\,dx + 2xy\,dy = d(xy^2)$. The solutions are the level curves

$$xy^2 = c.$$

EXAMPLE 3. $(xy \cos xy + \sin xy)\,dx + (x^2 \cos xy + e^y)\,dy = 0$.

Solution. $P = xy \cos xy + \sin xy, \qquad Q = x^2 \cos xy + e^y,$

$$\frac{\partial P}{\partial y} \equiv 2x \cos xy - x^2y \sin xy \equiv \frac{\partial Q}{\partial x}\cdot$$

The equation is exact and we seek $u(x, y)$ such that

$$\frac{\partial u}{\partial x} = xy \cos xy + \sin xy, \qquad \frac{\partial u}{\partial y} = x^2 \cos xy + e^y.$$

We integrate the *second* equation with respect to y:

$$u = x \sin xy + e^y + \phi(x),$$

$$\frac{\partial u}{\partial x} = xy \cos xy + \sin xy + \phi'(x).$$

Hence

$$xy \cos xy + \sin xy + \phi'(x) = xy \cos xy + \sin xy,$$

$$\phi'(x) = 0, \quad \phi(x) = \text{const},$$

$$u = x \sin xy + e^y + \text{const},$$

$$x \sin xy + e^y = c \quad \text{(gen. sol.)}.$$

* **2–6 Justification of the test for exactness.** Let the equation

$$P(x, y)\, dx + Q(x, y)\, dy = 0 \tag{2–32}$$

be given. We assume that $P(x, y)$ and $Q(x, y)$ have continuous first partial derivatives for all (x, y) and that

$$\frac{\partial P}{\partial y} = \frac{\partial Q}{\partial x} \tag{2–33}$$

for all (x, y). (The effect of discontinuities is discussed in Section 2–6 of ODE.)

We now seek a function $u(x, y)$ such that

$$\frac{\partial u}{\partial x} = P(x, y), \qquad \frac{\partial u}{\partial y} = Q(x, y). \tag{2–34}$$

Since addition of a constant to u does not affect (2–34), we can impose the additional condition

$$u(0, 0) = 0. \tag{2–35}$$

For by adding a constant to a solution of Eqs. (2–34), we can always ensure that Eq. (2–35) is satisfied.

To find the function u, we first seek the values of u along the x-axis. Here $y = 0$ and $\partial u/\partial x = P(x, 0)$. Since $u(x, 0)$ depends on x alone and

(2–35) holds (see Fig. 2–3),

$$u(x_1, 0) = \int_0^{x_1} \frac{\partial u}{\partial x}\,dx + u(0, 0) = \int_0^{x_1} \frac{\partial u}{\partial x}\,dx$$
$$= \int_0^{x_1} P(x, 0)\,dx. \tag{2–36}$$

Similarly, we can find the values of u along the y-axis:

$$u(0, y_1) = \int_0^{y_1} \frac{\partial u}{\partial y}\,dy + u(0, 0) = \int_0^{y_1} Q(0, y)\,dy. \tag{2–37}$$

From Eq. (2–36) we can find the value of u at (x_1, y_1):

$$u(x_1, y_1) - u(x_1, 0) = \int_0^{y_1} \frac{\partial u}{\partial y}(x_1, y)\,dy = \int_0^{y_1} Q(x_1, y)\,dy,$$

$$u(x_1, y_1) = u(x_1, 0) + \int_0^{y_1} Q(x_1, y)\,dy$$
$$= \int_0^{x_1} P(x, 0)\,dx + \int_0^{y_1} Q(x_1, y)\,dy. \tag{2–38}$$

Similarly, from (2–37)

$$u(x_1, y_1) = u(0, y_1) + \int_0^{x_1} P(x, y_1)\,dx$$
$$= \int_0^{x_1} P(x, y_1)\,dx + \int_0^{y_1} Q(0, y)\,dy. \tag{2–39}$$

We have now obtained two separate expressions (2–38) and (2–39) for the value of u at (x_1, y_1); however, the two are equal, for their difference is

$$\int_0^{x_1} P(x, 0)\,dx + \int_0^{y_1} Q(x_1, y)\,dy - \int_0^{x_1} P(x, y_1)\,dx - \int_0^{y_1} Q(0, y)\,dy$$
$$= \int_0^{y_1} [Q(x_1, y) - Q(0, y)]\,dy - \int_0^{x_1} [P(x, y_1) - P(x, 0)]\,dx$$
$$= \int_0^{y_1}\int_0^{x_1} \frac{\partial Q}{\partial x}(x, y)\,dx\,dy - \int_0^{x_1}\int_0^{y_1} \frac{\partial P}{\partial y}(x, y)\,dy\,dx.$$

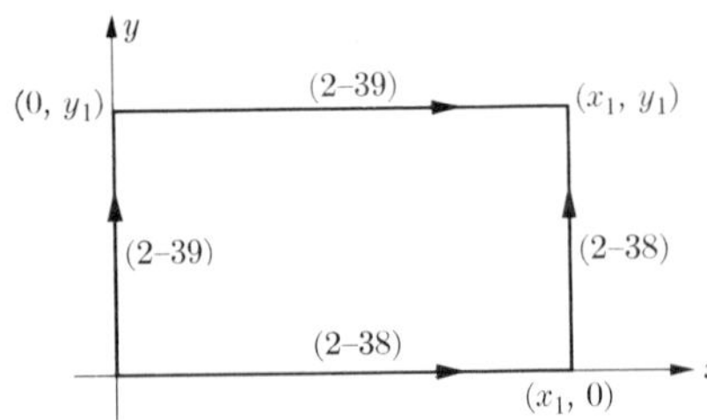

FIG. 2–3. Solution of exact equation by integration.

Both terms represent double integrals over the rectangle: $0 \leqq x \leqq x_1$, $0 \leqq y \leqq y_1$. Since $\partial Q/\partial x \equiv \partial P/\partial y$, the double integrals are equal and the difference is 0. Therefore (2–38) and (2–39) agree.

We now show that (2–34) holds at an arbitrary point (x_1, y_1). From Eq. (2–39), with y_1 held constant [see Eq. (1–44)], we find

$$\frac{\partial u}{\partial x_1} = \frac{\partial}{\partial x_1}\int_0^{x_1} P(x, y_1)\, dx = P(x_1, y_1).$$

Similarly, from Eq. (2–38), with x_1 held constant,

$$\frac{\partial u}{\partial y_1} = \frac{\partial}{\partial y_1}\int_0^{y_1} Q(x_1, y)\, dy = Q(x_1, y_1).$$

Thus (2–34) holds and Eq. (2–32) is exact.

Solution of initial value problem. If the general solution of an exact equation is obtained in the form $u(x, y) = c$, then the solution through (x_0, y_0) is obtained by choosing c so that $u(x_0, y_0) = c$. Hence the equation of the particular solution is

$$u(x, y) - u(x_0, y_0) = 0. \tag{2–40}$$

(The locus (2–40) may consist of several curves, one of which will define the particular solution sought.) When the variables are separable, (2–40) reduces to

$$\int_{x_0}^{x} P(x)\, dx + \int_{y_0}^{y} Q(y)\, dy = 0. \tag{2–41}$$

PROBLEMS

1. Show that the following equations are exact, and find all solutions:

(a) $2xy\, dx + (x^2 + 1)\, dy = 0$,

(b) $(2x + y)\, dx + (x - 2y)\, dy = 0$,

(c) $(15x^2y^2 - y^4)\, dx + (10x^3y - 4xy^3 + 5y^4)\, dy = 0$,

(d) $e^{x^2y}(1 + 2x^2y)\, dx + x^3e^{x^2y}\, dy = 0$,

(e) $[x \cos(x + y) + \sin(x + y)]\, dx + x \cos(x + y)\, dy = 0$,

(f) $3xy(1 + x^2)^{1/2}\, dx + [(1 + x^2)^{3/2} + \sin y]\, dy = 0$,

(g) $(x^2 + y^2)^2 (x\,dx + y\,dy) + 2\,dx + 3\,dy = 0$,
(h) $[(y\,dx - x\,dy)/y^2] + x\,dx = 0$,
(i) $(2xy^2 + 2xye^{2x} + e^{2x}y)\,dx + (2x^2y + xe^{2x})\,dy = 0$,
(j) $[(y - x)\,dx - 2x\,dy]/(x + y)^3 = 0$.

2. Find the particular solution specified:
(a) $(2x + y + 1)\,dx + (x + 3y + 2)\,dy = 0$; $y = 0$ when $x = 0$;
(b) $(3x + y + 5)^3(3\,dx + dy) + 2\,dx - dy = 0$; $y = 1$ when $x = -2$;
(c) $x^2\,dx + ye^y\,dy = 0$; $y = 1$ when $x = 0$;
(d) $e^{x^2}\,dx + \sin(1 + y^2)\,dy = 0$; $y = 0$ when $x = 0$;
(e) $ye^{-x^2}\,dx + [\int_0^x e^{-t^2}\,dt + y]\,dy = 0$; $y = 1$ when $x = 1$.

3. Find the general solution of the equation

$$(x + y)\,dx + x\,dy = 0,$$

(a) by means of (2–38); (b) by means of (2–39).

ANSWERS

1. (a) $x^2y + y = c$, (b) $x^2 + xy - y^2 = c$, (c) $5x^3y^2 - xy^4 + y^5 = c$, (d) $xe^{x^2y} = c$, (e) $x\sin(x + y) = c$, (f) $y(1 + x^2)^{3/2} - \cos y = c$, (g) $(x^2 + y^2)^3 + 12x + 18y = c$, (h) $2x + x^2y = cy$, (i) $x^2y^2 + xe^{2x}y = c$, (j) $x = c(x + y)^2$.

2. (a) $2x^2 + 2xy + 3y^2 + 2x + 4y = 0$, (b) $(3x + y + 5)^4 + 4(2x - y + 5) = 0$, (c) $x^3 + 3e^y(y - 1) = 0$, (d) $\int_0^x e^{t^2}\,dt + \int_0^y \sin(1 + t^2)\,dt = 0$, (e) $2y\int_0^x e^{-t^2}\,dt + y^2 = 2\int_0^1 e^{-x^2}\,dx + 1$.

3. $x^2 + 2xy = c$.

2–7 Integrating factors.

If an equation

$$P(x, y)\,dx + Q(x, y)\,dy = 0 \tag{2–42}$$

is not exact, we can attempt to make it exact by multiplying by a suitable function of x and y. For example, the equation

$$y\,dx - x\,dy = 0 \tag{2–43}$$

is not exact, but it becomes exact when multiplied by y^{-2}, for

$$\frac{y\,dx - x\,dy}{y^2} \equiv d\left(\frac{x}{y}\right). \tag{2–44}$$

We say that y^{-2} is an *integrating factor* for Eq. (2–43). Similarly,

$$2y\,dx + x\,dy = 0 \tag{2–45}$$

becomes exact on multiplication by x:

$$2xy\,dx + x^2\,dy \equiv d(x^2y) \equiv 0, \tag{2–45a}$$

so that x is an integrating factor.

It should be noted that multiplication of the differential equation by the integrating factor may introduce new discontinuities in the coefficients and may also introduce extraneous solutions (curves along which the integrating factor is zero). In the case of (2–43), the factor y^{-2} is discontinuous when $y = 0$. In the case of (2–45), the factor x is zero when $x = 0$, so that $x = 0$ is a solution of (2–45a); it happens to be a solution of (2–45) also. In general, the differential equation is changed when multiplied by the factor and a careful analysis is needed to ensure that no solutions are lost or gained in the process.

If an integrating factor has been found, then the given equation is replaced by an exact equation which can be solved by the methods of the preceding sections. Hence, except for the difficulties mentioned in the preceding paragraph, the general solution of the given equation is known.

EXAMPLE 1. $(xy + y - 1)\,dx + x\,dy = 0.$

Solution. Here e^x is an integrating factor, for

$$e^x(xy + y - 1)\,dx + xe^x\,dy = 0 \tag{2–46}$$

is exact:

$$\frac{\partial}{\partial y}\,e^x(xy + y - 1) \equiv e^x(x + 1) \equiv \frac{\partial}{\partial x}\,(xe^x).$$

We readily find the solutions of the new equation

$$xye^x - e^x = c.$$

Since e^x is never 0, the integrating factor introduces no complications and (2–46) gives the general solution of the given equation [there is one singular point: (0, 1), through which two solutions pass: $x = 0$ and $xy = 1 - e^{-x}$].

EXAMPLE 2. $(3xy + y^2)\,dx + (3xy + x^2)\,dy = 0$. Here the equation is not exact, but becomes exact when multiplied by $(x + y)$. For

$$(x + y)(3xy + y^2)\,dx + (x + y)(3xy + x^2)\,dy = 0$$

is exact, as is readily verified. In fact, the equation can be written

$$d\,[(x + y)^2 xy] = 0,$$

so that the solutions of the new equation are

$$(x + y)^2 xy = c.$$

Now the line $x + y = 0$ appears as a solution; however, it is not extraneous, since it is a solution of the original differential equation.

These two examples suggest the very great variety of integrating factors that may occur. It is natural to ask whether every equation $P\,dx + Q\,dy = 0$ has an integrating factor. It can be proved that an integrating factor does always exist, provided attention is restricted to a suitably small domain (Section 12–11 of ODE); however, this fact does not help to find integrating factors for particular problems (any more than the existence theorem of Section 1–7 helps us to find solutions).

The difficult problem of finding integrating factors for particular equations challenges the ingenuity. Here are some suggestions which are often helpful.

First note four commonly occurring exact differentials:

$$d(xy) = y\,dx + x\,dy, \tag{2–47}$$

$$d\left(\frac{y}{x}\right) = \frac{x\,dy - y\,dx}{x^2}, \tag{2–48}$$

$$d\arctan\frac{y}{x} = \frac{x\,dy - y\,dx}{x^2 + y^2}, \tag{2–49}$$

$$d\tfrac{1}{2}\log(x^2 + y^2) = \frac{x\,dx + y\,dy}{x^2 + y^2}. \tag{2–50}$$

Next observe that *if* $du = P\,dx + Q\,dy$, *then* $P\,dx + Q\,dy$ *remains an exact differential when multiplied by any continuous function of the function u.* For example,

$$2x\,dx + 2y\,dy = d(x^2 + y^2) = du,$$

$$(x^2 + y^2)(2x\,dx + 2y\,dy) = u\,du = d\left(\frac{u^2}{2}\right) \qquad (u = x^2 + y^2),$$

$$\frac{2x\,dx + 2y\,dy}{x^2 + y^2} = \frac{du}{u} = d\log u \qquad (u = x^2 + y^2).$$

The above explains (2–50), and we see that (2–49) is obtained from (2–48) by the reasoning:

$$\frac{x\,dy - y\,dx}{x^2 + y^2} = \frac{1}{1 + (y^2/x^2)}\,\frac{x\,dy - y\,dx}{x^2} = \frac{1}{1 + u^2}\,du = d\arctan u,$$

where $u = y/x$.

Given a particular equation, we can try to recognize an *exact portion* of the expression $P\,dx + Q\,dy$. We then try to multiply this *part* by an appropriate function $f(u)$ (where u is the function whose differential appears) in order to make the remaining portion exact.

Example 3. $(xy^2 + y)\,dx + x\,dy = 0$. This can be written

$$xy^2\,dx + d(xy) = 0.$$

We can multiply by a function of xy without spoiling the exactness of the second group. If we multiply by $(xy)^{-2}$ we remove y^2 from the first term:

$$\frac{dx}{x} + \frac{1}{(xy)^2}\,d(xy) = 0,$$

$$\log|x| - \frac{1}{xy} = c.$$

Example 4. $(x + 3y^2)\,dx + 2xy\,dy = 0$. Here $x\,dx$ is exact. We try to multiply by some function of x which will make $3y^2\,dx + 2xy\,dy$ exact. If we call this function $v(x)$, then we want

$$3y^2v\,dx + 2xvy\,dy = 0$$

to be an exact differential equation. Hence, by Eq. (2–33),

$$6yv \equiv 2y(xv' + v)$$

is the condition imposed. Accordingly, for $y \neq 0$,

$$6v = 2xv' + 2v,$$

$$xv' - 2v = 0,$$

$$x\frac{dv}{dx} - 2v = 0.$$

By separation of variables, we find that $v = x^2$ is a solution. Hence x^2 is the integrating factor sought. The new equation and general solution are found to be

$$(x^3 + 3x^2y^2)\,dx + 2x^3y\,dy = 0,$$

$$\frac{x^4}{4} + x^3y^2 = c.$$

Example 5. $(3y + 8xy^2)\,dx + (2x + 6x^2y)\,dy = 0$. Here we consider the group $3y\,dx + 2x\,dy$, which is not exact, but becomes so after multiplication by $(xy)^{-1}$, which has the effect of separating the variables:

$$(xy)^{-1}(3y\,dx + 2x\,dy) = \frac{3\,dx}{x} + \frac{2\,dy}{y}$$

$$= d(3 \log x + 2 \log y) = d(\log x^3y^2).$$

If the whole equation is multiplied by $(xy)^{-1}$, it becomes

$$3\frac{dx}{x} + 2\frac{dy}{y} + 8y\,dx + 6x\,dy = 0.$$

The first two terms together are exact and will remain exact when multiplied by any function of $\log x^3y^2$ or by any function of x^3y^2. We let $z = x^3y^2$ and try to choose $v(z)$ so that $v(z)(8y\,dx + 6x\,dy)$ is exact. Hence, by Eq. (2–33),

$$\frac{\partial}{\partial y}(8yv) = \frac{\partial}{\partial x}(6xv),$$

$$8v + 8y\frac{\partial v}{\partial y} = 6v + 6x\frac{\partial v}{\partial x},$$

$$8v + 8yv'(z)2x^3y = 6v + 6xv'(z)3x^2y^2,$$

$$2zv'(z) - 2v = 0.$$

Therefore we can choose $v = z$. The equation now becomes

$$zd \log z + 8x^3y^3\,dx + 6x^4y^2\,dy = 0,$$

$$z\frac{dz}{z} + d(2x^4y^3) = 0,$$

$$x^3y^2 + 2x^4y^3 = c.$$

The methods illustrated may not always be successful, but they are worth trying.

2–8 Linear equation of first order. A differential equation of first order is said to be linear if it can be written in the form

$$y' + p(x)y = q(x). \tag{2–51}$$

In differential form this equation is

$$[p(x)y - q(x)]\,dx + dy = 0.$$

The term $q(x)\,dx$ by itself is exact and will remain so after multiplication by a function of x, $v(x)$. We try to make the group $p(x)y\,dx + dy$ exact by multiplying by $v(x)$; that is,

$$v(x)p(x)y\,dx + v(x)\,dy = 0$$

is to be an exact equation. Accordingly, by Eq. (2–33),

$$v(x)p(x) = v'(x),$$

$$p(x)\,dx = \frac{dv}{v},$$

and we can choose $v = e^{\int p\,dx}$. The original equation becomes

$$v'(x)y\,dx + v(x)\,dy - v(x)q(x)\,dx = 0;$$

therefore

$$yv(x) - \int v(x)q(x)\,dx = c,$$

$$ye^{\int p\,dx} - \int e^{\int p\,dx}q(x)\,dx = c,$$

$$y = e^{-\int p\,dx}\int e^{\int p\,dx}q\,dx + ce^{-\int p\,dx}. \tag{2–52}$$

Equation (2–52) is a general formula for the solutions of the linear equation (2–51). Because of its importance, we state the result as a theorem:

THEOREM. *Let $p(x)$ and $q(x)$ be continuous for $a < x < b$. Let particular choices of the indefinite integrals $\int p\,dx$ and $\int e^{\int p\,dx} q\,dx$ be made. Then (2–52) gives all solutions of (2–51) over the interval $a < x < b$. In particular, for each point (x_0, y_0), $a < x_0 < b$, c can be chosen uniquely so that (2–52) passes through (x_0, y_0).*

Proof. We let $v = e^{\int p\,dx}$, so that v is continuous and

$$v' = e^{\int p\,dx} p(x) = pv.$$

If $y(x)$ is a solution of (2–51) for $a < x < b$, then successively

$$y' + py = q,$$

$$vy' + pvy = qv,$$

$$vy' + v'y = qv,$$

$$\frac{d}{dx}(vy) = qv,$$

$$vy = \int qv\,dx + c,$$

where the indefinite integral can be chosen as the given indefinite integral of qv. Now $v(x) \neq 0$. Hence we can divide by v:

$$y = v^{-1}\int qv\,dx + cv^{-1}; \tag{2–53}$$

therefore y has form (2–52). Next let y have form (2–52), so that (2–53) holds. We now reverse the steps, and arrive finally at the equation $y' + py = q$. Since v is continuous and $v \neq 0$, all the steps are reversible, and we conclude that every function (2–52) defines a solution of (2–51).

We can write (2–52) as

$$y = r(x) + \frac{c}{v(x)}.$$

The condition that when $x = x_0$, $y = y_0$, leads to the equation

$$y_0 = r(x_0) + \frac{c}{v(x_0)} \qquad [v(x_0) \neq 0].$$

Hence $c = v(x_0)[y_0 - r(x_0)]$. With this value of c (and only with this value) the initial condition is satisfied.

EXAMPLE. $y' + xy = x$. Here $p = x$ and $v = e^{x^2/2}$. Multiplying by v, we find

$$e^{x^2/2}y' + xe^{x^2/2}\,y = xe^{x^2/2},$$

$$e^{x^2/2}y = \int xe^{x^2/2}\,dx = e^{x^2/2} + c,$$

$$y = 1 + ce^{-x^2/2}.$$

The linear equation is of fundamental importance for applications. Accordingly, much of the following chapter is devoted to linear equations, and examples are given of typical applications.

PROBLEMS

1. Find an integrating factor for each of the following differential equations and obtain the general solution:

(a) $(x + 2y)\,dx + x\,dy = 0$,
(b) $(x + 3y)\,dx + x\,dy = 0$,
(c) $y\,dx + (y - x)\,dy = 0$,
(d) $2y^2\,dx + (2x + 3xy)\,dy = 0$,
(e) $(x^2 + y^2 + x)\,dx + y\,dy = 0$,
(f) $y\,dx + (x + x^2y^4)\,dy = 0$,
(g) $(2 + 2y^3)\,dx + 3xy^2\,dy = 0$,
(h) $y\,dx + (y^3 - 2x)\,dy = 0$,
(i) $(3y + 3e^xy^{2/3})\,dx + x\,dy = 0$,
(j) $(x + x^2y + y^3)\,dx + (y - x^3 - xy^2)\,dy = 0$,
(k) $(xy + y^2)\,dx + (xy - x^2)\,dy = 0$,
(l) $(y^3 - 2x^2y)\,dx + (2xy^2 - x^3)\,dy = 0$,
(m) $(5y - 6x)\,dx + x\,dy = 0$,
(n) $(\sin y + x^2 + 2x)\,dx + \cos y\,dy = 0$,
(o) $(3x - y^2)\,dx - 4xy\,dy = 0$.

2. Find the general solution of each of the following linear differential equations:

(a) $(dy/dx) + 3y = x$,
(b) $(dy/dx) + [y/(x + 1)] = \sin x$,
(c) $(\sin^2 x - y)\,dx - \tan x\,dy = 0$,
(d) $(y^2 - 1)\,dx + (y^3 - y + 2x)\,dy = 0$,
(e) $(dx/dt) + x = e^{2t}$.

3. Find the particular solution indicated:

(a) $(3xy + 2)\,dx + x^2\,dy = 0$; $y = 1$ when $x = 1$;
(b) $xy' + 2y = 2x \cos 2x + 2 \sin 2x$; $y = 1$ when $x = \pi$.

4. (a) An equation of form

$$y' + p(x)y = q(x)y^n \qquad (n \neq 1)$$

is called a *Bernoulli equation.* Show that the substitution $u = y^{1-n}$ reduces the equation to a linear equation for u as function of x. Obtain a formula analogous to (2–52) for the general solution.

(b) Show that the equation

$$[p(x)y^{k+1} + q(x)y^m]\,dx + r(x)y^k\,dy = 0 \qquad (m \neq k + 1)$$

can be written as a Bernoulli equation.

(c) Determine which of the equations of Prob. 1 are Bernoulli equations for y as a function of x or for x as a function of y.

5. Show that $v(x, y)$ is an integrating factor of the differential equation $P\,dx + Q\,dy = 0$ if and only if

$$Q\frac{\partial v}{\partial x} - P\frac{\partial v}{\partial y} = v\left(\frac{\partial P}{\partial y} - \frac{\partial Q}{\partial x}\right).$$

(*Additional problems* are given at the end of the chapter.)

ANSWERS

1. (a) $x^3 + 3x^2y = c$; (b) $x^4 + 4x^3y = c$; (c) $x + y\log|y| = cy$ and $y = 0$; (d) $y\log|x^2y^3| - 2 = cy$, $x = 0$ and $y = 0$; (e) $2x + \log(x^2 + y^2) = c$; (f) $xy^4 - 3 = 3cxy$, $y = 0$, $x = 0$; (g) $x^2(y^3 + 1) = c$; (h) $x + y^3 = cy^2$, $y = 0$; (i) $xy^{1/3} + e^x = c$; (j) $y = x\tan\{-[2(x^2 + y^2)]^{-1} + c\}$; (k) $x + y\log|xy| = cy$, $y = 0$, $x = 0$; (l) $x^2y^4 - x^4y^2 = c$; (m) $x^5y = x^6 + c$; (n) $e^x(\sin y + x^2) = c$; (o) $x(x - y^2)^2 = c$.

2. (a) $9y = 3x - 1 + ce^{-3x}$; (b) $(x + 1)y = \sin x - (x + 1)\cos x + c$; (c) $3y\sin x = \sin^3 x + c$; (d) $2x(y - 1) = (y + 1)[4y - y^2 - \log(y + 1)^4 + c]$, $y = -1$; (e) $3x = e^{2t} + ce^{-t}$.

3. (a) $x^3y + x^2 = 2$, (b) $x^2y = x^2\sin 2x + \pi^2$.

4. (a) $y = v^{-1}[(1 - n)\int v^{1-n}q\,dx + c]^{1/(1-n)}$, $v = e^{\int p\,dx}$; (c) parts (a), (b), (c), (e), (f), (g), (h), (i), (m), (o).

2–9 Method of substitution. One very general way to attack the first order equation $P\,dx + Q\,dy = 0$ is to introduce new variables u, v by the equations

$$x = \phi(u, v), \qquad y = \psi(u, v). \tag{2–54}$$

We shall consider the process formally, give examples, and then point out assumptions which should be satisfied to ensure that the steps to be taken have meaning.

From (2–54) we obtain

$$dx = \frac{\partial\phi}{\partial u}du + \frac{\partial\phi}{\partial v}dv, \qquad dy = \frac{\partial\psi}{\partial u}du + \frac{\partial\psi}{\partial v}dv. \tag{2–55}$$

Hence x, y, dx, dy are expressed in terms of u, v, du, dv, and the differential equation $P\,dx + Q\,dy = 0$ becomes a differential equation in u, v:

$$P[\phi(u, v), \psi(u, v)]\left(\frac{\partial \phi}{\partial u}\,du + \frac{\partial \phi}{\partial v}\,dv\right) \\ + Q[\ldots, \ldots]\left(\frac{\partial \psi}{\partial u}\,du + \cdots\right) = 0. \qquad (2\text{–}56)$$

When we collect terms, (2–56) becomes

$$P_1(u, v)\,du + Q_1(u, v)\,dv = 0. \qquad (2\text{–}57)$$

Let us suppose that the general solution of (2–57) has been found in form

$$U(u, v) = c. \qquad (2\text{–}58)$$

From (2–54) we obtain u, v as functions of x, y,

$$u = F(x, y), \qquad v = G(x, y). \qquad (2\text{–}59)$$

Substitution in (2–58) yields

$$U[F(x, y), G(x, y)] = c, \qquad (2\text{–}60)$$

which represents the general solution of $P\,dx + Q\,dy = 0$.

EXAMPLE 1. $\quad 3x^5\,dx - y(y^2 - x^3)\,dy = 0.$

Solution. We set

$$u = x^3, \qquad v = y^2, \qquad du = 3x^2\,dx, \qquad dv = 2y\,dy.$$

The equation becomes homogeneous:

$$u\,du - \tfrac{1}{2}(v - u)\,dv = 0.$$

Solution by the method of Section 2–4 yields

$$(v - 2u)(v + u)^2 = c;$$

hence

$$(y^2 - 2x^3)(y^2 + x^3)^2 = c$$

is the general solution of the given equation.

EXAMPLE 2.

$$(x\sqrt{x^2+y^2} + x^2y + y^2 + y^3)\,dx + (y\sqrt{x^2+y^2} - x^3 - xy - xy^2)\,dy = 0.$$

Solution. We introduce polar coordinates:

$$x = r\cos\theta, \qquad y = r\sin\theta, \qquad dx = \cos\theta\,dr - r\sin\theta\,d\theta,$$
$$dy = \sin\theta\,dr + \cos\theta\,d\theta.$$

The equation becomes

$$(r^2\cos\theta + r^3\sin\theta\cos^2\theta + r^2\sin^2\theta + r^3\sin^3\theta)(\cos\theta\,dr - r\sin\theta\,d\theta)$$
$$+ (r^2\sin\theta - r^3\cos^3\theta - r^2\sin\theta\cos\theta - r^3\sin^2\theta\cos\theta)$$
$$\times (\sin\theta\,dr + r\cos\theta)\,d\theta = 0,$$
$$r^2\,dr - (r^3\sin\theta + r^4)\,d\theta = 0,$$

which is a Bernoulli equation (Prob. 4 in Section 2–8) that becomes linear after the substitution $u = r^{-1}$. The solutions are found to be

$$re^{\cos\theta}\left(c - \int e^{-\cos\theta}\,d\theta\right) = 1.$$

The solution can be rewritten in rectangular coordinates if desired. If this is to be done, it is simpler to replace the indefinite integral of $e^{-\cos\theta}$ by

$$\int_0^\theta e^{-\cos t}\,dt$$

and then to set $\theta = \tan^{-1}(y/x)$.

Discussion of the method. The equations (2–54) can be regarded as a transformation, or mapping, of a region in the uv-plane into the xy-plane. We want to be able to solve for u, v in terms of x, y as in (2–59), which means that *we must assume a one-to-one correspondence between the points of a domain in the uv-plane and those of a domain in the xy-plane*, as suggested in Fig. 2–4. Under such a correspondence the family of solution curves of the given differential equation is replaced by a curve family in the uv-plane. If the functions (2–54) and (2–59) have continuous partial derivatives, then it follows from calculus that each curve in the uv-domain satisfies (2–57); conversely, each solution of (2–57) corresponds to a solution of $P\,dx + Q\,dy = 0$.

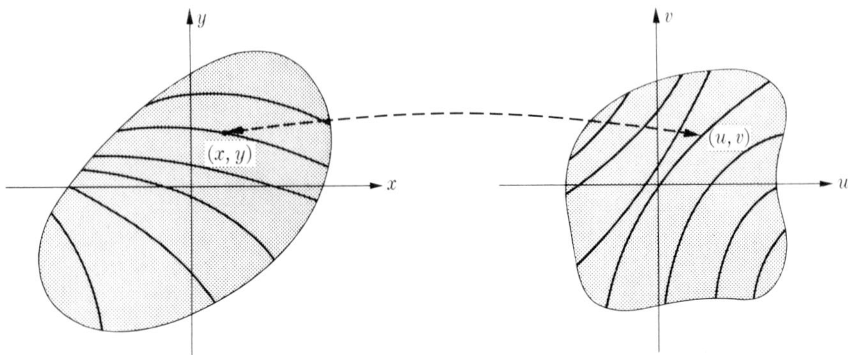

FIG. 2–4. Change of variables in first order equation.

The requirement that the correspondence be one-to-one is ordinarily satisfied only if attention is restricted to sufficiently small domains in the xy-plane and the uv-plane. In Example 1, the transformation is given by $u = x^3$, $v = y^2$; this correspondence is one-to-one if, for example, $y > 0$ and $v > 0$. The inverse functions are $x = u^{1/3}$, $y = v^{1/2}$. To ensure that these have continuous partial derivatives, we must make a further restriction; for example, $u > 0$, $x > 0$. Thus we apparently obtain only the solutions in the first quadrant: $x > 0, y > 0$. However, a similar analysis applies to each of the other quadrants. The lines $x = 0$, $y = 0$ are solution curves; the origin is a singular point.

In Example 2, the transformation is given by $x = r \cos \theta$, $y = r \sin \theta$ and is one-to-one if, for example, $r > 0$ and $-\pi < \theta < \pi$. Under these restrictions the solutions are meaningful and provide the solutions in the xy-plane without the negative x-axis. To study the solutions near the omitted line, we can require $r > 0$, $0 < \theta < 2\pi$, and the same formula is obtained.

In certain cases we do not need to assume the transformation to be one-to-one. A much simpler reasoning is sufficient. Given the differential equation $P\,dx + Q\,dy = 0$, we suppose the functions $u(x, y)$, $v(x, y)$ to be such that (in a certain domain)

$$P_1(u, v)\,du + Q_1(u, v)\,dv \equiv P\,dx + Q\,dy$$

when u, v, $du = (\partial u/\partial x)\,dx + (\partial u/\partial y)\,dy$, $dv = (\partial v/\partial x)\,dx + (\partial v/\partial y)\,dy$ are expressed in terms of x and y. Suppose further that we have found an integrating factor V for the equation $P_1\,du + Q_1\,dv = 0$, that is, that

$$dU(u, v) = VP_1\,du + VQ_1\,dv,$$

so that the solutions are given by $U(u, v) = c$. Then we can also write

$$dU = V(P_1\,du + Q_1\,dv) = V(P\,dx + Q\,dy);$$

that is, when u and v are expressed in terms of x and y, $V(u, v) = V[u(x, y), v(x, y)]$ becomes an integrating factor for $P\,dx + Q\,dy = 0$ and the solutions are given by $U[u(x, y), v(x, y)] = c$. The crucial fact is that *it may not be necessary to solve for x and y in terms of u and v.*

Example 1 fits the conditions described. For, with $u = x^3$, $v = y^2$, we have

$$u\,du - \tfrac{1}{2}(v - u)\,dv \equiv 3x^5\,dx - y(y^2 - x^3)\,dy.$$

PROBLEMS

1. Apply the given transformation to obtain a differential equation in the new variables; then obtain the general solution of the given differential equation:

(a) $(2x + y)\,dx + (x + 5y)\,dy = 0$; $u = x - y$, $v = x + 2y$;
(b) $3x^2ye^y\,dx + x^3e^y(y + 1)\,dy = 0$; $u = x^3$, $v = ye^y$;
(c) $(2x - 3y)\,dx - 3x\,dy = 0$; $u = x^2 - 3xy$, $v = x + y$;
(d) $(x + 2y)\,dx + (y - 2x)\,dy = 0$; $x = r\cos\theta$, $y = r\sin\theta$;
(e) $(3x^3 + xy^2 - x^2y^2 - y^4)\,dx + (3x^2y + y^3 + x^3y + xy^3)\,dy = 0$; $x = r\cos\theta$, $y = r\sin\theta$.

2. Find an appropriate transformation of variables and obtain the general solution:

(a) $e^x\sin y\,dx + e^x\cos y\,dy = 0$;
(b) $(x^2 + y^2)^3(y\,dx + x\,dy) + 6xy(x^2 + y^2)^2(x\,dx + y\,dy) = 0$;
(c) $2(x^3 - xy^3)\,dx + 3(x^2y^2 + y^5)\,dy = 0$.

3. Show that an appropriate translation of axes: $x = u + h$, $y = v + k$, converts

$$(a_1x + b_1y + c_1)\,dx + (a_2x + b_2y + c_2)\,dy = 0$$

($a_1, b_1, c_1, a_2, b_2, c_2$ constants) into a homogeneous equation in u, v, provided $a_1b_2 - a_2b_1 \neq 0$. Show that, when $a_1b_2 - a_2b_1 = 0$, the equation can be written in the form

$$[k_1(\alpha x + \beta y) + c_1]\,dx + [k_2(\alpha x + \beta y) + c_2]\,dy = 0.$$

Show that, if $\alpha^2 + \beta^2 \neq 0$, the substitution $x = \alpha u + \beta v$, $y = \beta u - \alpha v$ now leads to a separation of variables.

4. Find all solutions of the following equations (see Prob. 3):

(a) $(x + 2y - 1)\,dx + (2x - y - 7)\,dy = 0$;
(b) $(x + y + 1)\,dx + (2x + 2y + 1)\,dy = 0$;
(c) $(3x - 3y + 2)\,dx + (2x - 2y + 1)\,dy = 0$;
(d) $(2x + 3y)\,dx + (3x + 2y + 1)\,dy = 0$.

5. Show that the introduction of polar coordinates: $x = r\cos\theta$, $y = r\sin\theta$ leads to a separation of variables in a homogeneous equation $y' = F(x, y)$.

ANSWERS

1. (a) $u\,du + v\,dv = 0$, $2x^2 + 2xy + 5y^2 = c$; (b) $u\,dv + v\,du = 0$, $x^3ye^y = c$; (c) $du = 0$, $x^2 - 3xy = c$; (d) $r\,dr - 2r^2\,d\theta = 0$, $r = ce^{2\theta}$; (e) $r^3(1 + 2\cos^2\theta)\,dr + r^5\sin\theta\,d\theta = 0$, $r = c\exp[(\sqrt{2}/2)\tan(\sqrt{2}\cos\theta)]$.

2. (a) $e^x \sin y = c$, (b) $xy(x^2 + y^2)^3 = c$, (c) $\log(x^4 + y^6) + 2\arctan(x^2/y^3) = c$.

4. (a) $x^2 + 4xy - y^2 - 2x - 14y = c$; (b) $x + 2y + \log|x + y| = c$ and $x + y = 0$; (c) $\log|5x - 5y + 3| + 15x + 10y = c$, $5x - 5y + 3 = 0$; (d) $x^2 + 3xy + y^2 + y = c$.

MISCELLANEOUS PROBLEMS

For each of the following first order differential equations determine whether the equation has separable variables, is homogeneous, is linear, or is exact, and find the general solution.

1. $y' = (x + 1)/y$.
2. $y' + y = 2x + 1$.
3. $(2xy - y + 2x)\,dx + (x^2 - x)\,dy = 0$.
4. $y' = (x^2 - 1)/(y^2 + 1)$.
5. $[\{y/(xy + 1)\} + x^2]\,dx + [x\,dy/(xy + 1)] = 0$.
6. $y \sin\log x\,dx - \tan y\,dy = 0$.
7. $y' = [(x + \sqrt{x^2 - y^2})/y]$.
8. $(2x\sin xy + x^2y\cos xy)\,dx + x^3\cos xy\,dy = 0$.
9. $y' = y + e^y$.
10. $(2x - y)\,dx + (x + 2y)\,dy = 0$.
11. $(2x + y + 1)\,dx + (x + 3y + 2)\,dy = 0$.
12. $y' = xy^2 + 2xy$.
13. $(y - x^2 - 2xy)\,dx + (x^2 - x)\,dy = 0$.
14. $y' = (2xe^{-2x} - 2y^3)/3y^2$.
15. $(y + y^2)\,dx + (x - 2y - 4y^2 - 2y^3)\,dy = 0$.
16. $(dy/dx) + [(4x^3y + y^4)/(x^4 + 4xy^3)] = 0$.
17. $dy/dx = [2x(4x^2 - y^3)]/[3y^2(2x^2 + y^3)]$.
18. $(2y^2 + xy)\,dx + (y^2 - x^2 - xy)\,dy = 0$.
19. $(2x^3y^2 + 3x^2y^3 - 1)\,dx + (2x^4y + x^3y^2 - 1)\,dy = 0$.
20. $(x^3 + xy^2 - x^2y - y^3 + y^2)\,dx + (x^2y + y^3 + x^3 + xy^2 - xy)\,dy = 0$.
21. $t(dx/dt) + x = t^3$.
22. $(1 + 3x + 3y - x^2 + 2xy - y^2)\,dx$ $+ (1 - 3x - 3y + x^2 - 2xy + y^2)\,dy = 0$.
23. $(3xe^{3x}\sin 2y + e^{3x}\sin 2y)\,dx + (2xe^{3x}\cos 2y + 2y)\,dy = 0$.
24. $y' = x^2y^2 + xy^2 - x^2y - y^2 - xy + y$.
25. $(5x^2y^3 + 4xy^2 + 3y)\,dx + (4x^3y^2 + 3x^2y + 2x)\,dy = 0$.

ANSWERS

1. $y^2 = (x+1)^2 + c$. 2. $y = 2x - 1 + ce^{-x}$. 3. $x^2y - xy + x^2 = c$. 4. $y^3 + 3y = x^3 - 3x + c$. 5. $(xy+1)^3 = ce^{-x^3}$. 6. $\int \sin \log x \, dx - \int (\tan y/y) \, dy = c$. 7. $x + \sqrt{x^2 - y^2} = c$. 8. $x^2 \sin xy = c$. 9. $\int [dy/(y + e^y)] = x + c$. 10. $r = ce^{-\theta/2}$ (polar coords.). 11. $2x^2 + 2xy + 3y^2 + 2x + 4y = c$. 12. $\log |y/(y+2)| = x^2 + c$, $y = 0$, $y = -2$. 13. $x + y = c(x^2 + y)$. 14. $y^3e^{2x} = x^2 + c$. 15. $y^2 - [xy/(1+y)] = c$. 16. $x^4y + xy^4 = c$. 17. $(y^3 + 4x^2)^2(y^3 - x^2)^3 = c$. 18. $(x+y)e^{x/y} = c$. 19. $x^3y^2 + 1 = c(x+y)$. 20. $r = ce^{-\theta} + \frac{1}{2}(\sin\theta - \cos\theta)$(polar coords.). 21. $4xt - t^4 = c$. 22. $9(x-y)^2 + 21y - 33x + 2 = ce^{3(y-x)}$. 23. $y^2 + xe^{3x} \sin 2y = c$. 24. $y(1 - ce^{(2x^3+3x^2-6x)/6}) = 1$. 25. $x^5y^4 + x^4y^3 + x^3y^2 = c$.

SUGGESTED REFERENCES

1. AGNEW, RALPH, *Differential Equations*. New York: McGraw-Hill, 1942.

2. FORSYTH, A. R., *Theory of Differential Equations*, Vols. 1–6. Cambridge, Eng.: Cambridge University Press, 1890–1906.

3. KAMKE, E., *Differentialgleichungen, Lösungsmethoden und Lösungen*, Vol. 1, 2nd ed. Leipzig: Akademische Verlagsgesellschaft, 1943.

4. THOMAS, GEORGE B., *Calculus*. Reading, Mass.: Addison-Wesley, 1953.

CHAPTER 3

APPLICATIONS OF FIRST ORDER EQUATIONS

3–1 Orthogonal trajectories. Let there be given a family of curves in a domain D in the xy-plane. We assume that each curve has a well-defined tangent at each point and that exactly one curve passes through each point of D, as suggested in Fig. 3–1.

Now let us suppose that a second family of curves is given in D, with similar properties, and that each curve of the second family meets each curve of the first family at *right angles*. Then we say that the second family forms a set of *orthogonal trajectories* of the first family; similarly, the first family is a set of orthogonal trajectories of the second. (The word *trajectory* is synonymous with *solution curve;* the term arose in mechanics.)

If the first family consists of the solutions of a differential equation

$$P(x, y)\, dx + Q(x, y)\, dy = 0, \tag{3–1}$$

then, under reasonable assumptions, the second family is *uniquely* defined as the family of solutions of the differential equation

$$Q(x, y)\, dx - P(x, y)\, dy = 0 \tag{3–2}$$

in D. For example, if $P^2 + Q^2 \neq 0$ in D and $P(x, y), Q(x, y)$ have continuous first partial derivatives in D, then the existence theorem (Section

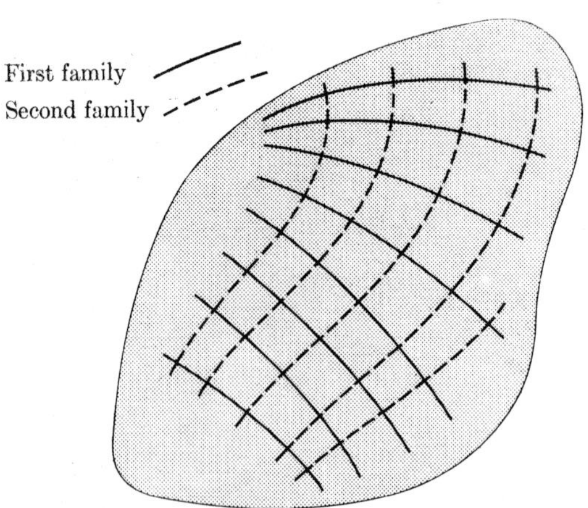

Fig. 3–1. Orthogonal trajectories.

1–7) guarantees a unique solution of (3–1) or of (3–2) through each point of D. The corresponding slopes are

$$\frac{dy}{dx} = -\frac{P}{Q}, \qquad \frac{dy}{dx} = \frac{Q}{P}. \tag{3–3}$$

Since these are negative reciprocals of each other (one of the two may be ∞), the corresponding curves are orthogonal.

If the first family is given as the primitive of (3–1) in the form $F(x, y, c) = 0$, then Eq. (3–1) can be obtained as in Section 1–9 by differentiating and eliminating c. From (3–1) we obtain (3–2) by interchanging coefficients and changing sign. The orthogonal trajectories are then the solutions of (3–2).

EXAMPLE 1. Find the orthogonal trajectories of the circles $x^2 + y^2 = c$.

Solution.

$$2x\,dx + 2y\,dy = 0,$$

$$y\,dx - x\,dy = 0,$$

$$\frac{dx}{x} - \frac{dy}{y} = 0,$$

$$y = cx, \qquad x = 0.$$

The orthogonal trajectories are the rays through the origin. The origin itself is a singular point for both families.

EXAMPLE 2. Find the orthogonal trajectories of the family $x^2 - cx + 4y = 0$.

Solution.

$$2x - c + 4y' = 0, \tag{3–4}$$

$$x^2 - x(2x + 4y') + 4y = 0, \tag{3–5}$$

$$4xy' - 4y + x^2 = 0. \tag{3–6}$$

We have used derivatives instead of differentials; hence we replace y' by $-1/y'$ to obtain the orthogonal trajectories:

$$\frac{-4x}{y'} - 4y + x^2 = 0, \qquad -4x\,dx + (x^2 - 4y)\,dy = 0.$$

The substitution $u = x^2$ leads to a linear equation for u as a function of y. The solutions are found to be

$$(x^2 - 4y - 8)e^{-y/2} = c.$$

There are two common errors in finding orthogonal trajectories. The first is to fail to eliminate the constant from the given primitive; in Example 2 this would lead to the use of (3–4) instead of (3–6) as the differential equation of the given family. The second error is to forget to replace y' by $-1/y'$, so that the given family is obtained instead of the orthogonal trajectories.

PROBLEMS

1. Find the family of orthogonal trajectories for each of the following families of curves, and graph both families in each case:
(a) $y^2 = 4cx$, (b) $x^2 + y^2 + cx = 0$,
(c) $x^2 + y^2 + 2cy - 1 = 0$, (d) $y = ce^{-2x}$,
(e) the family of all circles through $(1, 1)$ and $(-1, -1)$,
(f) the family of similar ellipses: $(x^2/a^2) + (y^2/4a^2) = 1$.

2. (a) Let a family of curves be the family of solutions of a differential equation $y' = f(x, y)$. Let a second similar family have the property that at each point (x, y) the angle from the tangent to the curve of the first family through (x, y) to the tangent of the second family through (x, y) is α (rad). Show that the second family satisfies the differential equation

$$y' = \frac{f(x, y) + \tan\alpha}{1 - f(x, y)\tan\alpha}.$$

(b) Find the family of curves whose tangents form the angle α with the circles $x^2 + y^2 = c^2$.

(c) Find the family of curves whose tangents form the angle $\pi/4$ with the hyperbolas $xy = c$.

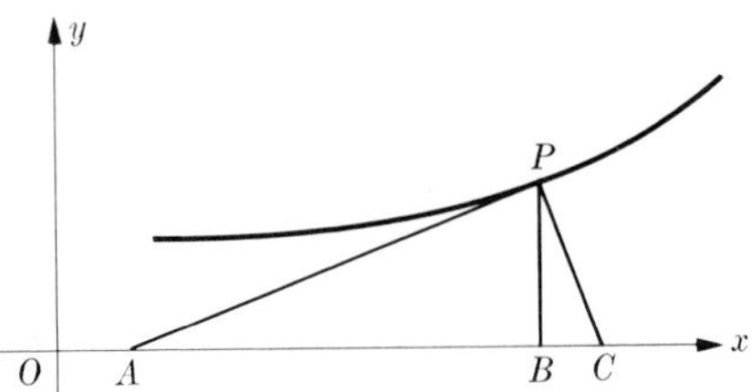

FIGURE 3–2

3. In Fig. 3–2 a general curve $y = f(x)$ is shown; $P(x, y)$ is an arbitrary point on the curve, AP is tangent to the curve, and PC is normal to the curve. Find $f(x)$ in each of the following cases:
(a) $OA = BP$ for all P; when $x = 2$, $y = 1$;
(b) $OA = AB$ for all P; when $x = 3$, $y = 1$;
(c) $(BP)^2 = BC$ for all P; when $x = 1$, $y = 1$.

ANSWERS

1. (a) $2x^2 + y^2 = c^2$, (b) $x^2 + y^2 + cy = 0$, (c) $c(x^2 + y^2) - x + c = 0$, (d) $y^2 = x + c$, (e) $c(x^2 + y^2) - x - y + 2c = 0$, (f) $y^4 = cx$, $x = 0$.

2. (b) $r = ce^{-\theta\tan\alpha}$ (in polar coordinates), (c) $x^2 - 2xy + y^2 = c$.

3. (a) $2y - y\log|y| = x$, (b) $9y = x^2$, (c) $y = e^{x-1}$.

3–2 Properties of the solutions of linear equations. Linear differential equations of first and higher orders are of fundamental importance for applications. In fact it can be stated that, with a few exceptions, the only mechanisms which are fully understood are those which obey linear equations.

The first order linear equation can be used to illustrate many basic properties of the linear equations. To emphasize that it is usually the *time* which is the independent variable, the equation will be written in the form

$$a\,D_t x + x = F(t), \tag{3–7}$$

where $D_t x$ denotes dx/dt. Throughout the following, except where otherwise indicated, it will be assumed that a is a positive constant.

Case I. $F(t) = 0$. The general solution is found by (2–52) or by separation of variables to be

$$x = ce^{-t/a}. \tag{3–8}$$

These curves are plotted for the case $a = 1$ in Fig. 3–3. They illustrate a phenomenon of very common occurrence, known as *exponential decay.* Examples are the fading out of a light bulb when the current is turned off, the cooling of a thermometer to the temperature of the surrounding medium, the decay of radium, the reaction rates in various chemical reactions. In all cases the system is approaching a state of equilibrium, represented by the line $x = 0$. The rate of approach to the equilibrium state is

$$\left|\frac{dx}{dt}\right| = \left|\frac{x}{a}\right|,$$

and is proportional to the difference $|x|$ between the present state and the

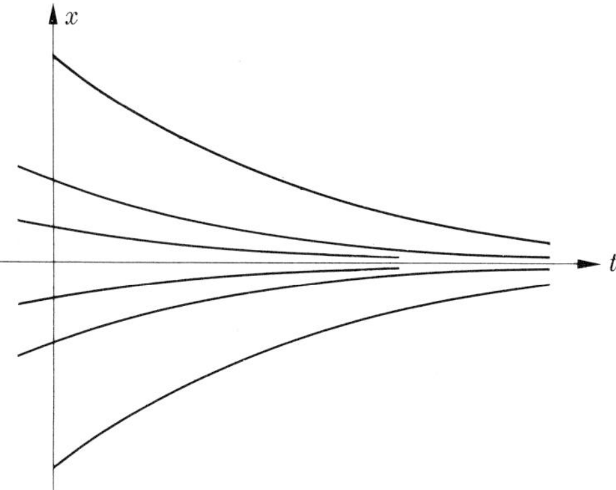

Fig. 3–3. Exponential decay.

equilibrium state. For $t = 0$, $x = c$, so that $c = x_0$, the *initial value* of x. For $t = a$, $x = x_0e^{-1}$; for $t = 2a$, $x = x_0e^{-2}$. In general, the values of x at equally spaced times form a *geometric progression*, approaching 0 as t increases.

The number a measures the rate of approach to 0. The larger a is, the slower the rate. The number a has the dimension of time and is often termed the *time constant* or *solution time.* It has been assumed here that a is positive. If a is negative, the solutions increase in absolute value as time increases, and the system is *unstable.* This case has applications in many practical problems: growth of population, growth of bacteria, growth of money at compound interest.

Case II. $F(t) = K =$ constant. The solutions are at once found to be

$$x = K + ce^{-t/a}. \tag{3-9}$$

It is clear that the only effect is to translate the picture of Fig. 3–3 along the x-direction, as shown in Fig. 3–4. The equilibrium solution is now the line $x = K$.

Case III. $F(t)$ a discontinuous function, piecewise constant, as shown in Fig. 3–5. Such a function is known as a *step-function.*

The meaning of a solution of Eq. (3–7) when $F(t)$ is discontinuous requires some discussion. We shall here consider $x(t)$ to be a solution if $x(t)$

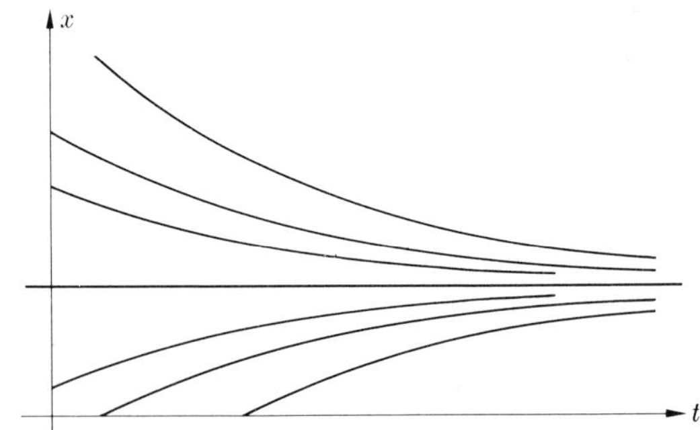

Fig. 3–4. Response to constant input.

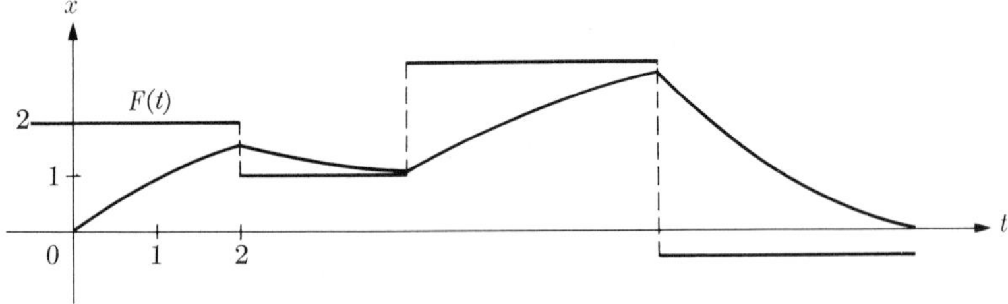

Fig. 3–5. Follow-up of step-function input.

is continuous and $x(t)$ satisfies the differential equation wherever $F(t)$ is continuous. One can verify that the existence theorem of Section 1–7 continues to apply to Eq. (3–7), when $F(t)$ is a step-function.

One can deduce the form of the solution when $F(t)$ is as in Fig. 3–5 by following physical reasoning. Let us assume that $x(0) = 0$. The mechanism described by x knows only the values of $F(t)$ in the present and past. For $t < 2$, it cannot anticipate that $F(t)$ will jump at $t = 2$. Accordingly, between $t = 0$ and $t = 2$ the solution is the same as that of Case II, with the constant $K = 2$. As t increases from 0 to 2, x increases, approaching the line $x = 2$ exponentially. When $t = 2$, F jumps to the new value 1; the mechanism proceeds to approach this value of x exponentially. The process repeats itself in the other intervals.

The situation can be described in the following way. The function $F(t)$ serves as an *input*, the solution $x(t)$ as an *output*. If there were no "mechanism," a would equal 0, and the output would equal the input. In any case, the output, $x(t)$, tries to stay with the input, $F(t)$. Thus, by ignoring the term in $D_t x$, an approximate solution $x = F(t)$ is obtained. The accuracy of the approximation depends on the size of a, which governs the speed of "follow-up."

If $F(t)$ is now replaced by an arbitrary (within reason) function of t, it can be approximated by a step-function, and similar conclusions are reached.

If a is allowed to vary with time, again the results are similar. The speed of follow-up is fluctuating, rather than steady. If a becomes negative, the solutions are unstable and are receding from, rather than following, $F(t)$.

From the general formula (2–52), further information can be obtained. For the case at hand, with $a =$ const, the formula becomes

$$x = e^{-t/a} \int e^{t/a} F(t)\, dt + ce^{-t/a}, \tag{3–10}$$

or, in terms of an initial condition $x(0) = x_0$,

$$x = e^{-t/a} \int_0^t e^{u/a} F(u)\, du + x_0 e^{-t/a}. \tag{3–11}$$

Varying the initial value of x affects the second term, but does not affect the first term. If a is positive, the second term approaches 0 exponentially, is a "transient." Thus for large values of t the solution is effectively independent of the initial conditions; the differential equation has, in this sense, only *one solution*.

If $F(t)$ is multiplied by a constant k, then the solution $x(t)$ is also, except for a transient, multiplied by the constant k. If $F(t)$ is a sum of two functions $F_1(t)$ and $F_2(t)$, then the solution $x(t)$ is, apart from transients, the

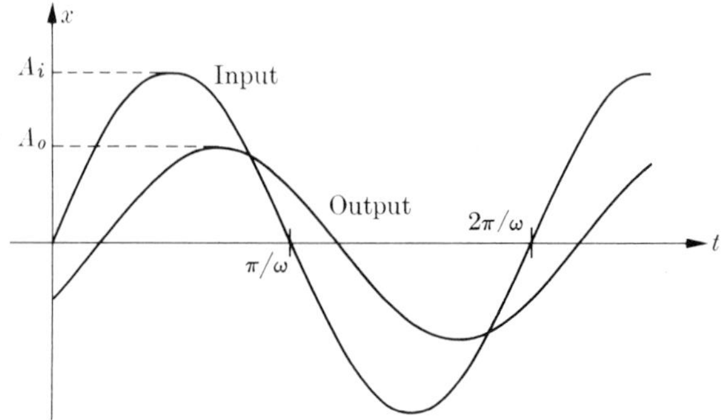

FIG. 3–6. Response to sinusoidal input.

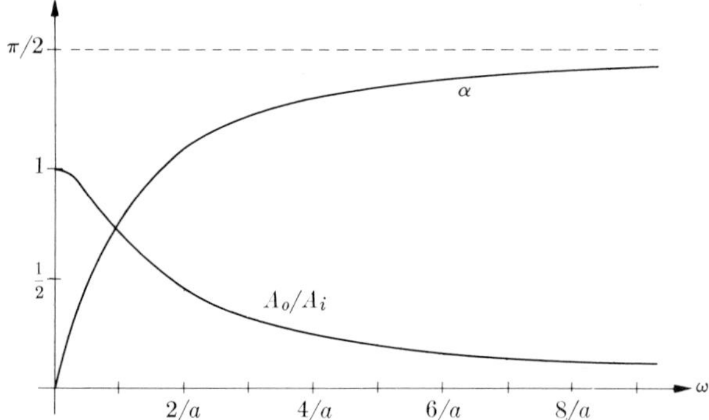

FIG. 3–7. Amplification and phase lag for sinusoidal input.

sum of two solutions $x_1(t)$ and $x_2(t)$, corresponding to F_1 and F_2 respectively. In other words, the *output depends linearly on the input.* These conclusions follow immediately from Eq. (3–11). They embody the *superposition principle* (see Section 4–4).

If $F(t)$ is simple harmonic: $F(t) = A_i \sin \omega t$, then so is the solution $x(t)$, except for a transient:

$$x(t) = A_o \sin(\omega t - \alpha) + ce^{-t/a}. \tag{3–12}$$

The frequency ω is the same for input and output, but the output amplitude A_o is less than the input amplitude A_i and there is a lag in phase. This is shown in Fig. 3–6. More specifically, one finds

$$A_o = \frac{A_i}{\sqrt{1 + a^2\omega^2}}, \qquad \alpha = \arctan(a\omega), \quad 0 < \alpha < \frac{\pi}{2}; \tag{3–13}$$

these relations are portrayed in Fig. 3–7, in which the "amplification factor" A_o/A_i and phase lag are graphed against ω. Since $A_o < A_i$, the amplification factor is less than 1, so that the input is diminished rather than amplified. The results stated here follow from Eq. (3–11) (see Prob. 2 below, following Section 3–3).

A more thorough discussion of the properties of solutions of the first order linear equation is given in Chapter 3 of ODE.

3–3 Physical applications of the linear equation. We give here several specific examples of phenomena whose laws are expressed by linear equations of first order. In each case the equation must be considered as an idealization of what is observed. For restricted ranges of the variables, the accuracy is in general very good.

A. *Heat conduction.* If a body at temperature x is immersed in a medium at temperature F, then the temperature of the body will approach temperature F at a rate which is proportional to the difference between x and F:

$$D_t x = k(F - x) \qquad (k > 0), \tag{3–14}$$

or

$$\frac{1}{k} D_t x + x = F. \tag{3–14a}$$

If F also varies with time, then $F(t)$ serves as input, the actual temperature as output. (See Reference 3, p. 221.)

B. *Motion against friction.* If a particle of mass m moves with velocity $v = D_t x$ along a line (the x-axis), and is subject to no force other than frictional resistance proportional to velocity, then the variation of velocity is governed by the linear equation

$$m\, D_t v + kv = 0. \tag{3–15}$$

(An example is that of a boy sliding on ice.) If, in addition, a force $f(t)$ is applied, the equation becomes

$$m\, D_t v + kv = f(t). \tag{3–16}$$

In particular, $f(t)$ may be constant; this case is illustrated by a body, (e.g., a parachute) falling against air resistance.

C. *Electric circuits.* If a circuit contains only a resistance R, a capacitance C, and an emf $\mathcal{E}$, as in Fig. 3–8, then the charge on the capacitor varies with time t according to the linear equation:

$$R\, D_t q + \frac{1}{C} q = \mathcal{E}. \tag{3–17}$$

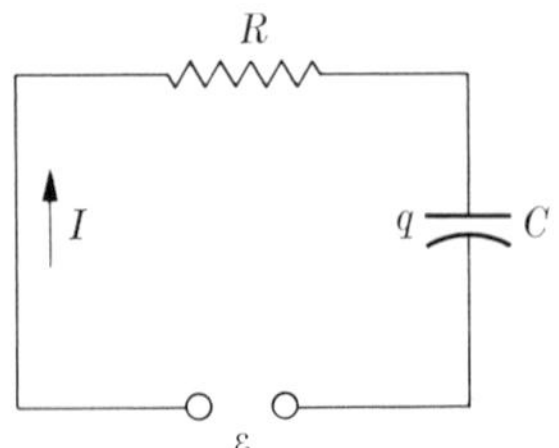

FIG. 3–8. $\mathcal{E}RC$-circuit.

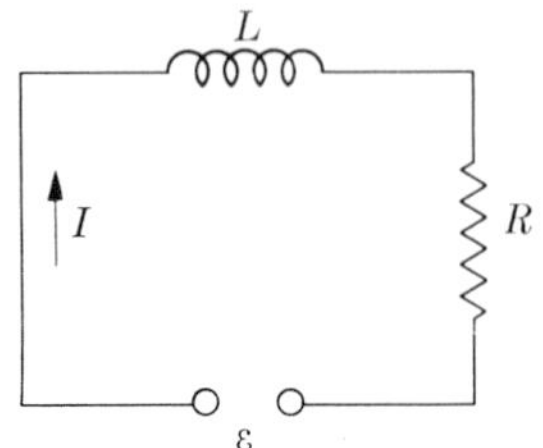

FIG. 3–9. $\mathcal{E}RL$-circuit.

Here the emf $\mathcal{E}$ may depend on time t and, in particular, be sinusoidal:

$$\mathcal{E} = \mathcal{E}_0 \sin \omega t. \tag{3–18}$$

The current I in the circuit is simply the rate of change of the charge q:

$$D_t q = I. \tag{3–19}$$

Hence the current I obeys the equation

$$R\, D_t I + \frac{1}{C} I = D_t \mathcal{E}. \tag{3–20}$$

If the circuit contains only an inductance L, a resistance R, and an emf $\mathcal{E}$, as in Fig. 3–9, then the current obeys the linear equation:

$$L\, D_t I + RI = \mathcal{E} \tag{3–21}$$

(see Reference 6).

D. *Radioactive decay.* A substance such as radium disintegrates at a rate proportional to the mass remaining. If x is the mass at time t, we have

$$D_t x = -kx \qquad (k > 0). \tag{3–22}$$

If more of the substance is being produced (e.g., in a nuclear reactor) at rate $f(t)$, then the total mass x obeys the equation

$$D_t x + kx = f(t). \tag{3–23}$$

E. *Growth of population.* Consider, for example, a population in a friendly environment that permits unlimited expansion. The number of offspring and the number of deaths in a short time interval are then approximately proportional to the size of the population at the beginning of the interval. Idealizing the process as a continuous one, we obtain the differential equation

$$D_t x = kx \qquad (k > 0), \tag{3–24}$$

where x is a number which measures the size of the population. If, in addition to the natural growth, there are gains or losses in population due to immigration or emigration, then (3–24) becomes

$$D_t x = kx + f(t). \tag{3–25}$$

In all five examples, the principles discussed above find immediate application. All but the last example represent stable systems, and the output can be considered as some sort of imitation of the input.

PROBLEMS

1. Evaluate and plot the solution such that $x = 0$ for $t = 0$ for the following differential equations:

(a) $D_t x + x = 1$, (b) $10 D_t x + x = 1$,
(c) $D_t x + x = \sin t$, (d) $10 D_t x + x = \sin t$.

Compare output with input in each case.

2. (a) Show that, if a is a positive constant, then the general solution of the differential equation

$$a\, D_t x + x = A_i \sin \omega t$$

is given by

$$x = A_o \sin (\omega t - \alpha) + ce^{-t/a},$$

where

$$A_o = \frac{A_i}{\sqrt{1 + a^2\omega^2}}, \qquad \tan \alpha = a\omega, \quad 0 \leqq \alpha < \pi/2.$$

(b) Verify the graphs of Fig. 3–7.

3. A thermometer which reads 75°F indoors is taken outdoors. After five minutes it reads 65°; after another five minutes it reads 60°. What is the outdoor temperature?

4. If the temperature of a body is changing rapidly, the instantaneous reading of a thermometer in the body will not agree with that of the body. Let us assume the reading r to be related to the actual temperature x by a linear equation $a\, D_t r + r = x$, $(a > 0)$. Discuss the manner in which r will vary when the temperature of the medium surrounding the body varies.

5. Mr. Smith and Mr. Brown both order coffee at the lunch counter and receive their cups at the same time. Mr. Smith adds cream at once but does not drink his coffee until five minutes later; Mr. Brown waits five minutes, then adds cream and begins to drink. Who drinks the hotter coffee?

6. (a) A man weighing (with his load) 200 lb makes a parachute jump and reaches a steady velocity of 10 mi/hr. Find the force due to air resistance when his speed is 5 mi/hr.

(b) If the same man jumps again from a height of h feet and takes 10 sec to open his parachute, how low can h be if he is to strike the ground with a speed less than 20 mi/hr.

7. In an $\mathcal{E}RC$-circuit ($R > 0, C > 0$), let $\mathcal{E}$ vary sinusoidally as in (3–18) and let $q = 0$ for $t = 0$. Find q and I in terms of t and show that, apart from transients, they are sinusoidal. Compare the phases of q, I, and $\mathcal{E}$.

8. The half-life of a radioactive substance is the time needed for one-half of a given amount to disintegrate. Express this in terms of the time constant.

9. The population of the United States from 1790 on, at ten-year intervals, was as follows, in millions: 3.9, 5.3, 7.2, 9.6, 12.9, 17, 23, 31, 39, 50, 63, 76, 92, 108, 122, 135, 150. If the growth obeys the law $D_t x = k(t)x$, discuss the behavior of $k(t)$ and its deviation from constancy. Choose some reasonable average value for k and predict the population in the years 2000, 2100, 2500, and 3000.

ANSWERS

1. (a) $1 - e^{-t}$; (b) $1 - e^{-0.1t}$; (c) $\frac{1}{2}(\sin t - \cos t + e^{-t})$;
(d) $\dfrac{\sin t - 10 \cos t + 10e^{-t}}{101}$.

3. 55°. 5. Mr. Smith. 6. (a) 100 lb, (b) 1754 ft.

7. $q = k \sin(\omega t - \alpha) + k \sin\alpha \exp(-t/(RC))$, where
$k = C\mathcal{E}_0(1 + R^2C^2\omega^2)^{-1/2}$, $\alpha = \arctan RC\omega$, $0 < \alpha < \pi/2$.
$I = k\omega \cos(\omega t - \alpha) - (k/(RC)) \sin\alpha \exp(-t/(RC))$.
Phases: $\omega t - \alpha$, $\omega t - \alpha + \frac{1}{2}\pi$, ωt.

8. $a \log 2$.

***3–4 Other applications of the first order equation.** Applications of linear equations are given above; here we confine ourselves to applications of nonlinear equations.

A. *Particle moving on a line.* Let a particle of mass m move on the x-axis subject to a force F which depends only on the position of the particle. Newton's second law gives the differential equation

$$m \frac{d^2x}{dt^2} = F(x). \tag{3–26}$$

Now if $v = dx/dt$, then

$$\frac{d^2x}{dt^2} = \frac{dv}{dt} = \frac{dv}{dx}\frac{dx}{dt} = v\frac{dv}{dx}. \tag{3–27}$$

Hence Eq. (3–26) becomes a first order equation:

$$mv\frac{dv}{dx} = F(x). \qquad (3\text{–}28)$$

The solutions are obtained by separation of variables:

$$mv\,dv = F(x)\,dx,$$

$$m\frac{v^2}{2} = \int F(x)\,dx + c_1. \qquad (3\text{–}29)$$

Let

$$U(x) = -\int F(x)\,dx, \qquad (3\text{–}30)$$

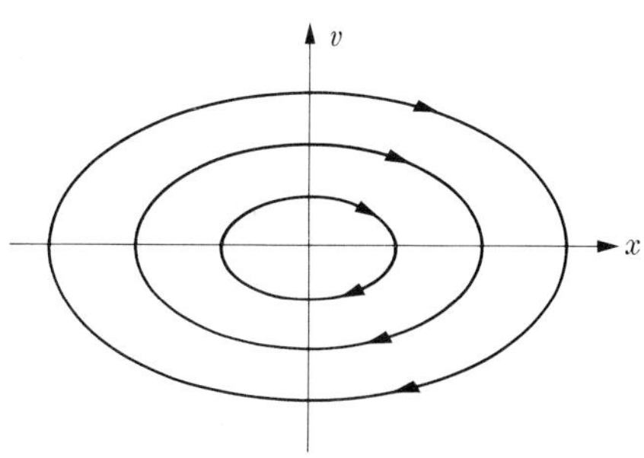

Fig. 3–10. Velocity versus displacement for motion subject to Hooke's law.

for some particular choice of the indefinite integral. Then (3–29) becomes

$$m\frac{v^2}{2} + U(x) = c_1. \qquad (3\text{–}31)$$

The term $\frac{1}{2}mv^2$ represents the *kinetic energy* of the particle; the function $U(x)$ (determined up to an additive constant) is called the *potential energy*. Hence (3–31) states:

$$\text{kinetic energy} + \text{potential energy} = \text{const} \qquad (3\text{–}32)$$

for each motion of the system. Equation (3–32) is the *law of conservation of energy* for the case considered. The constant on the right is called the *total energy*.

If, for example, $F(x) = -kx$ (Hooke's law), where $k > 0$, then the curves (3–31) in the xv-plane are ellipses (Fig. 3–10):

$$\tfrac{1}{2}mv^2 + \tfrac{1}{2}kx^2 = c_1. \qquad (3\text{–}33)$$

When $v > 0$, x increases as t increases, so that the motion is to the right; when $v < 0$, x decreases as t increases. The motion of the particle on the x-axis is a projection of the motion on the ellipse; hence the particle oscillates back and forth, with maximum displacement $\sqrt{2c_1/k}$.

The time t can be found in terms of x from (3–31), for (3–31) gives

$$\frac{dx}{dt} = v = \pm\sqrt{\frac{2}{m}[c_1 - U(x)]}, \quad \pm\sqrt{\frac{2}{m}}\,dt = \frac{dx}{\sqrt{c_1 - U(x)}},$$

$$\pm\sqrt{\frac{2}{m}}\,t = \int\frac{dx}{\sqrt{c_1 - U(x)}} + c_2. \qquad (3\text{–}34)$$

The plus sign applies to the upper half-plane ($v > 0$), the minus sign to the lower half.

If the particle is subject to a friction which depends only on velocity, in addition to the force F, then Eq. (3–28) is replaced by

$$mv\,\frac{dv}{dx} = F(x) + G(v). \tag{3–35}$$

This is a first order equation, to which some of the methods of Chapter 2 may be applicable. When the force depends in any way on position and velocity we are led to a first order equation:

$$mv\,\frac{dv}{dx} = F(x, v). \tag{3–36}$$

When the force depends only on velocity v and time t, the differential equation can be written

$$m\,\frac{dv}{dt} = F(v, t), \tag{3–37}$$

which is again of first order. If the general solution is obtained in the form

$$\phi(v, t) = c_1, \tag{3–38}$$

then replacement of v by dx/dt leads to a first order equation for x in terms of t.

B. *Motion of the planets.* It can be shown that, to a first approximation, each planet moves in a plane as though it were attracted by a fixed mass at the center of the sun. (See Chapter 5 of Reference 5 at the end of this chapter.) We choose coordinate axes with origin at the sun and introduce polar coordinates relative to these axes. We denote by **F** the force acting on the planet and by F_r, F_θ its components along the r- and θ-directions, as indicated in Fig. 3–11. Then

$$F_r = -\frac{k}{r^2}, \qquad F_\theta = 0, \tag{3–39}$$

since all the force is toward the sun and since the force is proportional to the inverse square of the distance.

It is shown in the calculus that the components a_r, a_θ of the acceleration vector are

$$a_r = \frac{d^2r}{dt^2} - r\omega^2, \qquad a_\theta = 2\omega\,\frac{dr}{dt} + r\,\frac{d\omega}{dt}, \tag{3–40}$$

where $\omega = d\theta/dt$ is the angular velocity. (See p. 360 of Reference 7 at the end of this chapter.) Since $ma_r = F_r$, $ma_\theta = F_\theta$, where m is the mass of the planet, we conclude that

$$m\left(\frac{d^2r}{dt^2} - r\omega^2\right) = -\frac{k}{r^2}, \qquad m\left(2\omega\frac{dr}{dt} + r\frac{d\omega}{dt}\right) = 0. \tag{3–41}$$

These differential equations govern the motion.

From the second part of (3–41) we obtain the first order equation

$$2\omega\, dr + r\, d\omega = 0, \tag{3–42}$$

for which r is an integrating factor, and we find

$$r^2\omega = h, \tag{3–43}$$

where h is a constant. The quantity $mr^2\omega$ is termed the angular momentum (more precisely, the xy-component of angular momentum) and Eq. (3–43) expresses the *conservation of angular momentum.* If $h = 0$, then either $r \equiv 0$ or

$$\omega = \frac{d\theta}{dt} \equiv 0.$$

This implies that θ is constant and that the planet moves on a straight line through the sun. Such a path can be followed by a meteor which falls into the sun.

For fixed nonzero h, the first part of (3–41) becomes

$$m\left(\frac{d^2r}{dt^2} - \frac{h^2}{r^3}\right) = -\frac{k}{r^2}\cdot \tag{3–44}$$

This second order equation governs the variation of r with time t. To study this, we introduce the new variable

$$u = \frac{1}{r} \tag{3–45}$$

and seek a differential equation for u in terms of θ, rather than t. Now, by Eq. (3–43),

$$\frac{dr}{dt} = -\frac{1}{u^2}\frac{du}{dt} = -\frac{1}{u^2}\frac{du}{d\theta}\frac{d\theta}{dt} = -\frac{\omega}{u^2}\frac{du}{d\theta} = -h\frac{du}{d\theta}\cdot$$

Similarly,

$$\frac{d^2r}{dt^2} = \frac{d}{dt}\left(-h\frac{du}{d\theta}\right) = \frac{d}{d\theta}\left(-h\frac{du}{d\theta}\right)\frac{d\theta}{dt} = -h\frac{d^2u}{d\theta^2}\,hu^2.$$

Accordingly, (3–44) becomes

$$m\left(-h^2u^2\frac{d^2u}{d\theta^2} - h^2u^3\right) = -ku^2$$

or, with the abbreviation $K = k/mh^2$, $(h \neq 0)$,

$$\frac{d^2u}{d\theta^2} + u = K. \tag{3–46}$$

This equation has the same form as (3–26) and we analyze it in the same way:

$$v = \frac{du}{d\theta}, \qquad v\frac{dv}{du} + u = K, \qquad \int v\,dv + \int(u - K)\,du = \frac{c_1^2}{2},$$

$$v^2 + (u - K)^2 = c_1^2, \qquad v = \pm\sqrt{c_1^2 - (u - K)^2},$$

$$\frac{du}{\sqrt{c_1^2 - (u - K)^2}} = \pm d\theta, \qquad \cos^{-1}\frac{u - K}{c_1} = \pm\theta - c_2,$$

$$u - K = c_1 \cos(\pm\theta - c_2). \tag{3–47}$$

The $\pm$ sign can be absorbed in the constants c_1, c_2. With $r = 1/u$, we finally find

$$r = \frac{1}{K + c_1\cos(\theta - c_2)}\cdot \tag{3–48}$$

It is shown in analytic geometry that the equation of a conic section with a focus at the origin is

$$r = \frac{l}{1 + e\cos(\theta - \beta)}, \tag{3–49}$$

where e is the eccentricity, $\theta = \beta$ is the axis of symmetry through the focus, and l is one-half the latus rectum (see Fig. 3–11). From (3–48) we conclude that each planet moves in an orbit which is a conic section, clearly an ellipse ($e < 1$). Comets follow approximately parabolic orbits ($e = 1$); bodies passing the solar system at great speed follow hyperbolic orbits ($e > 1$).

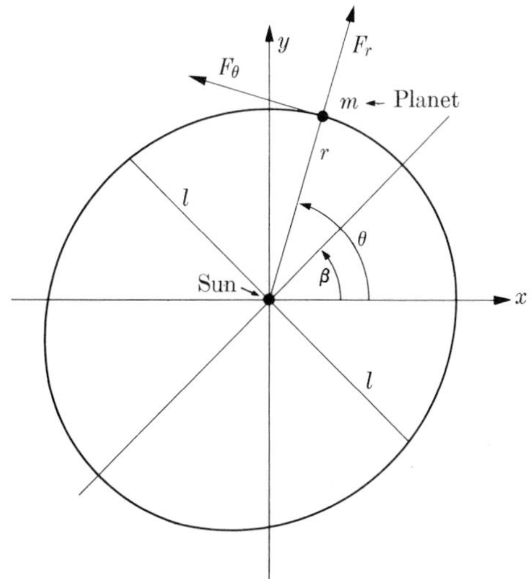

FIG. 3–11. Motion of a planet.

C. *Chemical processes.* We visualize first a process in which compound C is formed from compounds A and B, and we assume that the rate of formation of C is proportional to the amounts of A and B present. If x denotes the amount of C (e.g., in grams), and a, b denote the amounts of A and B, then we have

$$\frac{dx}{dt} = kab. \tag{3–50}$$

Now the amount of A present at time t equals an initial amount a_0 minus the amount used up to form C; the latter amount will be αx, where α is a constant. Similar reasoning applies to compound B. Hence

$$a = a_0 - \alpha x, \qquad b = b_0 - \beta x. \tag{3–51}$$

The constants α and β are such that x grams of C are formed of αx grams of A and βx grams of B. From (3–50) and (3–51) we obtain the differential equation

$$\frac{dx}{dt} = k(a_0 - \alpha x)(b_0 - \beta x), \tag{3–52}$$

which can be solved by separation of variables (Prob. 7 below).

Now we discuss the qualitative properties of the solutions of (3–52). We note, first of all, that particular solutions are given by

$$x = \frac{a_0}{\alpha}, \qquad x = \frac{b_0}{\beta}. \tag{3–53}$$

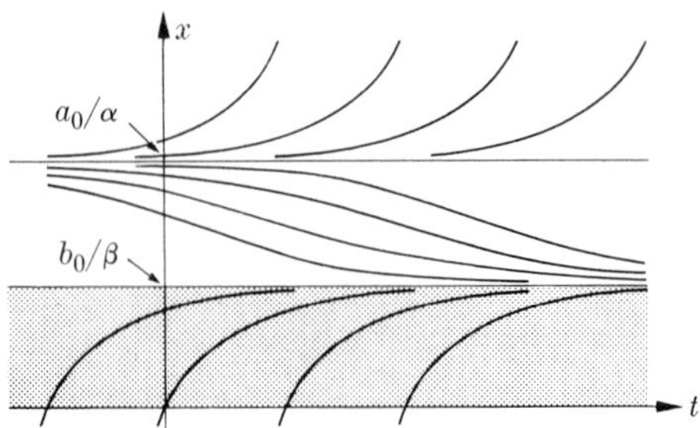

FIG. 3–12. Approach to equilibrium in a chemical process.

If $a_0/\alpha > b_0/\beta$, then these are distinct lines parallel to the t-axis (Fig. 3–12). Furthermore, since dx/dt is positive below the line $x = b_0/\beta$, negative between the two lines, and positive above the line a_0/α, we deduce that the solutions have the appearance of Fig. 3–12. We note that the isoclines are lines $x =$ const, from which it follows that a solution curve remains such after translation to the left or right. (In the diagram of Fig. 3–12 only the shaded portion has physical meaning, for x must be positive, and so also must $a = a_0 - \alpha x$, $b = b_0 - \beta x$.)

In more complicated processes, where compound C may be formed from three or more substances, Eq. (3–52) is replaced by the general equation

$$\frac{dx}{dt} = k(a_1 - \alpha_1 x)(a_2 - \alpha_2 x) \cdots (a_n - \alpha_n x). \tag{3–54}$$

The qualitative analysis is similar to that just given (Prob. 8 below).

D. *Growth of population.* The rate of growth of any population (human, animal, bacterial) is determined by the number of individuals present at a given time and by the environment. For example, the maximum food supply will limit the number of individuals who can live in a given region. When the population is very small, the environment has little effect (e.g., the food supply appears unlimited). If x is a measure of the population at time t, the simplest law postulated is

$$\frac{dx}{dt} = kx \ (k = \text{const}). \tag{3–55}$$

It would be meaningless to choose x, which is an integer, as the actual population; for then dx/dt would be either zero or infinite (Fig. 3–13); but we can choose a smooth function which approximates the true population and for which the differential equation (3–55) has meaning.

The effect of the environment can be taken into account in many ways. We can assume that the maximum allowable value of x (e.g., because of exhaustion of the food supply) is x_0, and postulate the differential equation

$$\frac{dx}{dt} = kx(x_0 - x), \qquad x \leqq x_0. \tag{3–56}$$

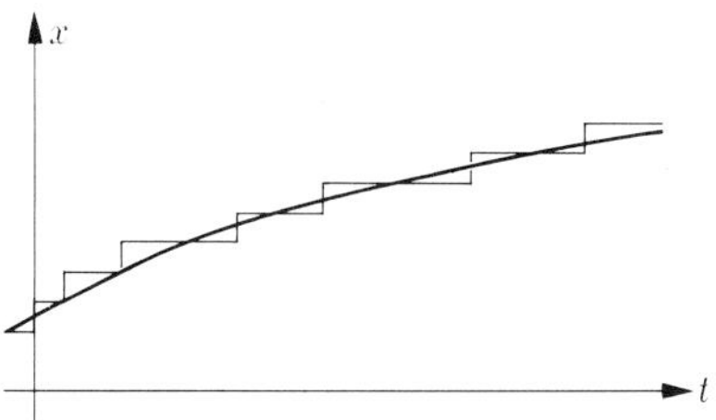

FIG. 3–13. Population growth approximated by a smooth curve.

An interesting variant of (3–56) is obtained by assuming that because of technological improvements, x_0 is a slowly increasing function of t. For example, we might assume

$$\frac{dx}{dt} = kx(at + b - x),$$

$$x < at + b, \tag{3–57}$$

where a, b are constants. Analysis of the solutions by isoclines leads to the diagram of Fig. 3–14. Equation (3–57) is reduced to a linear equation by the substitution $y = 1/x$ (Prob. 9 below), and hence the solutions can be obtained explicitly.

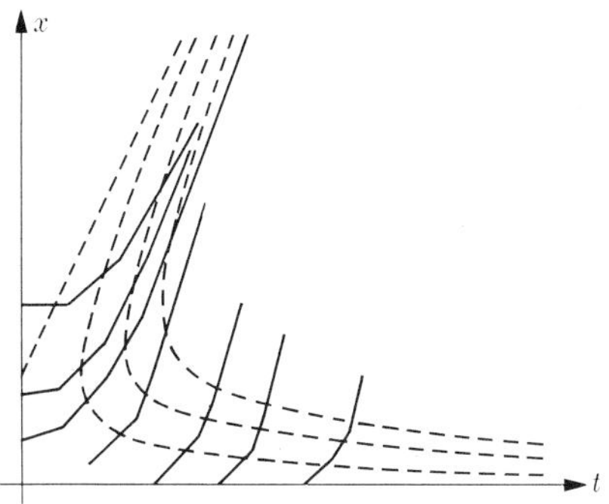

FIG. 3–14. Population growth with improving environment.

E. *A nonlinear electric circuit.* To a first approximation, electric circuits are described by linear differential equations (see Section 3–3). Here, however, we consider a circuit containing a nonlinear element, for which the analysis is considerably more difficult.

The circuit chosen (Fig. 3–15) contains an inductance L, resistance R, and applied emf $v(t)$. In linear theory the current I obeys the differential equation

$$L\frac{dI}{dt} + RI = v(t), \tag{3–58}$$

but we must now take into account nonlinearities in the inductance term, which are very pronounced if the coil contains an iron bar. In this case, (3–58) is replaced by the equation

$$\frac{d\Lambda(I)}{dt} + RI = v(t), \tag{3–59}$$

where $\Lambda(I)$ is the magnetic flux caused by current I. The function $\Lambda(I)$

is given empirically by experiments with different materials. It is, in fact, a two-valued function (Fig. 3–16), with one value for increasing I and another for decreasing I; its graph is the "hysteresis loop."

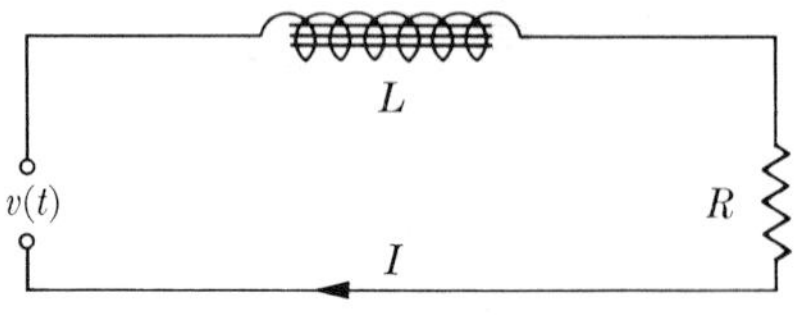

FIG. 3–15. Electric circuit with nonlinear inductance.

We shall approximate $\Lambda(I)$ by a single-valued function, which does fit the average values fairly well:

$$\Lambda(I) = b \sinh^{-1}(aI), \tag{3–60}$$

where a and b are constants. Since

$$\frac{d\Lambda(I)}{dt} = \frac{d\Lambda}{dI}\frac{dI}{dt}, \tag{3–61}$$

Eq. (3–59) becomes

$$\frac{ab}{\sqrt{1 + a^2 I^2}} \frac{dI}{dt} + RI = v(t), \tag{3–62}$$

which is a nonlinear differential equation for I in terms of t.

If the applied voltage v is constant, the variables in (3–62) can be separated (Prob. 10 below). The solutions have the qualitative appearance of Fig. 3–17. If $v(t)$ is sinusoidal,

$$v = v_0 \sin \omega t, \tag{3–63}$$

the equation is difficult to solve. Graphical solution leads to a diagram such as that of Fig. 3–18 (Prob. 10 below).

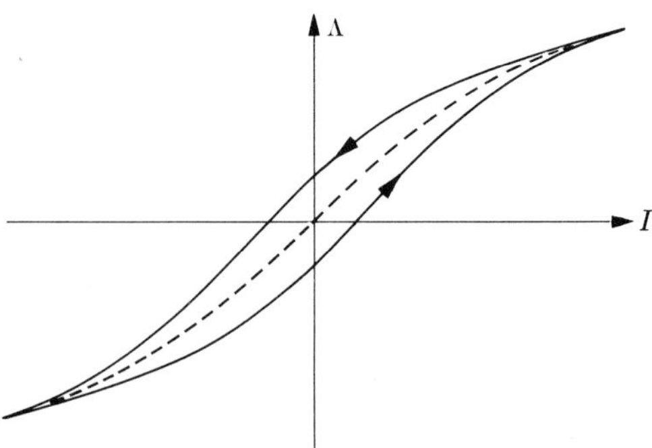

FIG. 3–16. Magnetic flux versus current.

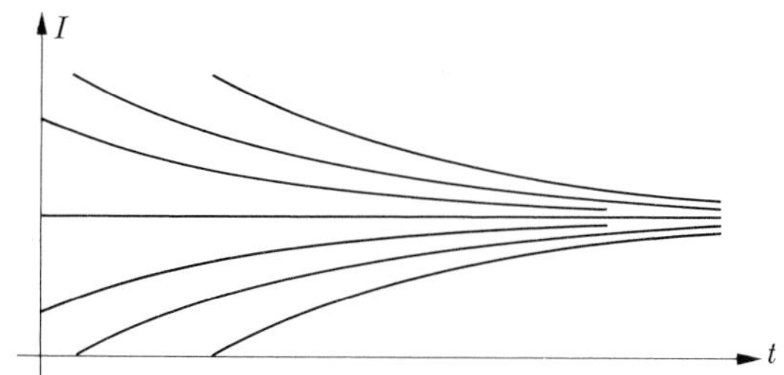

FIG. 3–17. Current in nonlinear circuit with constant applied emf.

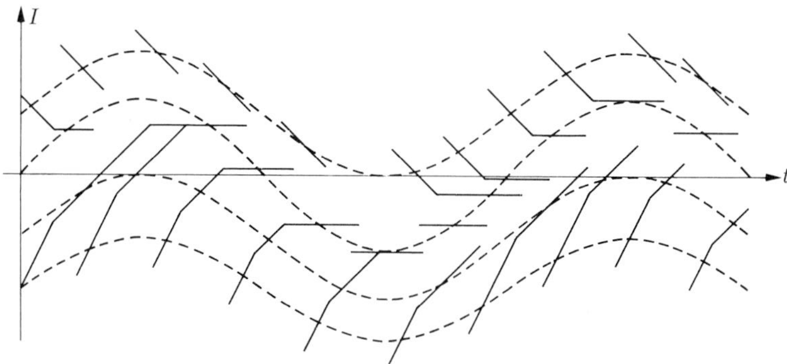

FIG. 3–18. Current in nonlinear circuit with sinusoidal applied emf.

Remarks. The examples chosen are only a few of the many types which occur in all the sciences. They illustrate the type of reasoning by which one may gain information on the physical system from the differential equation itself.

PROBLEMS

1. Let a particle of mass m move on the x-axis subject to a force $F(x, v)$, so that $m(d^2x/dt^2) = F$. Let $x = 0$ and $v = v_0$ when $t = 0$. Find v in terms of x and t in terms of x for each of the following cases:

(a) $F = -mg$ (falling body),
(b) $F = -kx - mg$ (mass suspended by a spring),
(c) $F = -kx - ax^3$ (nonlinear spring),
(d) $F = -kmb/(x - b)^2$ (attraction by inverse square law),
(e) $F = -bv - hv^3$ (nonlinear friction).

Throughout, m, g, b, k, a, b, h denote positive constants.

2. Let a particle of mass m move on the x-axis subject to a force $F = -kx + g(v)$, where k is a positive constant and $g(v) = -bv^2$ when $v \geqq 0$, $g(v) = bv^2$ when $v \leqq 0$, $b = \text{const} > 0$. Find v in terms of x and plot the corresponding curves in the xv-plane. Give a physical interpretation.

3. Let a particle of mass m move on the x-axis subject to a force F; let $x = x_0$, $v = v_0$ when $t = 0$. Find x and v in terms of t for each of the following cases (m, g, b, k are constants):

(a) $F = -mg - bv$,
(b) $F = -bv + k \sin t$,
(c) $F = bv^3 e^{-kt}$.

4. The motion of a *simple pendulum* (Fig. 3–19) can be described by equating the tangential force $-mg \sin \theta$ to m times the acceleration component a_θ. Hence, by (3–40),

$$mL \frac{d\omega}{dt} = -mg \sin \theta.$$

Show that $d\omega/dt = \omega(d\omega/d\theta)$, find ω in terms of θ, and analyze the motion graphically in the $\omega\theta$-plane.

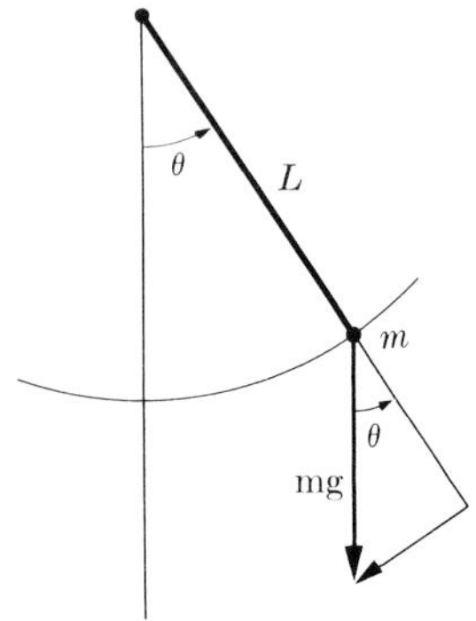

FIG. 3–19. Simple pendulum.

5. Show that, for a planet moving about the sun, conservation of angular momentum (Eq. 3–43) implies that the radius vector of the planet sweeps out area at a constant rate.

6. Find the path of a planet if the gravitational force is replaced by an attractive force proportional to distance.

7. Find the general solution of Eq. (3–52).

8. Discuss with the aid of isoclines the qualitative nature of the solutions of Eq. (3–54).

9. Solve each of the following equations and interpret the results in terms of population growth: (a) Eq. (3–55), (b) Eq. (3–56), (c) Eq. (3–57). [*Hint* for (c): Set $y = 1/x$.]

10. (a) Find the solutions of Eq. (3–62) when v is a constant. (b) Analyze the solutions of Eq. (3–62) graphically with the aid of isoclines for the case $v = v_0 \sin \omega t$ (see Fig. 3–18).

ANSWERS

1. (a) $v^2 - v_0^2 = -2gx$, $x = v_0 t - \frac{1}{2}gt^2$; (b) $\frac{1}{2}m(v^2 - v_0^2) = -mgx - \frac{1}{2}kx^2$, $x = (mg/k) \cos \beta t + (v_0/\beta) \sin \beta t - (mg/k)$, $\beta = (k/m)^{1/2}$; (c) $\frac{1}{2}m(v^2 - v_0^2) = -\frac{1}{2}kx^2 - \frac{1}{4}ax^4$, $t = \pm \int_0^x (v_0^2 - km^{-1}u^2 - \frac{1}{2}am^{-1}u^4)^{-1/2}\, du$; (d) $\frac{1}{2}(v^2 - v_0^2) = kx(x-b)^{-1}$, $t = \pm \int_0^x [v_0^2 + 2ku(u-b)^{-1}]^{-1/2}\, du$; (e) $v = [cv_0 - \tan(bcx/m)]/[c + c^2 v_0 \tan(bcx/m)]$, $t = \int_0^x [c + c^2 v_0 \tan(bcu/m)]/[cv_0 - \tan(bcu/m)]\, du$.

2. $(v^2 - \frac{1}{2}mkb^{-2} \pm kb^{-1}x)e^{\pm 2bx/m} = \text{const}$, plus for $v \geqq 0$, minus for $v \leqq 0$.

3. (a) $v = e^{-bt/m}(v_0 + gmb^{-1}) - gmb^{-1}$, $x = x_0 - mgtb^{-1} + (1 - e^{-bt/m})\, b^{-2}(m^2 g + mbv_0)$; (b) $v = (b^2 + m^2)^{-1}[\{(b^2 + m^2)v_0 + km\}e^{-bt/m} + k(b \sin t -$

$m \cos t)]$, $x = (b^3 + m^2b)^{-1}[\{-mv_0(b^2 + m^2) - km^2\}e^{-bt/m} - kb(b \cos t + m \sin t)] + x_0 + (mv_0 + k)/b$; (c) $v^2 = kmv_0^2/[2bv_0^2(e^{-kt} - 1) + km]$, $x = x_0 + v_0\int_0^t [km/\{2bv_0^2(e^{-ku} - 1) + km\}]^{1/2}\, du$.

4. $L\omega^2 = 2g \cos \theta + c$.

6. $r^2[c_1 + (c_1^2 - K)^{1/2} \sin (2\theta + c_2)] = 1$, $K = km^{-1}h^{-2}$. By converting to rectangular coordinates, we can verify that the path is an ellipse with *center* at the origin.

7. $x = (a_0 - b_0ce^{qt})(\alpha - \beta ce^{qt})^{-1}$, $q = k(a_0\beta - b_0\alpha)$; $x = b_0/\beta$, $x = a_0/\alpha$.

9. (a) $x = ce^{kt}$; (b) $x = cx_0e^{kx_0t}(1 + ce^{kx_0t})^{-1}$;
(c) $x = -e^{pt^2+qt}[k\int e^{pt^2+qt}\, dt + c]^{-1}$, $p = \frac{1}{2}ka$, $q = kb$.

10. (a) $I = [ke^{2\beta t} - 2ce^{\beta t} - kc^2][a(e^{2\beta t} + 2kce^{\beta t} - c^2)]^{-1}$, $\beta t > \log |c|$, $k = av_0/R$, $\beta = Rq/(ab)$, $q = (1 + k^2)^{1/2}$.

SUGGESTED REFERENCES

1. DRAPER, CHARLES S., MCKAY, WALTER, and LEES, SIDNEY, *Instrument Engineering*, Vols. 1 and 2 (esp. Vol. 2, Chap. 18). New York: McGraw-Hill, 1952–1953.

2. LAWDEN, DEREK F., *Mathematics of Engineering Systems*. New York: John Wiley and Sons, Inc., 1954.

3. LEMON, HARVEY B., and FERENCE, MICHAEL, JR., *Analytical Experimental Physics*. Chicago: University of Chicago Press, 1943.

4. MCLACHLAN, N. W., *Ordinary Non-Linear Differential Equations in Engineering and Physical Sciences*. London: Oxford University Press, 1950.

5. MOULTON, F. R., *Celestial Mechanics*, 2nd ed. New York: Macmillan, 1914.

6. SKILLING, HUGH H., *Transient Electric Currents*. New York: McGraw-Hill, 1937.

7. THOMAS, GEORGE B., *Calculus*. Reading, Mass.: Addison-Wesley, 1953.

8. TRIMMER, JOHN D., *Response of Physical Systems*. New York: John Wiley and Sons, Inc., 1950.

CHAPTER 4

LINEAR EQUATIONS OF ARBITRARY ORDER

4–1 Linear differential equations. An ordinary linear differential equation of order n is a differential equation of form

$$a_0(x)D_x^n y + a_1(x)D_x^{n-1}y + \cdots + a_{n-1}(x)D_x y + a_n(x)y = Q(x), \quad (4\text{–}1)$$

where $D_x y = y'$, $D_x^2 y = y''$, ... It will be assumed here that the coefficients $a_0(x)$, $a_1(x)$, ..., $a_n(x)$, and the right-hand member $Q(x)$ are defined and continuous in some interval (perhaps infinite) of the x-axis and that $a_0(x) \neq 0$ in this interval. The fundamental theorem of Section 1–7 then implies that there is one and only one solution $y = y(x)$ of (4–1) that satisfies given initial conditions

$$y(x_0) = y_0, \qquad y'(x_0) = y_0', \qquad \ldots, \qquad y^{(n-1)}(x_0) = y_0^{(n-1)} \quad (4\text{–}2)$$

at a point x_0 of the interval.

The following are examples of linear equations:

$$y'' + y = \sin 2x, \quad (4\text{–}3)$$

$$x^2y'' - xy' + e^x y = \log x \qquad (x > 0), \quad (4\text{–}4)$$

$$D_x^5 y - xD_x^3 y + x^3 D_x y = 0, \quad (4\text{–}5)$$

$$y'' + y = 0, \quad (4\text{–}6)$$

$$y' + x^2 y = e^x. \quad (4\text{–}7)$$

If $Q(x) \equiv 0$, the equation (4–1) is called a *homogeneous linear equation* (not to be confused with the homogeneous first order equation of Section 2–4). Thus Eqs. (4–5), (4–6) are homogeneous; the other examples are *nonhomogeneous.* If we replace $Q(x)$ by 0 in a general equation (4–1), we obtain a new homogeneous equation, which we call the *related homogeneous equation* of Eq. (4–1). Thus Eq. (4–6) is the related homogeneous equation of Eq. (4–3).

If the coefficients $a_0(x)$, $a_1(x)$, ..., $a_n(x)$ are all constants, hence independent of x, the equation (4–1) is said to have *constant coefficients,* even though $Q(x)$ may depend on x. Thus (4–3) and (4–6) have constant coefficients; the other examples do not.

4–2 Linear independence. We call n functions $y_1(x), \ldots, y_n(x)$ *linearly independent* over a given interval if no one function is expressible as a linear combination of the others, with constant coefficients, over the interval. If the functions are not linearly independent over the interval, they are termed *linearly dependent.* For example, the functions

$$y_1(x) = \cos 2x, \qquad y_2(x) = \cos^2 x, \qquad y_3(x) = \sin^2 x$$

are linearly dependent for all x, since $y_1(x) \equiv y_2(x) - y_3(x)$ for all x. The functions $y_1 = 1$, $y_2 = x$, $y_3 = x^2$ are linearly independent for all x. For if, for example,

$$x^2 \equiv A \cdot 1 + B \cdot x$$

with constant A, B, then the quadratic function $x^2 - Bx - A$ would be identically 0; but the quadratic equation $x^2 - Bx - A = 0$ has at most two roots, so that there is a contradiction. Similarly, relations of form $x \equiv A \cdot 1 + B \cdot x^2$ and $1 \equiv A \cdot x + B \cdot x^2$ are found to be impossible.

The definition of linear independence can be rephrased as follows: *the functions $y_1(x), \ldots, y_n(x)$ are linearly independent over a given interval, if an identity*

$$k_1 y_1(x) + \cdots + k_n y_n(x) \equiv 0 \tag{4–8}$$

with constant $k_1, k_2, \ldots$ can hold over the given interval only if $k_1 = 0$, $k_2 = 0, \ldots, k_n = 0$. If the new condition holds, then no one function is expressible as a linear combination of the others; if, for example,

$$y_n(x) \equiv A_1 y_1(x) + \cdots + A_{n-1} y_{n-1}(x), \tag{4–9}$$

then Eq. (4–8) holds with $A_1 = k_1$, $A_2 = k_2, \ldots, A_{n-1} = k_{n-1}$, $-1 = k_n$, so that not all k's are zero. If the new condition fails, then one function is expressible as a linear combination of the others; for if (4–8) holds and, for example, $k_n \neq 0$, then (4–8) can be solved for $y_n(x)$ to give a relation (4–9) with $A_1 = -(k_1/k_n), \ldots, A_{n-1} = -(k_{n-1}/k_n)$. Thus the two definitions of linear independence are equivalent.

The importance of the concept of linear independence for linear differential equations can be illustrated by considering the example

$$y''' - y'' - y' + y = 0. \tag{4–10}$$

We verify that $y = e^x$ is a solution of this equation; from the form of the equation, $y = c_1 e^x$ will also be a solution for each choice of the constant c_1. Similarly, $y = c_2 x e^x$ and $y = c_3 e^{-x}$ are found to be solutions, with c_2, c_3

constant. Finally, we observe that the sum of such solutions is a solution; that is,

$$y = c_1e^x + c_2xe^x + c_3e^{-x} \tag{4–11}$$

is a solution. Since (4–11) contains three arbitrary constants, it appears to be the general solution. By the existence theorem of Section 1–7 we can prove that (4–11) is the general solution of Eq. (4–10) by showing that the c's can be chosen so that (4–11) satisfies *prescribed initial conditions:*

$$y(x_0) = y_0, \qquad y'(x_0) = y_0', \qquad y''(x_0) = y_0''. \tag{4–12}$$

From (4–11) we find that (4–12) will be satisfied if

$$\begin{aligned} y_0 &= c_1e^{x_0} + c_2x_0e^{x_0} + c_3e^{-x_0}, \\ y_0' &= c_1e^{x_0} + c_2e^{x_0}(x_0+1) - c_3e^{-x_0}, \\ y_0'' &= c_1e^{x_0} + c_2e^{x_0}(x_0+2) + c_3e^{-x_0}. \end{aligned} \tag{4–13}$$

These are simultaneous linear equations for c_1, c_2, c_3. The determinant of coefficients is

$$\begin{vmatrix} e^{x_0} & x_0e^{x_0} & e^{-x_0} \\ e^{x_0} & e^{x_0}(x_0+1) & -e^{-x_0} \\ e^{x_0} & e^{x_0}(x_0+2) & e^{-x_0} \end{vmatrix} = e^{4x_0} \neq 0.$$

Hence Eqs. (4–13) can be solved uniquely for c_1, c_2, c_3 and (4–11) is the general solution of (4–10).

Now the functions e^x, e^{-x}, $\cosh x$ are also solutions of Eq. (4–10), so that the same reasoning would lead us to the expression

$$y = c_1e^x + c_2e^{-x} + c_3\cosh x \tag{4–14}$$

for the general solution. If we attempt to prove that (4–14) is the general solution by showing that arbitrary initial conditions can be satisfied, we are led to contradictory equations. For example, the initial conditions

$$\text{for } x = 0\text{:} \quad y = 1, \qquad y' = 0, \qquad y'' = 0$$

cannot be satisfied. They lead to the contradictory equations

$$1 = c_1 + c_2 + c_3, \qquad 0 = c_1 - c_2, \qquad 0 = c_1 + c_2 + c_3.$$

What is the reason for the difficulty? A close inspection of Eq. (4–14) reveals that it contains effectively only *two* arbitrary constants. For $\cosh x = \frac{1}{2}(e^x + e^{-x})$, so that (4–14) can be written

$$y = c_1e^x + c_2e^{-x} + \tfrac{1}{2}c_3(e^x + e^{-x}) = C_1e^x + C_2e^{-x},$$

where $C_1 = c_1 + \frac{1}{2}c_3$, $C_2 = c_2 + \frac{1}{2}c_3$. Since there are only *two* arbitrary constants at our disposal, it is clear why the *three* initial conditions cannot be satisfied.

The reduction of the number of arbitrary constants in (4–14) was possible because the three functions e^x, e^{-x}, $\cosh x$ are *linearly dependent*, for

$$\cosh x \equiv \tfrac{1}{2}e^x + \tfrac{1}{2}e^{-x}.$$

A similar reduction cannot be made in (4–11), since the functions e^x, xe^x, e^{-x} are *linearly independent*. It will be seen that the general solution of a linear differential equation has the form

$$y = y^*(x) + c_1y_1(x) + \cdots + c_ny_n(x), \tag{4–15}$$

where $y_1(x), \ldots, y_n(x)$ are *linearly independent* solutions of the related homogeneous equation and $y^*(x)$ is one particular solution of the given equation. However, if $y_1(x), \ldots, y_n(x)$ are linearly dependent, the number of arbitrary constants in (4–15) can be reduced and (4–15) fails to provide the general solution.

4–3 Fundamental theorem. Test for linear independence. We can now state a general existence theorem for linear differential equations.

THEOREM 1. *Let the linear differential equation*

$$a_0(x)D_x^ny + a_1(x)D_x^{n-1}y + \cdots + a_n(x)y = Q(x) \tag{4–16}$$

be given, with the related homogeneous equation

$$a_0(x)D_x^ny + a_1(x)D_x^{n-1}y + \cdots + a_n(x)y = 0. \tag{4–17}$$

Let $a_0(x), \ldots, a_n(x)$, $Q(x)$ be defined and continuous over an interval of the x-axis and let $a_0(x) \neq 0$ on this interval.

There exists a set of n functions which are solutions of Eq. (4–17) and are linearly independent over the given interval. If $y_1(x), \ldots, y_n(x)$ is such a set of linearly independent solutions of Eq. (4–17) over the given *interval, then*

$$y = c_1y_1(x) + \cdots + c_ny_n(x) \tag{4–18}$$

is the general solution of Eq. (4–17).

There exist solutions of the nonhomogeneous equation Eq. (4–16) *over the given interval. If* $y = y^*(x)$ *is one such solution and* $y_1(x), \ldots, y_n(x)$ *are chosen as above, then*

$$y = y^*(x) + c_1y_1(x) + \cdots + c_ny_n(x) \tag{4–19}$$

is the general solution of Eq. (4–16).

The proof of this theorem is given in Chapter 12 of ODE. One striking difference from the general existence theorem of Section 1–7 is that *all solutions of the linear equation* (4–16) *are valid over the whole interval under consideration.* For a nonlinear equation this need not be so (Prob. 6 below).

Remark. Theorem 1 implies that we cannot find $n + 1$ linearly independent solutions of the homogeneous equation (4–17). For let $y_1(x), \ldots, y_{n+1}(x)$ be such linearly independent solutions. Then $y_1(x), \ldots, y_n(x)$ are also linearly independent; indeed, a relation

$$k_1y_1(x) + \cdots + k_ny_n(x) \equiv 0,$$

with not all k's equal to zero, is a special case of a relation of form

$$k_1y_1(x) + \cdots + k_ny_n(x) + k_{n+1}y_{n+1}(x) \equiv 0,$$

with not all k's equal to zero. Hence the general solution of (4–17) is given by

$$y = c_1y_1(x) + \cdots + c_ny_n(x).$$

Now $y_{n+1}(x)$ is also a solution of (4–17). Therefore by Theorem 1, for some choice of the c's,

$$y_{n+1}(x) \equiv c_1y_1(x) + \cdots + c_ny_n(x).$$

This makes $y_1(x), \ldots, y_{n+1}(x)$ linearly dependent, contrary to assumption.

We proceed to illustrate the theorem by examples.

EXAMPLE 1. $y'' + y = 0$. The functions $\sin x$ and $\cos x$ are solutions for all x, since $(\sin x)'' = -\sin x$, $(\cos x)'' = -\cos x$. The two functions are linearly independent, since neither one is a constant times the other. Hence by Theorem 1 the general solution is

$$y = c_1 \sin x + c_2 \cos x. \tag{4–20}$$

To check the correctness of this result, we replace y by $c_1 \sin x + c_2 \cos x$ in the differential equation. The left-hand side becomes

$$-c_1 \sin x - c_2 \cos x + (c_1 \sin x + c_2 \cos x)$$

or

$$c_1(-\sin x + \sin x) + c_2(-\cos x + \cos x). \tag{4–21}$$

Since this is identically 0, the solutions do check. The terms were grouped in a special way in (4–21) to illustrate the fact that replacing y by $c_1 \sin x + c_2 \cos x$ is the same as

(c_1 times the result of replacing y by $\sin x$)
plus
(c_2 times the result of replacing y by $\cos x$).

In other words, the left-hand side of the differential equation "operates" on each term of (4–20) separately and constants factor out. Since $\sin x$ and $\cos x$ are solutions, each leads to a zero term, and the final result is zero, as desired. This reasoning can be extended to the general case of (4–17). Since $y_1(x), \ldots, y_n(x)$ are solutions, each gives rise to a zero term when (4–18) is substituted in (4–17). The constants factor out and the result is zero.

It remains to verify that the constants c_1 and c_2 can be chosen to match the given initial conditions

$$\text{for } x = x_0\text{:} \quad y = y_0, \qquad y' = y'_0. \tag{4–22}$$

We must solve the equations

$$\begin{aligned} y_0 &= c_1 \sin x_0 + c_2 \cos x_0, \\ y'_0 &= c_1 \cos x_0 - c_2 \sin x_0. \end{aligned} \tag{4–23}$$

The unique solution is

$$c_1 = y_0 \sin x_0 + y'_0 \cos x_0, \qquad c_2 = y_0 \cos x_0 - y'_0 \sin x_0.$$

Thus, for this example, the theorem above (for the homogeneous case) is completely verified.

Let us re-examine the last steps. Why was it possible to solve (4–23) for c_1, c_2? Equations (4–23) are linear equations in the unknowns c_1, c_2, and the determinant of the coefficients is

$$\begin{vmatrix} \sin x_0 & \cos x_0 \\ \cos x_0 & -\sin x_0 \end{vmatrix} = -\sin^2 x_0 - \cos^2 x_0 = -1.$$

This determinant is never 0, hence solution is always possible. If we write the general solution as $c_1y_1(x) + c_2y_2(x)$, the equations (4–23) become

$$y_0 = c_1y_1(x_0) + c_2y_2(x_0),$$

$$y_0' = c_1y_1'(x_0) + c_2y_2'(x_0),$$

and the determinant of the coefficients is

$$W = \begin{vmatrix} y_1(x_0) & y_2(x_0) \\ y_1'(x_0) & y_2'(x_0) \end{vmatrix}$$

If the determinant is not equal to zero for any value of x_0 in the interval considered, then initial conditions can be satisfied. The determinant W is called the *Wronskian determinant* of the functions $y_1(x)$, $y_2(x)$ and the fact that it is not zero is *equivalent to linear independence of* $y_1(x)$, $y_2(x)$:

THEOREM 2. *Let $y_1(x), \ldots, y_n(x)$ be solutions of the homogeneous equation (4–17) over an interval. Then $y_1(x), \ldots, y_n(x)$ are linearly independent over the interval if and only if $W(x) \neq 0$ on the interval, where $W(x)$ is the Wronskian determinant:*

$$W(x) = \begin{vmatrix} y_1(x) & y_2(x) & \ldots & y_n(x) \\ y_1'(x) & y_2'(x) & & y_n'(x) \\ \vdots & & & \vdots \\ y_1^{(n-1)}(x) & y_2^{(n-1)}(x) & \ldots & y_n^{(n-1)}(x) \end{vmatrix} \tag{4–24}$$

Theorem 2 is a consequence of Theorem 1; for if $y_1(x), \ldots, y_n(x)$ are linearly independent, then $y = c_1y_1(x) + \cdots + c_ny_n(x)$ is the general solution of (4–17). Hence it must be possible to satisfy arbitrary initial conditions. This leads as above to simultaneous linear equations for $c_1, \ldots, c_n$, whose determinant is $W(x_0)$. Since these can be solved for $c_1, \ldots, c_n$ for arbitrary choice of $y_0, y_0', \ldots, y_0^{(n-1)}$, the determinant $W(x_0)$ must be different from 0. Conversely, if $W(x) \neq 0$, the functions must be linearly independent; otherwise, for appropriate constants $k_1, \ldots, k_n$ not all 0,

$$k_1y_1(x) + \cdots + k_ny_n(x) \equiv 0.$$

We differentiate this relation $n - 1$ times:

$$\begin{aligned} &k_1y_1'(x) + \cdots + k_ny_n'(x) \equiv 0, \\ &\vdots \\ &k_1y_1^{(n-1)}(x) + \cdots + k_ny_n^{(n-1)}(x) \equiv 0. \end{aligned}$$

Thus the k's satisfy n homogeneous equations. Since the k's are not all 0, the determinant of the coefficients must be zero for every x. But the determinant is $W(x)$, which we have assumed to be different from 0. Since this is a contradiction, the functions must be linearly independent.

EXAMPLE 2. $y'' + y = 2e^x$. Here $y^*(x) = e^x$ is a particular solution, for $(e^x)'' + e^x = 2e^x$. Hence, by the result of Example 1,

$$y = e^x + c_1 \cos x + c_2 \sin x \tag{4–25}$$

is the general solution. We can verify without difficulty that (4–25) always satisfies the differential equation and that the initial conditions can always be met. The only difference between this and the preceding example is that while the terms $c_1 \cos x$ and $c_2 \sin x$ give rise to zero terms, the term e^x gives rise to $e^x + e^x$, which just matches the right-hand side.

The "term-by-term" analyses here are a reflection of the basic fact that the differential equation is *linear*. The left-hand side acts on a given $y(x)$ as a *linear operator*. This point of view will be further discussed below.

EXAMPLE 3. $y''' - 6y'' + 11y' - 6y = 4 - 12x$. Here we verify that $y_1 = e^x$, $y_2 = e^{2x}$, $y_3 = e^{3x}$ are solutions of the related homogeneous equation. They are linearly independent, since

$$W(x) = \begin{vmatrix} e^x & e^{2x} & e^{3x} \\ e^x & 2e^{2x} & 3e^{3x} \\ e^x & 4e^{2x} & 9e^{3x} \end{vmatrix} = 2e^{6x} \neq 0.$$

We also verify that $y^* = 2x + 3$ is a solution of the nonhomogeneous equation. Hence

$$y = 2x + 3 + c_1e^x + c_2e^{2x} + c_3e^{3x}$$

is the general solution of the given equation.

In all the above examples, we have had the particular solutions given. Most of the rest of this chapter is devoted to methods for finding particular solutions.

PROBLEMS

1. Given the differential equation $x^2y'' + 4xy' + 2y = 0$,

(a) verify that $y = c_1x^{-2} + c_2x^{-1}$, $x > 0$, satisfies the equation for every choice of c_1 and c_2;

(b) verify that c_1 and c_2 can be chosen uniquely to satisfy the initial conditions $y = y_0$, $y' = y_0'$ for $x = x_0$, $(x_0 > 0)$.

Hence $y = c_1x^{-2} + c_2x^{-1}$ is the general solution for $x > 0$.

2. Follow the procedure of Prob. 1 to show that $y = x^2 + e^{-x}(c_1 \cos 2x + c_2 \sin 2x)$ is the general solution of the differential equation

$$y'' + 2y' + 5y = 5x^2 + 4x + 2.$$

3. Show that the following sets of functions are linearly independent for all x:

(a) e^{ax}, e^{bx}, e^{cx} (a, b, c distinct); (b) x, x^2, x^3;
(c) $\sin x$, $\cos x$, $\sin 2x$; (d) e^x, xe^x, $\sinh x$.

4. Determine which of the following sets of functions are linearly independent for all x:

(a) $\sinh x$, e^x, e^{-x}; (b) $\sin 3x$, $\sin x$, $\sin^3 x$;
(c) $1 + x$, $1 + 2x$, x^2; (d) $x^2 - x + 1$, $x^2 - 1$, $3x^2 - x - 1$.

5. Let $y_1(x)$ and $y_2(x)$ both be solutions of the differential equation

$$y'' + p(x)y' + q(x)y = 0, \qquad a < x < b.$$

Let $W(x) = y_1(x)y_2'(x) - y_1'(x)y_2(x)$ be the Wronskian determinant of the two solutions.

(a) Prove that $W'(x) = -p(x)W(x)$.
(b) Prove that $W(x) = ce^{-\int p(x)\,dx}$ for some constant c.
(c) Prove that if $W(x_0) = 0$ for some one x_0, $a < x_0 < b$, then $W(x) \equiv 0$, for $a < x < b$.
(d) Show that the result in (c) follows from Theorem 2.

6. Show that every solution of the *nonlinear* differential equation

$$y' = 1 + y^2$$

is defined over an interval of length at most π.

7. Let $y_1(x)$, $y_2(x)$, . . . , $y_n(x)$ be linearly independent over a certain interval. Let c_1, . . . , c_n, C_1, . . . , C_n be constants such that

$$c_1y_1(x) + \cdots + c_ny_n(x) \equiv C_1y_1(x) + \cdots + C_ny_n(x)$$

over the interval. Show that $c_1 = C_1$, . . . , $c_n = C_n$.

ANSWERS

4. (a), (b), (d) are linearly dependent. 6. Solutions are $y = \tan(x + c)$.

4–4 Differential operators. Superposition principle. It is convenient to write Dy for D_xy, D^2y for D_x^2y, and in general

$$D^ny \equiv D_x^ny \equiv \frac{d^ny}{dx^n} \qquad (n = 1, 2, \ldots). \tag{4–26}$$

Furthermore we can write $y'' + y \equiv D^2y + y \equiv (D^2 + 1)y$, $x^2y'' - x^3y' + 3y \equiv x^2D^2y - x^3Dy + 3y \equiv (x^2D^2 - x^3D + 3)y$, and in general

TABLE 4–1

y	$u = Ly,\ L = D^2 + 2D - 1$
e^{5x}	$34e^{5x}$
x^2	$2 + 4x - x^2$
$\sin x$	$-2\sin x + 2\cos x$
$2e^{5x} + x^2$	$68e^{5x} + 2 + 4x - x^2$

$$a_0(x)D_x^n y + a_1(x)D_x^{n-1}y + \cdots + a_n(x)y \equiv [a_0(x)D^n + a_1(x)D^{n-1} + \cdots + a_n(x)]y. \tag{4–27}$$

An expression

$$a_0(x)D^n + a_1(x)D^{n-1} + \cdots + a_n(x) \tag{4–28}$$

by itself will now be termed a (linear) *differential operator*. It describes an operation to be carried out on some function, but does not tell which function is "operated on." For example, $D^2 + 2D - 1$ is a differential operator; it stands for "formation of the second derivative of plus twice the first derivative of minus one times . . . " When the blank is filled in, we can compute the result of the operation. For example,

$$(D^2 + 2D - 1)e^{5x} = D^2e^{5x} + 2De^{5x} - e^{5x}$$
$$= 25e^{5x} + 10e^{5x} - e^{5x} = 34e^{5x}.$$

We can abbreviate a given differential operator (4–28) by a single letter, e.g., L. Then we write Ly for the result of applying L to a particular function y of x. For example, if $L = D^2 + 2D - 1$, then $L(e^{5x}) = 34e^{5x}$ as above. Accordingly, the operator L resembles a function, except that the independent and dependent variables are functions; if y is a function of x, then $Ly = u$ is another function. We can emphasize the similarity of operator to function by forming a table of values, such as Table 4–1.

Each operator L of form (4–28) is *linear*. By this we mean that if $y_1(x)$ and $y_2(x)$ are functions defined for $a < x < b$ and are such that Ly_1, Ly_2 have meaning, then for each pair of constants c_1, c_2,

$$L[c_1y_1(x) + c_2y_2(x)] = c_1L[y_1(x)] + c_2L[y_2(x)]. \tag{4–29}$$

For example, for the operator of Table 4–1,

$$L(2e^{5x} + x^2) = 2L(e^{5x}) + L(x^2);$$

this is in agreement with the table.

To prove (4–29) in general, we proceed as follows:

$$\{a_0(x)D^n + \cdots + a_n(x)\}[c_1y_1(x) + c_2y_2(x)]$$

$$= a_0(x)D^n[c_1y_1(x) + c_2y_2(x)] + \cdots + a_n(x)[c_1y_1(x) + c_2y_2(x)]$$

$$= a_0(x)[c_1D^ny_1(x) + c_2D^ny_2(x)] + \cdots + [c_1a_n(x)y_1(x) + c_2a_n(x)y_2(x)]$$

$$= c_1[a_0(x)D^ny_1 + \cdots + a_n(x)y_1] + c_2[a_0(x)D^ny_2 + \cdots + a_n(x)y_2]$$

$$= c_1\{a_0(x)D^n + \cdots + a_n(x)\}y_1 + c_2\{a_0(x)D^n + \cdots + a_n(x)\}y_2$$

$$= c_1Ly_1 + c_2Ly_2.$$

By repeated application of (4–29) we obtain the rule

$$L[c_1y_1(x) + \cdots + c_ny_n(x)] = c_1L[y_1(x)] + \cdots + c_nL[y_n(x)]. \quad (4\text{–}30)$$

A linear differential equation

$$a_0(x)D^ny + \cdots + a_n(x)y = Q \quad (4\text{–}31)$$

can be written in the abbreviated form

$$Ly = Q, \quad (4\text{–}32)$$

where $L = a_0(x)D^n + \cdots + a_n(x)$. If $y_1(x), \ldots, y_n(x)$ are solutions of the related homogeneous equation, then $Ly_1 = 0, \ldots, Ly_n = 0$. Hence, by (4–30),

$$L(c_1y_1 + \cdots + c_ny_n) = 0 \quad (4\text{–}33)$$

for every choice of the constants $c_1, \ldots, c_n$. If $y^*(x)$ is a solution of the nonhomogeneous equation (4–31), then $Ly^* = Q$. Hence by (4–30) and (4–33)

$$L(y^* + c_1y_1 + \cdots + c_ny_n) = Q. \quad (4\text{–}34)$$

Thus $y = y^* + c_1y_1 + \cdots + c_ny_n$ is a solution of (4–32) for every choice of $c_1, \ldots, c_n$. Furthermore, if $y(x)$ is any solution of the nonhomogeneous equation, then $L(y - y^*) = Ly - Ly^* = Q(x) - Q(x) = 0$. Hence $y - y^*$ is a solution of the homogeneous equation; that is, the general solution of the nonhomogeneous equation equals a particular solution $y^*(x)$ plus the general solution of the homogeneous equation. These remarks explain the *form* of the general solution of (4–31). (To complete the proof of Theorem 1, we would have to establish the *existence* of the solutions $y^*, y_1, \ldots, y_n$; this is done in Chapter 12 of ODE.)

Now let $y_1^*(x)$ satisfy (4–31) when $Q = Q_1(x)$, and let $y_2^*(x)$ satisfy (4–31) when $Q = Q_2(x)$; then $Ly_1^* = Q_1$, $Ly_2^* = Q_2$ and by (4–29),

$$L(c_1y_1^* + c_2y_2^*) = c_1Q_1 + c_2Q_2.$$

Hence $c_1y_1^* + c_2y_2^*$ is a solution of (4–31) when Q is replaced by $c_1Q_1 + c_2Q_2$. This result, which is known as the *superposition principle* (Section 3–2), can be stated as follows: *if the right-hand member of a nonhomogeneous linear differential equation is a linear combination of two functions Q_1, Q_2, then a particular solution is obtainable as the same linear combination of two solutions of the equation with Q_1, Q_2, respectively as right-hand members.* The principle can be extended to linear combinations of n functions $Q_1(x), \ldots, Q_n(x)$.

4–5 Linear differential equations with constant coefficients. Homogeneous case. Theorem 1 of Section 4–3 shows us how to form the general solution of a linear differential equation when we know a set of linearly independent solutions $y_1(x), \ldots, y_n(x)$ of the related homogeneous equation and one solution $y^*(x)$ of the nonhomogeneous equation. However, we as yet have no information on how to find $y_1(x), \ldots, y_n(x)$ and $y^*(x)$. For the general linear equation, obtaining this information presents difficulties, although infinite power series prove to be very helpful (Chapter 9).

For the special case of *constant coefficients* the problem is reducible to a standard problem of algebra and can be considered to be completely solved. Here we give the solution for the homogeneous case.

Let the given differential equation be

$$a_0D^ny + \cdots + a_{n-1}Dy + a_ny = 0 \tag{4–35}$$

or, in operator notation,

$$(a_0D^n + \cdots + a_n)y = 0. \tag{4–36}$$

The coefficients $a_0, \ldots, a_n$ are assumed to be constants and $a_0 \neq 0$.

We now seek a solution of the form $y = e^{rx}$, where r is constant. Substitution of this expression for y in the left-hand side of (4–35) yields

$$a_0r^ne^{rx} + \cdots + a_{n-1}re^{rx} + a_ne^{rx} \equiv f(r)e^{rx}, \tag{4–37}$$

where

$$f(r) = a_0r^n + a_1r^{n-1} + \cdots + a_{n-1}r + a_n. \tag{4–38}$$

We call $f(r)$ the *characteristic polynomial* associated with the given differential equation. We see that e^{rx} *will be a solution of the differential equation if* r *is chosen as a root of*

$$a_0 r^n + a_1 r^{n-1} + \cdots + a_{n-1} r + a_n = 0, \tag{4–39}$$

which we call the *characteristic equation* associated with the differential equation; it is simply the equation $f(r) = 0$. We note that if we write

$$L = a_0 D^n + \cdots + a_n, \tag{4–40}$$

then the differential equation is simply the equation

$$Ly = 0. \tag{4–41}$$

Equation (4–37) states that

$$L(e^{rx}) = f(r)e^{rx}, \tag{4–42}$$

and $f(r)$ is obtained from L by replacing D by r.

If now equation (4–39) has n distinct real roots $r_1, \ldots, r_n$, then the functions

$$y_1 = e^{r_1 x}, \qquad y_2 = e^{r_2 x}, \qquad \ldots, \qquad y_n = e^{r_n x} \tag{4–43}$$

are solutions of the differential equation. These functions are linearly independent for all x (Prob. 4 below). Hence the general solution sought is

$$y = c_1 e^{r_1 x} + \cdots + c_n e^{r_n x}. \tag{4–44}$$

It is shown in algebra that an equation of degree n has n roots. However, some of the n roots may be complex and some may be equal. It will be seen that Eq. (4–44) can be modified appropriately to cover these cases.

For example, the equation

$$y'' + y = 0 \qquad \text{or} \qquad (D^2 + 1)y = 0 \tag{4–45}$$

has the characteristic equation

$$r^2 + 1 = 0 \tag{4–46}$$

with roots $\pm i$, ($i = \sqrt{-1}$). Proceeding formally, we obtain the "solutions" e^{ix} and e^{-ix}. From these imaginary solutions we can form linear combinations which are real:

$$\cos x = \frac{e^{ix} + e^{-ix}}{2}, \qquad \sin x = \frac{e^{ix} - e^{-ix}}{2i}, \tag{4–47}$$

as follows from the Euler identity

$$e^{ix} = \cos x + i \sin x. \tag{4–48}$$

(See p. 534 of Reference 7 at the end of Chapter 3.) The functions

$$y_1(x) = \cos x, \qquad y_2(x) = \sin x,$$

are indeed linearly independent solutions of Eq. (4–45), and hence

$$y = c_1 \cos x + c_2 \sin x$$

is the general solution.

A similar analysis applies to complex roots in general. As is shown in algebra, for equations with real coefficients such roots come in pairs $a \pm bi$ (complex conjugates). From the two functions

$$e^{(a \pm bi)x} = e^{ax} (\cos bx \pm i \sin bx)$$

we obtain the two real functions

$$e^{ax} \cos bx, \quad e^{ax} \sin bx \tag{4–49}$$

as solutions of the corresponding differential equation. A proof is given in Section 4–8 of ODE.

If the characteristic equation has a multiple real root r, of multiplicity k, then it can be shown (Prob. 5 below) that the functions

$$e^{rx}, \quad xe^{rx}, \quad \ldots, \quad x^{k-1}e^{rx} \tag{4–50}$$

are solutions. If $a \pm bi$ is a pair of multiple complex roots, then we obtain as solutions the functions (4–49) and the functions obtained by multiplying these by $x, x^2, \ldots, x^{k-1}$.

We can summarize the rules as follows.

THEOREM 3. *Let there be given a homogeneous linear differential equation with constant coefficients:*

$$(a_0 D^n + \cdots + a_n)y = 0 \qquad (a_0 \neq 0) \tag{4–51}$$

with the characteristic equation

$$a_0 r^n + \cdots + a_n = 0. \tag{4–52}$$

After finding the n roots of (4–52), *we assign*

(i) *to each simple real root r the function* e^{rx};

(ii) *to each pair* $a \pm bi$ *of simple complex roots the functions* $e^{ax} \cos bx$, $e^{ax} \sin bx$;

(iii) *to each real root r of multiplicity k the functions* e^{rx}, xe^{rx}, ..., $x^{k-1}e^{rx}$;

(iv) *to each pair* $a \pm bi$ *of complex roots of multiplicity k the functions*

$$\begin{array}{llll} e^{ax}\cos bx, & xe^{ax}\cos bx, & \ldots, & x^{k-1}e^{ax}\cos bx, \\ e^{ax}\sin bx, & xe^{ax}\sin bx, & \ldots, & x^{k-1}e^{ax}\sin bx. \end{array}$$

The n functions $y_1(x), \ldots, y_n(x)$ *thus obtained are linearly independent solutions of* (4–51) *for all x, and*

$$y = c_1y_1(x) + \cdots + c_ny_n(x) \tag{4–53}$$

is the general solution of (4–51).

A proof of this theorem is given in Section 4–8 of ODE.

EXAMPLE 1. $y'' - y = 0$. The characteristic equation $r^2 - 1 = 0$ has the distinct roots $1, -1$; hence the general solution is

$$y = c_1e^x + c_2e^{-x}.$$

EXAMPLE 2. $(D^3 - D^2 + D - 1)y = 0$. The characteristic equation $r^3 - r^2 + r - 1 = 0$ has the distinct roots $1, i, -i$; hence the general solution is

$$y = c_1e^x + c_2 \cos x + c_3 \sin x.$$

EXAMPLE 3. $(D^2 + D + 1)y = 0$. The characteristic equation is $r^2 + r + 1 = 0$, with roots $\frac{1}{2}(-1 \pm \sqrt{3}i)$. Hence by part (ii) of the above theorem the general solution is

$$y = e^{-x/2}\left(c_1 \cos \frac{\sqrt{3}}{2}x + c_2 \sin \frac{\sqrt{3}}{2}x\right).$$

EXAMPLE 4. $(D^6 + 8D^4 + 16D^2)y = 0$. The characteristic equation is $r^6 + 8r^4 + 16r^2 = 0$ or

$$r^2(r^2 + 4)^2 = 0.$$

The roots are $0, 0, \pm 2i, \pm 2i$. By parts (iii) and (iv) of Theorem 3 the general solution is

$$y = c_1 + c_2x + c_3 \cos 2x + c_4 \sin 2x + c_5x \cos 2x + c_6x \sin 2x.$$

It thus appears that the homogeneous linear equation with constant coefficients is completely solved; once we have solved a certain algebraic equation, we can write down all solutions of the differential equation. However, in a practical sense this method is not always satisfactory, for the solution of an algebraic equation is not always simple or brief. (See Section 4–6 of ODE for a discussion of solution of algebraic equations.)

PROBLEMS

1. Find the general solution of each of the following equations:

(a) $(D^2 - 4)y = 0$, (b) $(D^2 + 4D)y = 0$,
(c) $(D^3 - 3D^2 + 3D - 1)y = 0$, (d) $(D^4 + 1)y = 0$,
(e) $(D^5 + 2D^3 + D)y = 0$, (f) $D_t x + 3x = 0$,
(g) $D_t^2 x + D_t x + 7x = 0$, (h) $D^5 y = 0$,
(i) $(D^5 + 1)y = 0$, (j) $(D^6 + 64)y = 0$,
(k) $(D^8 - 256)y = 0$, (l) $(36D^3 - 144D^2 + 191D - 84)y = 0$,
(m) $(D^3 + 5D^2 - 1)y = 0$, (n) $(D^4 - 5D^2 + D + 4)y = 0$,
(o) $(D^4 + D - 1)y = 0$, (p) $(D^4 + D^3 + D^2 + D + 1)y = 0$.

2. Find the solution which satisfies the given initial conditions:

(a) $(D^2 + 1)y = 0$; for $x = 0$: $y = 1$ and $y' = 0$;
(b) $D_t^2 x + D_t x - 3x = 0$; $x = 0$ and $D_t x = 1$ for $t = 0$.

3. Find a solution satisfying the given boundary conditions:

(a) $y'' - y' - 6y = 0$; $y = 1$ for $x = 0$, $y = 0$ for $x = 1$;
(b) $y'' + y = 0$; $y = 1$ for $x = 0$, $y = 2$ for $x = \pi/2$;
(c) $y'' + y = 0$; $y = 0$ for $x = 0$, $y = 0$ for $x = \pi$.

4. Let $r_1, \ldots, r_n$ be distinct real numbers. Prove that the functions $e^{r_1 x}, \ldots, e^{r_n x}$ are linearly independent for all x. Two possible methods are the following.

(a) Assume a relation $k_1 e^{r_1 x} + \cdots + k_n e^{r_n x} = 0$ to hold for all x, with not all $k_i = 0$. Assume the r's to be numbered so that $r_1 < r_2 \cdots < r_n$. Multiply by $e^{-r_n x}$ and let $x \to +\infty$ to conclude that $k_n = 0$. Then multiply by $e^{-r_{n-1} x}$ and let $x \to +\infty$ to conclude that $k_{n-1} = 0$; thus finally show that all k's must be zero.

(b) The Wronskian determinant is $W_n e^{(r_1 + \cdots + r_n)x}$, where

$$W_n = \begin{vmatrix} 1 & 1 & \cdots & 1 \\ r_1 & r_2 & & r_n \\ \vdots & & & \vdots \\ r_1^{n-1} & r_2^{n-1} & \cdots & r_n^{n-1} \end{vmatrix}$$

We can show by induction that so long as the r's are distinct, W_n cannot be 0.

This is clearly true for $n = 1$. If it is true for $n = k$, then form W_n for $n = k + 1$:

$$W_{k+1} = \begin{vmatrix} 1 & 1 & \dots & 1 \\ r_1 & r_2 & & r_{k+1} \\ \vdots & & & \vdots \\ r_1^k & r_2^k & \dots & r_{k+1}^k \end{vmatrix}$$

If we replace r_{k+1} by a variable r, then W_{k+1} becomes a polynomial, $P(r)$; the coefficient of r^k in $P(r)$ is a determinant W_k and, by induction assumption, is not 0. Hence $P(r)$ has degree k. Show that $P(r_1) = 0$, $P(r_2) = 0, \dots, P(r_k) = 0$ and that $P(r) \neq 0$ for r distinct from $r_1, \dots, r_k$. Therefore $W_{k+1} = P(r_{k+1}) \neq 0$, and the induction is complete.

Remark. The determinant W_n is known as a *Vandermonde determinant.* An extension of the argument of part (b) shows that

$$W_n = (r_2 - r_1)(r_3 - r_1)(r_3 - r_2) \cdots (r_n - r_{n-1}).$$

5. Let $L = a_0 D^n + \cdots + a_n$, where $a_0, \dots, a_n$ are constants. Let $f(r) = a_0 r^n + \cdots + a_n$.

(a) Prove: $L(xe^{rx}) = f(r)xe^{rx} + f'(r)e^{rx}$. [*Hint:* It is sufficient to prove the rule when L consists of one term $a_k D^k$; the general case then follows by addition. For this case, $D^k(xe^{rx})$ can be found by the Leibnitz rule for differentiation of products:

$$D^k(uv) = uD^k v + kDuD^{k-1}v + \frac{k(k-1)}{2!} D^2 u D^{k-2} v + \cdots + (D^k u)v.\Big]$$

(b) Prove that for $m = 1, 2, 3, \dots,$

$$L(x^m e^{rx}) = e^{rx}\left[f(r)x^m + mf'(r)x^{m-1} + \frac{m(m-1)}{2!} f''(r)x^{m-2} + \cdots \right].$$

[*Hint:* Proceed as in part (a).]

(c) If r_1 is a double root of $f(r)$, then $f(r_1) = 0, f'(r_1) = 0$. Set $r = r_1$ in the conclusion of part (a) to conclude that $xe^{r_1 x}$ must then be a solution of the differential equation $Ly = 0$.

(d) Reason as in part (c) to show that if r_1 is a root of multiplicity k of $f(r)$, then $e^{r_1 x}, xe^{r_1 x}, \dots, x^{k-1}e^{r_1 x}$ are solutions of the differential equation $Ly = 0$. Another proof of this result is given in Prob. 7 following Section 5–4.

ANSWERS

1. (a) $c_1 e^{2x} + c_2 e^{-2x}$; (b) $c_1 + c_2 e^{-4x}$; (c) $c_1 e^x + c_2 x e^x + c_3 x^2 e^x$; (d) $e^{ax}(c_1 \cos ax + c_2 \sin ax) + e^{-ax}(c_3 \cos ax + c_4 \sin ax)$, $a = \sqrt{2}/2$; (e) $c_1 + c_2 \cos x + c_3 \sin x + c_4 x \cos x + c_5 x \sin x$; (f) $c_1 e^{-3t}$;

(g) $e^{-t/2}(c_1 \cos bt + c_2 \sin bt)$, $b = 3\sqrt{3}/2$; (h) $c_1 + c_2x + c_3x^2 + c_4x^3 + c_5x^4$; (i) $c_1e^{-x} + e^{0.809x}(c_2 \cos 0.588x + c_3 \sin 0.588x) + e^{-0.309x}(c_4 \cos 0.951x + c_5 \sin 0.951x)$; (j) $c_1 \cos 2x + c_2 \sin 2x + e^{1.732x}(c_3 \cos x + c_4 \sin x) + e^{-1.732x}(c_5 \cos x + c_6 \sin x)$; (k) $c_1e^{2x} + c_2e^{-2x} + c_3 \cos 2x + c_4 \sin 2x + e^{ax}(c_5 \cos ax + c_6 \sin ax) + e^{-ax}(c_7 \cos ax + c_8 \sin ax)$, $a = \sqrt{2}$; (l) $c_1e^{(3/2)x} + c_2e^{(4/3)x} + c_3e^{(7/6)x}$; (m) $c_1e^{0.429x} + c_2e^{-4.96x} + c_3e^{-0.470x}$; (n) $c_1e^{1.22x} + c_2e^{1.78x} + c_3e^{-0.86x} + c_4e^{-2.15x}$; (o) $c_1e^{-1.22x} + c_2e^{0.73x} + e^{0.25x}(c_3 \cos 1.03x + c_4 \sin 1.03x)$; (p) $e^{0.309x}(c_1 \cos 0.951x + c_2 \sin 0.951x) + e^{-0.809x}(c_1 \cos 0.588x + c_2 \sin 0.588x)$.

2. (a) $\cos x$, (b) $(2/\sqrt{13})e^{-t/2} \sinh (\sqrt{13}t/2)$.

3. (a) $(e^{3x} - e^{5-2x})/(1 - e^5)$, (b) $\cos x + 2 \sin x$, (c) $c \sin x$.

***4–6 Complex form of solution of homogeneous linear differential equations.** We return to the discussion of Section 4–5. When the characteristic equation has complex roots $a \pm bi$, we can proceed formally and introduce the terms

$$c_1e^{(a+bi)x} + c_2e^{(a-bi)x} \tag{4–54}$$

in the solution. From the identity

$$e^{(a\pm bi)x} = e^{ax}(\cos bx \pm i \sin bx) \tag{4–55}$$

the real solution can then be recovered, for (4–54) becomes

$$e^{ax}[(c_1 + c_2) \cos bx + i(c_1 - c_2) \sin bx]. \tag{4–56}$$

If we now introduce new arbitrary constants:

$$C_1 = c_1 + c_2, \qquad C_2 = i(c_1 - c_2), \tag{4–57}$$

then (4–56) becomes

$$e^{ax}[C_1 \cos bx + C_2 \sin bx], \tag{4–58}$$

as in Section 4–5.

From (4–57) we find

$$c_1 = \tfrac{1}{2}(C_1 - iC_2), \qquad c_2 = \tfrac{1}{2}(C_1 + iC_2). \tag{4–59}$$

Now the constants C_1, C_2 are to be real, so that (4–58) gives the usual real solution. Hence (4–59) shows that c_1, c_2 are *conjugate complex numbers:* $c_2 = \bar{c}_1$. If c_1, c_2 are any pair of conjugate complex constants, then

$C_1 = c_1 + c_2$ and $C_2 = i(c_1 - c_2)$ will be real, and (4–54) is equivalent to the real solution (4–58). Thus we can write our real solutions as

$$c_1 e^{(a+bi)x} + \bar{c}_1 e^{(a-bi)x} \quad \text{or} \quad c_1 e^{rx} + \bar{c}_1 e^{\bar{r}x},$$

where $r = a + bi$, $\bar{r} = a - bi$.

EXAMPLE 1. $y'' + y = 0$. The characteristic equation has roots $\pm i$. The general solution can be written in the two forms

$$y = C_1 \cos x + C_2 \sin x, \tag{4–60}$$

$$y = ce^{ix} + \bar{c}e^{-ix}. \tag{4–61}$$

Here C_1, C_2 are arbitrary *real* constants, while c is an arbitrary *complex* constant. If the characteristic equation has several complex roots, possibly multiple, as in Example 2, a similar procedure can be followed.

EXAMPLE 2. $(D^6 + 2D^5 + 4D^4 + 4D^3 + 5D^2 + 2D + 2)y = 0$. The characteristic equation can be written as $(r^2 + 1)^2(r^2 + 2r + 2) = 0$, so that the roots are $\pm i$, $\pm i$, $-1 \pm i$. The solutions can be written in the form

$$y = C_1 \cos x + C_2 \sin x + C_3\, x \cos x + C_4\, x \sin x + e^{-x}(C_5 \cos x + C_6 \sin x)$$

or in the form

$$\begin{aligned} y &= c_1 e^{ix} + \bar{c}_1 e^{-ix} + c_2 x e^{ix} + \bar{c}_2 x e^{-ix} \\ &\qquad + e^{-x}(c_3 e^{ix} + \bar{c}_3 e^{-ix}) \\ &= e^{ix}(c_1 + c_2 x + c_3 e^{-x}) + e^{-ix}(\bar{c}_1 + \bar{c}_2 x + \bar{c}_3 e^{-x}), \end{aligned}$$

where c_1, c_2, c_3 are arbitrary complex constants.

EXAMPLE 3. $(D^3 - 3D^2 + 7D - 5)y = 0$. The characteristic roots are 1, $1 \pm 2i$. The solutions can be written

$$y = c_1 e^x + e^x(c_2 e^{2ix} + \bar{c}_2 e^{-2ix}),$$

where c_1 is real, but c_2 is complex.

***4–7 General theory of complex solutions.** The preceding discussion has been purely formal, and a complex solution such as (4–61) appears simply as another way of writing the real solution (4–60). However, we can take a more general point of view which enables us to calculate freely with complex solutions.

By a *complex function* of a *real variable* is meant a function $F(x)$ which assigns a complex number to each x (of a certain interval). Thus

$$F(x) = x^2 + i(x^3 - 1)$$

is such a function; typical values are as follows:

$$F(0) = -i, \qquad F(1) = 1, \qquad F(2) = 4 + 7i.$$

Other examples of complex functions are the following:

$$F(x) = \cos x + i \sin x = e^{ix},$$

$$F(x) = e^{2x} \cos x + ie^{2x} \sin x = e^{(2+i)x}.$$

The value of a complex function $F(x)$ for each x is a complex number $w = u + iv$, where u and v are real. We call u the *real part* of w, and v the *imaginary part* of w; in symbols,

$$w = u + iv, \qquad u = \text{Re}\,(w), \qquad v = \text{Im}\,(w). \tag{4-62}$$

In general, a complex function $F(x)$ can be written as

$$F(x) = f(x) + ig(x),$$

where f and g are real, and the equation $w = F(x)$ is equivalent to the two real equations

$$u = f(x), \qquad v = g(x).$$

Operations on complex functions are similar to those for real functions; we can add, subtract, multiply, and divide complex functions defined over the same interval, except for division by $0 = 0 + i0$. We can also take limits; the equation

$$\lim_{x \to x_0} F(x) = a + ib \tag{4-63}$$

means that $F(x)$ is to be arbitrarily close to $a + ib$ for x sufficiently close to x_0. It is easily seen that (4-63) is equivalent to the two equations

$$\lim_{x \to x_0} f(x) = a, \qquad \lim_{x \to x_0} g(x) = b, \tag{4-64}$$

if $F(x) = f(x) + ig(x)$. From the definition or from (4–64) we can verify that the theorem on limit of sum, product, and quotient remains valid.

The *derivative* of a complex function is defined exactly as for real functions:

$$F'(x) = \lim_{\Delta x \to 0} \frac{F(x + \Delta x) - F(x)}{\Delta x}. \tag{4–65}$$

Since we can take limits in real and imaginary parts separately, (4–65) is the same as

$$F'(x) = f'(x) + ig'(x), \tag{4–66}$$

wherever both $f'(x)$ and $g'(x)$ exist.

EXAMPLE 1. If $w = F(x) = x^2 + i(x^3 - 1)$, then $F'(x) = 2x + 3x^2 i$.

We also use other standard notations for the derivative: w', dw/dx, $D_x w$. Higher derivatives are defined as usual, and we find

$$F''(x) = f''(x) + ig''(x), \quad \ldots \tag{4–67}$$

The basic rules of calculus continue to hold:

$$[F(x) + G(x)]' = F'(x) + G'(x), \qquad (F \cdot G)' = FG' + F'G,$$
$$\left(\frac{F}{G}\right)' = \frac{GF' - FG'}{G^2}, \tag{4–68}$$

provided F and G have derivatives over the interval considered and there is no division by zero. The proofs are left as exercises (Prob. 3 below).

EXAMPLE 2. If $w = e^{ix} = \cos x + i \sin x$, then $D_x w = -\sin x + i \cos x = i(\cos x + i \sin x) = ie^{ix}$, $D_x^2 w = iD_x e^{ix} = i^2 e^{ix} = -e^{ix}$.

EXAMPLE 3. If $w = e^{(a+bi)x} = e^{ax}(\cos bx + i \sin bx)$, where a and b are real constants, then

$$\begin{aligned} D_x w &= e^{ax}[(a \cos bx - b \sin bx) + i(a \sin bx + b \cos bx)] \\ &= (a + bi)e^{ax}(\cos bx + i \sin bx) \\ &= (a + bi)e^{(a+bi)x}, \\ D_x^2 w &= (a + bi)D_x e^{(a+bi)x} = (a + bi)^2 e^{(a+bi)x}, \end{aligned}$$

and in general

$$D_x^n w = (a + bi)^n e^{(a+bi)x} \qquad (n = 1\ 2, \ldots). \tag{4–69}$$

A *definite integral* can also be defined as a limit or, more simply, by the equation

$$\int_a^b F(x)\,dx = \int_a^b [f(x) + ig(x)]\,dx = \int_a^b f(x)\,dx + i\int_a^b g(x)\,dx. \qquad (4\text{–}70)$$

The indefinite integral is defined as usual:

$$\int F(x)\,dx = G(x) + C \quad \text{if} \quad G'(x) = F(x), \qquad (4\text{–}71)$$

where C is an arbitrary *complex* constant. The integrals have the familiar properties. In particular,

$$\int_a^b F'(x)\,dx = F(b) - F(a) = F(x)\Big|_a^b. \qquad (4\text{–}72)$$

Let a linear differential equation be given:

$$(a_0 D_x^n + \cdots + a_n)y = Q(x). \qquad (4\text{–}73)$$

A complex function $F(x) = f(x) + ig(x)$ is said to be a *solution* of the equation over some interval if

$$a_0 D_x^n F(x) + \cdots + a_n F(x) \equiv Q(x) \qquad (4\text{–}74)$$

over the interval. The coefficients a_0, a_1, ... may be functions of x; in fact, the coefficients and $Q(x)$ may be complex functions.

EXAMPLE 4. $y = e^{ix}$ is a solution of $y'' + y = 0$ (see Example 2 above).

EXAMPLE 5. $y = e^{(1+2i)x}$ is a solution of the equation $y'' - 2y' + 5y = 0$. For

$$(D_x^2 - 2D_x + 5)e^{(1+2i)x} \equiv [(1 + 2i)^2 - 2(1 + 2i) + 5]e^{(1+2i)x} \equiv 0.$$

EXAMPLE 6. $y = e^{ix}$ is a solution of $(ix - 1)y'' + xy' - y = 0$.

EXAMPLE 7. $y = 1 - ix + ce^{-ix}$ is a solution of $y' + iy = x$, for every choice of the complex constant c. This solution can be obtained by the general method for first order linear equations (Section 2–8). For e^{ix} is the integrating factor, and

$$e^{ix}y = \int xe^{ix}\,dx = \frac{xe^{ix}}{i} - \int \frac{e^{ix}}{i}\,dx = \frac{xe^{ix}}{i} + e^{ix} + c$$

by integration by parts. Hence $y = 1 - ix + ce^{-ix}$, and this is the general complex solution.

If the coefficients $a_0, \ldots$ and the function $Q(x)$ are real, there are, in general, complex solutions of Eq. (4–73); see Examples 4 and 5 above. The real part of every such complex solution is a real solution. For if

$$a_0(D_x^n f + iD_x^n g) + \cdots + a_n(f + ig) = Q,$$

then we can compare real parts on both sides:

$$a_0 D_x^n f + \cdots + a_n f = Q;$$

that is, $f = \text{Re}\,(f + ig)$ is a solution. Every real solution f can be considered as the real part of a complex solution $f + i0$. Hence *if all complex solutions are known, all real solutions are obtained as all real parts of the complex solutions.*

A set of n complex functions is said to be *linearly independent* (with respect to complex coefficients) over a given interval if no one function can be expressed as a linear combination, with complex coefficients, of the others; this is equivalent to the statement that an identity

$$k_1 F_1(x) + \cdots + k_n F_n(x) \equiv 0,$$

where $k_1, \ldots, k_n$ are complex constants, can hold only if $k_1 = 0, k_2 = 0, \ldots, k_n = 0$. A theorem analogous to Theorem 1 (Section 4–3) holds for complex functions: the general solution of (4–74) has the form

$$y = y^*(x) + c_1 F_1(x) + \cdots + c_n F_n(x),$$

where $F_1(x), \ldots, F_n(x)$ are linearly independent complex solutions of the homogeneous equation. A proof is given in Chapter 12 of ODE. When the coefficients are constant, the following basic theorem applies.

THEOREM 4. *Let there be given a homogeneous linear differential equation with constant coefficients (possibly complex),*

$$(a_0 D_x^n + \cdots + a_n)y = 0 \qquad (a_0 \neq 0). \tag{4–75}$$

Let $r_1, \ldots, r_n$ be the roots of the characteristic equation

$$a_0 r^n + \cdots + a_n = 0. \tag{4–76}$$

To each root r of multiplicity k assign the functions $e^{rx}, xe^{rx}, \ldots, x^{k-1}e^{rx}$.

Then the n functions so obtained are linearly independent complex solutions of (4–75), so that the general solution is

$$y = e^{r_1 x}(c_1 + c_2 x + \cdots + c_{k_1} x^{k_1 - 1}) + \cdots \tag{4–77}$$

The proof is given in Section 4–8 of ODE.

Remark. For the real case we now have three ways of writing the solutions. We illustrate these for the equation $y'' + y = 0$:

$$y = C_1 \cos x + C_2 \sin x, \qquad y = ce^{ix} + \bar{c}e^{-ix}, \qquad y = \mathrm{Re}\,(c_1 e^{ix} + c_2 e^{-ix}). \tag{4–78}$$

Here C_1, C_2 are arbitrary real constants; c, c_1, and c_2 are arbitrary complex constants.

PROBLEMS

1. Write the general real solution of each of the following equations in terms of complex constants and their conjugates:

(a) $y'' + 4y = 0$, (b) $y'' + 4y' + 5y = 0$,
(c) $(D^5 + 6D^3 + 9D)y = 0$, (d) $(D^5 + D^4 + D^3 + D^2 + D + 1)y = 0$.

2. Differentiate each of the following functions:

(a) $xe^{(1+i)x}$, (b) $(e^{ix} - e^{-ix})/(e^{ix} + e^{-ix})$,
(c) $(e^{ix} - e^{-ix})^3$, (d) $(1 + ix)^4$.

3. Prove the validity of the following rules for complex functions $F(x)$, $G(x)$, assuming existence of the derivatives concerned over some interval:

(a) $[F(x) + G(x)]' = F'(x) + G'(x)$ [*Hint:* Use (4–66).],
(b) $[F(x)G(x)]' = F(x)G'(x) + F'(x)G(x)$,

(c) $\left[\dfrac{1}{G(x)}\right]' = -\dfrac{G'(x)}{[G(x)]^2}$ $[G(x) \neq 0]$,

(d) $\left[\dfrac{F(x)}{G(x)}\right]' = \dfrac{G(x)F'(x) - F(x)G'(x)}{[G(x)]^2}$ $[G(x) \neq 0]$.

[*Hint:* For (d) apply the results of parts (b) and (c).]

4. Prove that $e^{a+bi} \neq 0$ for every complex number $a + bi$.

5. Find the general complex solution of each of the following:

(a) $(D^2 + 4)y = 0$, (b) $(D^2 - 3iD - 2)y = 0$.

6. Obtain the general real solution as the real part of the general complex solution:

(a) $(D^2 + 9)y = 0$, (b) $(D^2 + 4D + 5)y = 0$,
(c) $(D^4 + 18D^2 + 81)y = 0$, (d) $(D^3 - 6D^2 + 10D)y = 0$.

ANSWERS

1. (a) $ce^{2ix} + \bar{c}e^{-2ix}$; (b) $ce^{(-2+i)x} + \bar{c}e^{(-2-i)x}$; (c) $C_1 + c_2e^{rx} + \bar{c}_2e^{\bar{r}x} + c_3xe^{rx} + \bar{c}_3xe^{\bar{r}x}$, $r = \sqrt{3}i$, and C_1 is real; (d) $C_1e^{-x} + c_2e^{rx} + \bar{c}_2e^{\bar{r}x} + c_3e^{sx} + \bar{c}_3e^{\bar{s}x}$, where $r = e^{\pi i/3}$, $s = e^{2\pi i/3}$, and C_1 is real.

2. (a) $(1 + x + ix)e^{(1+i)x}$, (b) $4i/(e^{ix} + e^{-ix})^2$, (c) $3i(e^{ix} - e^{-ix})^2(e^{ix} + e^{-ix})$, (d) $4i(1 + ix)^3$.

5. (a) $c_1e^{2ix} + c_2e^{-2ix}$, (b) $c_1e^{ix} + c_2e^{2ix}$.

6. (a) Re $(c_1e^{3ix} + c_2e^{-3ix})$, (b) Re $(c_1e^{(-2+i)x} + c_2e^{(-2-i)x})$,
(c) Re $(c_1e^{3ix} + c_2e^{-3ix} + c_3xe^{3ix} + c_4xe^{-3ix})$,
(d) Re $(c_1 + c_2e^{(3+i)x} + c_3e^{(3-i)x})$.

4–8 The nonhomogeneous linear equation. Method of variation of parameters. By Theorem 1 of Section 4–3 the general solution of a linear equation such as

$$(a_0D^n + \cdots + a_n)y = Q(x) \tag{4–79}$$

has the form

$$y = y^*(x) + c_1y_1(x) + \cdots + c_ny_n(x), \tag{4–80}$$

where $y^*(x)$ is a particular solution of the nonhomogeneous equation (4–79) and $c_1y_1(x) + \cdots + c_ny_n(x)$ is the general solution of the related homogeneous equation

$$(a_0D^n + \cdots + a_n)y = 0;$$

the expression $c_1y_1(x) + \cdots + c_ny_n(x)$ is called the *complementary function*. At least when the coefficients are constant, we know how to find the complementary function, but we have as yet no inkling of how to find the particular solution $y^*(x)$ of the nonhomogeneous equation. Now, however, we discuss one method for finding $y^*(x)$. This method, called *variation of parameters,* is applicable to equations with variable or constant coefficients, but the complementary function must be known before the method can be applied. Other methods for finding $y^*(x)$ are described in Section 4–9 and in Chapter 5.

We illustrate our procedure for an equation of second order:

$$a_0y'' + a_1y' + a_2y = Q(x). \tag{4–81}$$

The complementary function $c_1y_1(x) + c_2y_2(x)$ is assumed known. We consider the two equations

$$y = c_1y_1(x) + c_2y_2(x),$$
$$y' = c_1y_1'(x) + c_2y_2'(x),$$

which are valid for solutions of the homogeneous equation. We now replace the constants c_1, c_2 by variables $v_1(x)$, $v_2(x)$ and consider the equations

$$\begin{aligned} y &= v_1(x)y_1(x) + v_2(x)y_2(x), \\ y' &= v_1(x)y_1'(x) + v_2(x)y_2'(x) \end{aligned} \tag{4–82}$$

as defining a *change* of variables. Instead of a second order equation for y, we obtain a system of two first order equations for v_1 and v_2. To find the system, we differentiate the first equation of (4–82):

$$y' = v_1y_1' + v_2y_2' + v_1'y_1 + v_2'y_2.$$

Subtraction of the second equation of (4–82) yields

$$v_1'y_1 + v_2'y_2 = 0, \tag{4–83}$$

which is the *first of the two equations sought.* Differentiation of the second of (4–82) yields

$$y'' = v_1y_1'' + v_2y_2'' + v_1'y_1' + v_2'y_2'. \tag{4–84}$$

We replace y, y', y'' by the expressions (4–82), (4–84) in the given differential equation (4–81):

$$\begin{aligned} a_0(v_1y_1'' + v_2y_2'' + v_1'y_1' + v_2'y_2') + a_1(v_1y_1' + v_2y_2') \\ + a_2(v_1y_1 + v_2y_2) = Q(x). \end{aligned}$$

This can be written as

$$\begin{aligned} v_1(a_0y_1'' + a_1y_1' + a_2y_1) + v_2(a_0y_2'' + a_1y_2' + a_2y_2) \\ + a_0(v_1'y_1' + v_2'y_2') = Q(x). \end{aligned}$$

But $y_1(x)$ is a solution of the homogeneous equation; hence the coefficient of v_1 is 0. For the same reason, the coefficient of v_2 is 0. Accordingly, we obtain the *second desired equation:*

$$a_0(v_1'y_1' + v_2'y_2') = Q(x). \tag{4–85}$$

Equations (4–83) and (4–85) are simultaneous equations for v_1', v_2'. They can be solved for v_1', v_2', and v_1, v_2 can then be obtained by integration.

EXAMPLE 1. $y'' - y = e^{3x}$. The complementary function is $c_1e^x + c_2e^{-x}$. Equations (4–83), (4–85) become

$$v_1'e^x + v_2'e^{-x} = 0, \qquad v_1'e^x - v_2'e^{-x} = e^{3x}.$$

Hence $2v_1' = e^{2x}$, $2v_2' = -e^{4x}$, and we can choose v_1 as $e^{2x}/4$, v_2 as $-e^{4x}/8$. Only one particular solution is needed in each case, hence

$$y^* = v_1e^x + v_2e^{-x} = \frac{1}{4}e^{3x} - \frac{1}{8}e^{3x} = \frac{e^{3x}}{8}$$

is the particular solution sought, and the general solution is

$$y = \tfrac{1}{8}e^{3x} + c_1e^x + c_2e^{-x}.$$

The method carries over to higher order equations.

THEOREM 5. *Let the function $a_0(x), \ldots, a_n(x)$, $Q(x)$ be continuous in some interval of x, within which $a_0(x) \neq 0$. Let $c_1y_1(x) + \cdots + c_ny_n(x)$ be the complementary function for the differential equation*

$$[a_0(x)D^n + \cdots + a_n(x)]y = Q(x).$$

Then a particular solution $y^*(x)$ is given by

$$y^*(x) = v_1(x)y_1(x) + \cdots + v_n(x)y_n(x),$$

where $v_1(x), \ldots, v_n(x)$ are chosen to satisfy the equations

$$\begin{aligned} &v_1'(x)y_1(x) + \cdots + v_n'(x)y_n(x) = 0,\\ &v_1'(x)y_1'(x) + \cdots + v_n'(x)y_n'(x) = 0,\\ &\vdots\\ &v_1'(x)y_1^{(n-2)}(x) + \cdots + v_n'(x)y_n^{(n-2)}(x) = 0,\\ &a_0[v_1'(x)y_1^{(n-1)}(x) + \cdots + v_n'(x)y^{(n-1)}(x)] = Q(x). \end{aligned} \tag{4–86}$$

Proof. The justification follows the reasoning for $n = 2$. The equations

$$\begin{aligned} &y = v_1y_1 + \cdots + v_ny_n,\\ &y' = v_1y_1' + \cdots + v_ny_n',\\ &\vdots\\ &y^{(n-1)} = v_1y_1^{(n-1)} + \cdots + v_ny_n^{(n-1)} \end{aligned} \tag{4–87}$$

are considered as defining the change of variables. Differentiation of the first and subtraction of the second yields the first of (4–86); differentiation of the second of (4–87) and subtraction of the third leads to the second of (4–86), and so on. Differentiation of the last of (4–87) gives

$$y^{(n)} = v_1 y_1^{(n)} + \cdots + v_n y_n^{(n)} + v_1' y_1^{(n-1)} + \cdots + v_n' y_n^{(n-1)}. \tag{4–88}$$

Multiplication of the equations (4–87) by $a_n(x)$, $a_{n-1}(x)$, ..., $a_1(x)$ and of (4–88) by $a_0(x)$ and addition of all n equations yields the last of (4–86) by virtue of the fact that $y_1(x), \ldots, y_n(x)$ are solutions of the homogeneous equation.

The equations (4–86) are n simultaneous linear equations for the unknowns $v_1'(x), \ldots, v_n'(x)$. The determinant of the coefficients is

$$a_0(x) \begin{vmatrix} y_1(x) & \cdots & y_n(x) \\ \vdots & & \vdots \\ y_1^{(n-1)}(x) & \cdots & y_n^{(n-1)}(x) \end{vmatrix} = a_0(x) W(x),$$

where $W(x)$ is the Wronskian determinant of the functions $y_1(x), \ldots, y_n(x)$. Since these functions must be linearly independent, Theorem 2 shows that $W(x) \not\equiv 0$. We have assumed $a_0(x) \neq 0$; therefore the determinant is not 0 and equations (4–86) have a unique solution for $v_1'(x), \ldots, v_n'(x)$. The solution can be expressed in terms of determinants:

$$v_1'(x) = \begin{vmatrix} 0 & y_2(x) & \cdots & y_n(x) \\ \vdots & & & \vdots \\ Q(x) & y_2^{(n-1)}(x) & \cdots & y_n^{(n-1)}(x) \end{vmatrix} \div [a_0(x) W(x)], \cdots$$

From this we see that $v_1'(x)$ equals a continuous function of x; hence integration is possible and we can obtain $v_1(x)$ (up to an arbitrary constant). Similarly, $v_2(x), \ldots, v_n(x)$ can be found. Since $v_1(x), \ldots, v_n(x)$ satisfy (4–86), it follows at once that $y^*(x) = v_1 y_1(x) + \cdots + v_n y_n(x)$ satisfies (4–87) and the given differential equation.

Example 2. $y'' + 2y' + 2y = e^{5x}$. The characteristic equation has the complex roots $-1 \pm i$. We apply the method of variation of parameters in terms of *complex* functions. If we obtain a complex particular solution, its real part will be a real particular solution (Section 4–7). We thus choose $y_1(x)$ to be $e^{(-1+i)x}$ and $y_2(x)$ to be $e^{(-1-i)x}$. Equations (4–86) become

$$v_1' e^{(-1+i)x} + v_2' e^{(-1-i)x} = 0,$$

$$v_1'(-1+i) e^{(-1+i)x} + v_2'(-1-i) e^{(-1-i)x} = e^{5x}.$$

Elimination gives the equations

$$v_1' = -\tfrac{1}{2}ie^{(6-i)x}, \qquad v_2' = \tfrac{1}{2}ie^{(6+i)x}.$$

Hence we can choose

$$v_1 = -\frac{1}{2}\frac{i}{6-i}e^{(6-i)x}, \qquad v_2 = \frac{1}{2}\frac{i}{6+i}e^{(6+i)x},$$

$$y^* = v_1y_1 + v_2y_2 = e^{5x}\left(-\frac{1}{2}\frac{i}{6-i} + \frac{1}{2}\frac{i}{6+i}\right) = \frac{e^{5x}}{37}\cdot$$

Example 3. $(D^3 - 7D^2 + 14D - 8)y = \log x$, $x > 0$. The complementary function is $c_1e^x + c_2e^{2x} + c_3e^{4x}$. The equations (4–86) become

$$v_1'e^x + v_2'e^{2x} + v_3'e^{4x} = 0,$$

$$v_1'e^x + 2v_2'e^{2x} + 4v_3'e^{4x} = 0,$$

$$v_1'e^x + 4v_2'e^{2x} + 16v_3'e^{4x} = \log x.$$

We can consider $v_1'e^x$, $v_2'e^{2x}$, $v_3'e^{4x}$ as the unknowns. We solve by determinants:

$$v_1'e^x = \begin{vmatrix} 0 & 1 & 1 \\ 0 & 2 & 4 \\ \log x & 4 & 16 \end{vmatrix} \div \begin{vmatrix} 1 & 1 & 1 \\ 1 & 2 & 4 \\ 1 & 4 & 16 \end{vmatrix} = \frac{\log x}{3}\cdot$$

Hence $v_1' = (e^{-x}\log x)/3$. Similarly, we find $v_2' = -(e^{-2x}\log x)/2$, $v_3' = (e^{-4x}\log x)/6$; accordingly,

$$\begin{aligned} y^* &= v_1y_1 + v_2y_2 + v_3y_3 \\ &= \tfrac{1}{3}e^x\int e^{-x}\log x\,dx - \tfrac{1}{2}e^{2x}\int e^{-2x}\log x\,dx + \tfrac{1}{6}e^{4x}\int e^{-4x}\log x\,dx. \end{aligned}$$

PROBLEMS

1. Find the general solution of each of the following by the method of variation of parameters:

(a) $y'' - y = e^x$;
(b) $y''' - 6y'' + 11y' - 6y = e^{4x}$;
(c) $y'' + y = \cot x$;
(d) $y'' + 4y = \sec 2x$;
(e) $y'' - y = 1/x$, $x > 0$;
(f) $y'' + 4y' + 5y = xe^x$.

2. Solve the first order linear equation $y' + p(x)y = Q(x)$ by first solving the related homogeneous equation and then obtaining a particular solution by variation of parameters.

3. Verify that $y = c_1x + c_2x^2$ is the general solution of the equation $x^2y'' - 2xy' + 2y = 0$ and find the general solution of the equation $x^2y'' - 2xy' + 2y = x^3$.

4. Verify that $y = c_1e^x + c_2x^{-1}$ is the complementary function for

$$x(x + 1)y'' + (2 - x^2)y' - (2 + x)y = (x + 1)^2$$

and find the general solution.

5. Let an equation of second order

$$y'' + a_1y' + a_2y = Q(x)$$

have constant coefficients a_1, a_2 and distinct characteristic roots r_1, r_2. Apply the method of variation of parameters to obtain the particular solution

$$y = \frac{e^{r_1x}}{r_1 - r_2}\int e^{-r_1x}Q(x)\,dx + \frac{e^{r_2x}}{r_2 - r_1}\int e^{-r_2x}Q(x)\,dx.$$

ANSWERS

1. (a) $c_1e^x + c_2e^{-x} + \frac{1}{2}xe^x$, (b) $c_1e^x + c_2e^{2x} + c_3e^{3x} + \frac{1}{6}e^{4x}$,
(c) $c_1 \cos x + c_2 \sin x - \sin x \log|\csc x + \cot x|$,
(d) $c_1 \cos 2x + c_2 \sin 2x + \frac{1}{4}\cos 2x \log|\cos 2x| + \frac{1}{2}x \sin 2x$,
(e) $c_1e^x + c_2e^{-x} + \frac{1}{2}e^x\int e^{-x}x^{-1}\,dx - \frac{1}{2}e^{-x}\int e^xx^{-1}\,dx$,
(f) $(5x - 3)e^x/50 + ce^{(-2+i)x} + \bar{c}e^{(-2-i)x}$.

3. $c_1x + c_2x^2 + \frac{1}{2}x^3$. 4. $c_1e^x + c_2x^{-1} - \frac{1}{2}(x + 2)$.

4-9 Method of undetermined coefficients. Consider a linear equation with constant coefficients:

$$(a_0D^n + \cdots + a_n)y = Q(x). \tag{4-89}$$

We seek a particular solution and do not assume the complementary function to be known. The following examples illustrate the method of undetermined coefficients.

EXAMPLE 1. $(D^2 - 3D + 7)y = 10e^{2x}$. We try to choose k so that ke^{2x} is a solution. Substitution yields the equations

$$4ke^{2x} - 6ke^{2x} + 7ke^{2x} = 10e^{2x}, \qquad 5k = 10, \qquad k = 2.$$

Hence $2e^{2x}$ is a particular solution. The complementary function is found to be

$$e^{3x/2}\left(c_1 \cos \frac{\sqrt{19}}{2} x + c_2 \sin \frac{\sqrt{19}}{2} x\right).$$

The general solution is the sum of the complementary function and $2e^{2x}$.

EXAMPLE 2. $(D^2 - 3D + 7)y = 10xe^{2x}$. If we set $y = kxe^{2x}$, we find it impossible to choose k so that the equation is satisfied, since $(D^2 - 3D + 7)xe^{2x}$ is of form $e^{2x}(ax + b)$. This suggests trying $y = e^{2x}(k_1x + k_2)$. The substitution in the equation can be arranged as follows:

$$\begin{array}{r|l} 7 & y \;\;= e^{2x}(k_1x + k_2) \\ -3 & y' \;= e^{2x}(2k_1x + 2k_2 + k_1) \\ 1 & y'' = e^{2x}(4k_1x + 4k_2 + 4k_1) \\ \hline & \end{array}$$

$$y'' - 3y' + 7y = e^{2x}(5k_1x + 5k_2 + k_1) \equiv 10xe^{2x}.$$

Hence

$$5k_1x + 5k_2 + k_1 \equiv 10x, \qquad 5k_1 = 10, \qquad 5k_2 + k_1 = 0,$$

and

$$k_1 = 2, \qquad k_2 = -\tfrac{2}{5}, \qquad y = e^{2x}(2x - \tfrac{2}{5}).$$

(See Prob. 8 below.)

The above examples suggest that, in general, if

$$Q = e^{ax}(b_0x^m + b_1x^{m-1} + \cdots),$$

our trial function should have the similar form

$$y = e^{ax}(k_1x^m + k_2x^{m-1} + \cdots).$$

The following example shows that this form will not always succeed.

EXAMPLE 3. $y'' - y = xe^x$. The substitution of $y = e^x(k_1x + k_2)$ leads to an impossible equation:

$$y'' - y = 2e^xk_1 \equiv xe^x.$$

The trouble can be traced to the fact that e^x is a solution of the homogeneous equation. We discover by experimenting that multiplication by x eliminates the difficulty; that is, we set $y = xe^x(k_1x + k_2) = e^x(k_1x^2 + k_2x)$ and can then determine the coefficients:

$$\begin{array}{r|lcl} -1 & y & = & e^x(k_1x^2 + k_2x) \\ 0 & y' & = & e^x[k_1x^2 + (2k_1 + k_2)x + k_2] \\ 1 & y'' & = & e^x[k_1x^2 + (4k_1 + k_2)x + 2k_1 + 2k_2] \\ \hline \end{array}$$

$$y'' - y = e^x(4k_1x + 2k_1 + 2k_2) \equiv xe^x.$$

Hence

$$4k_1x + 2k_1 + 2k_2 \equiv x, \qquad k_1 = \tfrac{1}{4}, \qquad k_2 = -\tfrac{1}{4},$$

$$y^* = e^x[(x^2/4) - (x/4)].$$

EXAMPLE 4. $y'' + 2y' + 2y = \sin 3x$. The substitution $y = k \sin 3x$ is ineffective, but $y = k_1 \cos 3x + k_2 \sin 3x$ leads to a solution:

$$\begin{array}{r|lcl} 2 & y & = & k_1 \cos 3x + k_2 \sin 3x \\ 2 & y' & = & 3k_2 \cos 3x - 3k_1 \sin 3x \\ 1 & y'' & = & -9k_1 \cos 3x - 9k_2 \sin 2x \\ \hline \end{array}$$

$$y'' + 2y' + 2y = \cos 3x\,(6k_2 - 7k_1) + \sin 3x\,(-7k_2 - 6k_1) \equiv \sin 3x,$$

$$6k_2 - 7k_1 = 0, \qquad -7k_2 - 6k_1 = 1,$$

$$k_1 = -\frac{6}{85}, \qquad k_2 = -\frac{7}{85},$$

$$y^* = \frac{1}{85}(-6 \cos 3x - 7 \sin 3x),$$

$$y = e^{-x}(c_1 \cos x + c_2 \sin x) + \frac{1}{85}(-6 \cos 3x - 7 \sin 3x).$$

We now describe the method precisely; the rules given are suggested by the preceding examples. A proof is given in Section 5–2.

Let $Q(x)$ have the form

$$e^{ax} \cos bx\,(p_0x^m + p_1x^{m-1} + \cdots + p_m) + e^{ax} \sin bx\,(q_0x^m + \cdots + q_m),$$

where some of the constants $a, b, p_0, p_1, \ldots, q_0, q_1, \ldots$ may be 0. If $a \pm bi$ is not a root of the characteristic equation

$$a_0r^n + \cdots + a_n = 0,$$

then there is a solution y^* of the differential equation (4–89) of form similar to that of Q:

$$y^* = e^{ax}\cos bx\,(k_1x^m + k_2x^{m-1} + \cdots) + e^{ax}\sin bx\,(l_1x^m + l_2x^{m-1} + \cdots).$$

The coefficients $k_1, k_2, \ldots, l_1, l_2, \ldots$ are determined by substitution of the expression for y^* in the differential equation and choosing the coefficients so that the equation becomes an identity. If $a \pm bi$ is a root of multiplicity h of the characteristic equation, then the trial function must be multiplied by x^h.

When the right-hand member is formed of two or more groups of terms, each associated with a different choice of $a \pm bi$, the particular solution is a sum of those for each group. This follows from the superposition principle (Section 4–4).

EXAMPLE 5. $y'' + y = x + 2\cos x + \sin x$. Here the term x corresponds to $a \pm bi$ equal to 0:

$$x = xe^{0x}\cos 0x,$$

while the terms $2\cos x + \sin x$ correspond to $a \pm bi$ equal to $\pm i$. Now 0 is not a root of the characteristic equation, but $\pm i$ are roots. Hence our trial function is

$$y^* = k_1x + k_2 + x(k_3\cos x + k_4\sin x).$$

Upon substituting, we find that $k_1 = 1$, $k_2 = 0$, $k_3 = -\frac{1}{2}$, $k_4 = 1$, and

$$y = c_1\cos x + c_2\sin x + x + x\sin x - \tfrac{1}{2}x\cos x$$

is the general solution.

PROBLEMS

1. Find the general solution of each of the following equations:

(a) $(D^2 - 9)y = e^x$,
(b) $(D^2 + 4)y = e^{2x}$,
(c) $(D^2 + 2D + 1)y = 5$,
(d) $(D^2 + 2D + 1)y = x + e^{4x}$,
(e) $(D^2 + 2D + 1)y = e^{-x} + e^x$,
(f) $(D^2 + 2D + 1)y = x^2e^{-x}$,
(g) $(D^2 + 4)y = 5\sin 3x + \cos 3x + \sin 2x$,
(h) $(D^2 + 4)y = x\cos 2x + 3e^{2x}\sin 2x$,
(i) $(D^3 + 3D^2 + 3D + 1)y = e^{-x}\sin x$,
(j) $(D^2 + 2D + 5)y = e^{-x}\cos 2x$.

2. Find a particular solution of each of the following:
(a) $(D^3 + D + 1)y = e^{3x}$,
(b) $(D^4 - D^3 + D - 1)y = e^x + 3x - 2$,
(c) $(D^5 + D^3 + D + 1)y = x^2 - x - 2$,
(d) $(D^4 + D^3 + D^2)y = 3x + 2$, (e) $(D^4 + D + 1)y = \cos 2x + 3$.

3. Obtain the solution satisfying the given initial conditions:
(a) $y'' + y = \sin x$; $y = 1$ and $y' = 0$ for $x = 0$;
(b) $y'' + 2y' + y = \cos x$; $y = 0$ and $y' = 0$ for $x = 0$.

4. Prove that a particular solution of the equation $(a_0 D^n + \cdots + a_n)y = e^{bx}$ is given by $e^{bx}/f(b)$, where $f(r) = a_0 r^n + \cdots + a_n$, provided $f(b) \neq 0$.

5. Prove that if the coefficients $a_0, \ldots, a_n$ are real and $y(x)$ is a complex solution of

$$(a_0 D^n + \cdots + a_n)y = F(x) = f(x) + ig(x),$$

then Re $[y(x)]$ is a solution of

$$(a_0 D^n + \cdots + a_n)y = f(x) = \text{Re}\,[F],$$

while Im $[y(x)]$ is a solution of

$$(a_0 D^n + \cdots + a_n)y = g(x) = \text{Im}\,[F].$$

6. Use the rule of Prob. 5 to obtain particular solutions of the following:
(a) $(D^2 + D + 2)y = \cos x = \text{Re}\,[e^{ix}]$,
(b) $(D^2 + D + 2)y = \sin x = \text{Im}\,[e^{ix}]$,
[*Hint:* Obtain a particular solution of $(D^2 + D + 2)y = e^{ix}$, then take real and imaginary parts.]
(c) $(D^2 + D + 2)y = e^{2x} \cos 3x = \text{Re}\,[e^{(2+3i)x}]$,
(d) $(D^2 + D + 2)y = xe^{2x} \cos 3x = \text{Re}\,[xe^{(2+3i)x}]$.

7. Show that if $h > 0$, $\lambda > 0$, $\omega > 0$, then a particular solution of

$$(D^2 + 2hD + \lambda^2)y = A \sin \omega x$$

is given by

$$y = \frac{A \sin \omega(x - \alpha)}{[(\lambda^2 - \omega^2)^2 + 4h^2\omega^2]^{1/2}}, \qquad \alpha = \tan^{-1} \frac{2h\omega}{\omega^2 - \lambda^2},$$

where $0 < \alpha < \pi$.

8. Example 2 in the text above leads to the identity

$$5k_1 xe^{2x} + (5k_2 + k_1)e^{2x} \equiv 10xe^{2x} + 0e^{2x}.$$

Show that the relations $5k_1 = 10$, $5k_2 + k_1 = 0$ follow from the *linear independence* of the functions xe^{2x}, e^{2x}. (See Prob. 7 following Section 4–3.)

ANSWERS

1. (a) $c_1e^{3x} + c_2e^{-3x} - (e^x/8)$, (b) $c_1 \cos 2x + c_2 \sin 2x + e^{2x}/8$, (c) $c_1e^{-x} + c_2xe^{-x} + 5$, (d) $c_1e^{-x} + c_2xe^{-x} + x - 2 + e^{4x}/25$, (e) $c_1e^{-x} + c_2xe^{-x} + x^2e^{-x}/2 + e^x/4$, (f) $c_1e^{-x} + c_2xe^{-x} + x^4e^{-x}/12$, (g) $c_1 \cos 2x + c_2 \sin 2x - \sin 3x - (\cos 3x)/5 - (x \cos 2x)/4$, (h) $c_1 \cos 2x + c_2 \sin 2x - (2x^2 \sin 2x + x \cos 2x)/16 + (3/20)e^{2x} (\sin 2x - 2 \cos 2x)$, (i) $c_1e^{-x} + c_2xe^{-x} + c_3x^2e^{-x} + e^{-x} \cos x$, (j) $e^{-x}(c_1 \cos 2x + c_2 \sin 2x + \frac{1}{4}x \sin 2x)$.

2. (a) $e^{3x}/31$, (b) $\frac{1}{2}xe^x - 3x - 1$, (c) $x^2 - 3x + 1$, (d) $\frac{1}{2}(x^3 - x^2)$, (e) $3 + (17 \cos 2x + 2 \sin 2x)/293$.

3. (a) $\cos x + \frac{1}{2} (\sin x - x \cos x)$, (b) $\frac{1}{2} (\sin x - xe^{-x})$.

6. (a) $\frac{1}{2} (\cos x + \sin x)$, (b) $\frac{1}{2} (\sin x - \cos x)$,
(c) $e^{2x}(15 \sin 3x - \cos 3x)/226$,
(d) $e^{2x}[x (-226 \cos 3x + 3390 \sin 3x) - 1194 \sin 3x + 1300 \cos 3x]/226^2$.

CHAPTER 5

OPERATIONAL METHODS FOR LINEAR DIFFERENTIAL EQUATIONS

In this chapter additional methods are given for finding the solutions of linear differential equations with constant coefficients. Historically the methods arose in the work of Heaviside as an exploitation of the remarkable algebraic properties of differential operators (Section 4–4 above). More recently the Laplace transform has been introduced to obtain similar results. The whole development is part of the evolution of the theory of linear operators or, more generally, of functional analysis.

5–1 Algebra of differential operators. Let $L_1 = a_0D^n + \cdots + a_n$, $L_2 = b_0D^m + \cdots + b_m$ be two differential operators; the coefficients may depend on x. The sum $L_1 + L_2$ is defined as the operator which, when applied to y, yields $L_1y + L_2y$. Thus

$$\begin{aligned}(L_1 + L_2)y &= L_1y + L_2y \\ &= (a_0D^n + \cdots + a_n)y + (b_0D^m + \cdots + b_m)y.\end{aligned}$$

The last two expressions can be combined into one by collecting terms of the same degree. Hence we conclude that differential operators are added as if they were polynomials in D; for example,

$$(xD^2 - D + 2) + (xD + x) = xD^2 + (x - 1)D + x + 2.$$

Multiplication of L_1 *on the left* by a constant k or by a function of x is defined similarly by the equations

$$(kL_1)y = k(L_1y), \qquad [g(x)L_1]y = g(x)(L_1y),$$

and we again conclude that the operation is the same as for polynomials. From the definitions given, these algebraic rules follow:

$$L_1 + L_2 = L_2 + L_1, \qquad L_1 + (L_2 + L_3) = (L_1 + L_2) + L_3,$$
$$g(x)(L_1 + L_2) = g(x)L_1 + g(x)L_2, \qquad k(L_1 + L_2) = kL_1 + kL_2.$$

We now define multiplication of operators. We define L_1L_2 as the operator such that

$$(L_1L_2)y = L_1(L_2y) \tag{5–1}$$

wherever the right-hand side has meaning. For example, $(D+1)(D-1)$ is evaluated as follows:

$$\begin{aligned}[(D+1)(D-1)]y &= (D+1)[(D-1)y] = (D+1)(Dy-y)\\ &= D(Dy-y)+Dy-y\\ &= D^2y-Dy+Dy-y = D^2y-y\\ &= (D^2-1)y.\end{aligned}$$

Accordingly, $(D+1)(D-1) = D^2-1$, just as for polynomials in D. However, the results are different *when the coefficients are variable.* Thus

$$\begin{aligned}[(xD+1)(xD-1)]y &= (xD+1)[(xD-1)y]\\ &= (xD+1)(xDy-y)\\ &= xD(xDy-y)+xDy-y\\ &= x(xD^2y+Dy-Dy)+xDy-y\\ &= x^2D^2y+xDy-y.\end{aligned}$$

Accordingly,

$$(xD+1)(xD-1) = x^2D^2+xD-1,$$

in disagreement with formal algebraic procedure. If we analyze the above example, we see that the difficulty arises from the application of D to xDy; the product rule is used, and a new term Dy is introduced because of the variable coefficient x. This complication cannot arise when the coefficients are constant, and we have the general rule:

Operators with constant coefficients can be multiplied as if they were polynomials in the variable D.

To prove this rule, we remark that each operator $a_0D^n+\cdots+a_n = L$ with constant coefficients can be completely specified by giving its characteristic polynomial $f(r) = a_0r^n+\cdots+a_n$; furthermore, $f(r)$ can be found from the equation

$$L(e^{rx}) = f(r)e^{rx}. \tag{5–2}$$

Now if $L_1 = a_0D^n+\cdots+a_n$, $L_2 = b_0D^m+\cdots+b_m$, then let $f(r) = a_0r^n+\cdots+a_n$, $g(r) = b_0r^m+\cdots+b_m$ be the associated characteristic polynomials. From the above definition of multiplication of operators, it follows that L_1L_2 is an operator with constant coefficients. To find the associated characteristic polynomial, we evaluate

$$(L_1L_2)e^{rx} = L_1(L_2e^{rx}) = L_1[g(r)e^{rx}] = g(r)L_1(e^{rx}) = g(r)f(r)e^{rx}.$$

Hence L_1L_2 has the characteristic polynomial $f(r)g(r)$, which shows that L_1L_2 is obtained from L_1, L_2 by multiplying them as if they were polynomials in D.

Operators with *constant coefficients* can now be added, multiplied, and multiplied by constants, just as polynomials in D. In particular, multiplication is *commutative, associative,* and *distributive:*

$$\begin{aligned} L_1L_2 &= L_2L_1, \\ L_1(L_2L_3) &= (L_1L_2)L_3, \\ L_1(L_2 + L_3) &= L_1L_2 + L_1L_3. \end{aligned} \tag{5–3}$$

Associativity and distributivity also hold for operators with variable coefficients, but commutativity fails in general (Probs. 2, 3 following Section 5–2).

5–2 Factorization of operators. Associated with each operator $a_0D^n + \cdots + a_n$ with constant coefficients is the characteristic polynomial $f(r) = a_0r^n + \cdots + a_n$. It is convenient to denote the operator itself by $f(D)$:

$$f(D) = a_0D^n + \cdots + a_n. \tag{5–4}$$

Of course, $f(D)$ is not a function of D in the ordinary sense.

If the roots $r_1, r_2, \ldots$ of the characteristic equation are known, then there is a corresponding factorization of $f(r)$:

$$f(r) = a_0(r - r_1)(r - r_2) \cdots (r - r_n). \tag{5–5}$$

Accordingly, we obtain a *factorization of* $f(D)$:

$$f(D) = a_0D^n + \cdots + a_n = a_0(D - r_1)(D - r_2) \cdots (D - r_n). \tag{5–6}$$

For we are allowed to multiply the expressions on the right of (5–6) as though D were a variable; (5–5) shows that the result is $f(D)$.

Factorization provides us with a new method for finding a particular solution of a nonhomogeneous equation.

EXAMPLE 1. $(D^2 - 1)y = e^{-x}$. We write the equation in factored form:

$$[(D + 1)(D - 1)]y = e^{-x}$$

or

$$(D + 1)[(D - 1)y] = e^{-x}.$$

This suggests introduction of an auxiliary variable:

$$(D-1)y = u, \qquad (D+1)u = e^{-x}.$$

The second equation is a first order linear equation for u; when u has been found, we treat the first equation as a first order equation for y:

$$u = e^{-x}\int e^{x}e^{-x}\,dx = xe^{-x},$$

$$y = e^{x}\int e^{-x}u\,dx = e^{x}\int xe^{-2x}\,dx$$

$$= e^{x}\left(\frac{xe^{-2x}}{-2} + \frac{e^{-2x}}{-4}\right) = -\frac{1}{2}xe^{-x} - \frac{1}{4}e^{-x}.$$

We have carried no arbitrary constants, since we seek only a particular solution. Furthermore, $-\frac{1}{4}e^{-x}$ is part of the complementary function, so that $-\frac{1}{2}xe^{-x}$ is itself a particular solution.

EXAMPLE 2. $(D^2-1)y = 2(\sec^3 x - \sec x)$. The procedure used in Example 1 leads to the equations

$$(D-1)y = u, \qquad (D+1)u = 2(\sec^3 x - \sec x),$$

$$u = 2e^{-x}\int e^{x}(\sec^3 x - \sec x)\,dx, \qquad y = e^{x}\int e^{-x}u\,dx.$$

It happens that the integrals can be expressed in terms of elementary functions:

$$\int e^{x}(\sec^3 x - \sec x)\,dx = \tfrac{1}{2}e^{x}(\sec x\tan x - \sec x),$$

$$u = \sec x\tan x - \sec x,$$

$$y = e^{x}\int e^{-x}(\sec x\tan x - \sec x)\,dx$$

$$= e^{x}(e^{-x}\sec x) = \sec x.$$

EXAMPLE 3. $(D^2+1)^3y = \sin 2x$. Here the equation is given in factored form. We now introduce two auxiliary variables:

$$(D^2+1)y = u, \qquad (D^2+1)u = v, \qquad (D^2+1)v = \sin 2x.$$

We could factor the quadratic expressions into linear factors:

$$D^2 + 1 = (D + i)(D - i)$$

and split the equations further; however, this procedure is not needed in this case. By undetermined coefficients we find, successively,

$$v = \frac{\sin 2x}{-3}, \qquad u = \frac{\sin 2x}{9}, \qquad y = \frac{\sin 2x}{-27}.$$

Justification of the method of undetermined coefficients. We now give a proof that the rule of Section 4–9 does provide a particular solution of a nonhomogeneous equation

$$Ly \equiv a_0 y^{(n)} + \cdots + a_n = Q(x) \equiv p(x)e^{ax} \cos bx + q(x)e^{ax} \sin bx,$$

where $p(x)$ and $q(x)$ are polynomials of degree at most m. Let the characteristic roots be $r_1, \ldots, r_n$, so that

$$L = a_0(D - r_1) \cdots (D - r_n).$$

From the form given, $Q(x)$ is a particular solution of an equation $L_1 y = 0$, where

$$L_1 = [(D - a)^2 + b^2]^{m+1}.$$

This we see by writing out the general solution of the equation $L_1\, y = 0$. Now let y be a solution of the equation $Ly = Q$. We multiply by L_1 on both sides:

$$L_1 L y = L_1 Q = 0.$$

Hence y is also a solution of the equation $L_1 L y = 0$; that is,

$$a_0[(D - a)^2 + b^2]^{m+1}(D - r_1) \cdots (D - r_n)y = 0.$$

The general solution of this equation consists of the general solution of the equation $Ly = 0$, that is, the complementary function $y_c(x)$, plus additional terms arising from the new roots $a \pm bi$. The additional terms have the form described for the trial function in the rule of Section 4–9; we denote the sum of these terms by $y_k(x)$. Thus $y = y_c(x) + y_k(x)$. Substitution in the equation $Ly = Q$ gives

$$L[y_c(x) + y_k(x)] = Q.$$

But $L[y_c(x)] = 0$, and hence

$$L[y_k(x)] = Q.$$

Therefore, for appropriate choice of the k's, $y_k(x)$ is a particular solution.

PROBLEMS

1. Combine and simplify the following:
(a) $x^2(D^2 - D + 1) + x[xD^2 + (x + 1)D - 2]$,
(b) $(D - 1)^2 + (D + 1)^2$,
(c) $(D - 1)(D^2 + D + 1)$,
(d) $(xD - 1)(D + 2)$,
(e) $(x^2D^2 - e^x)(e^xD + x)$.

2. Verify the following inequalities:
(a) $(xD + x)(xD - 1) \neq (xD - 1)(xD + x)$,
(b) $(D + e^x)(e^xD + 1) \neq (e^xD + 1)(D + e^x)$.

3. Let L_1, L_2, L_3 be arbitrary differential operators with coefficients which have derivatives of all orders over an interval.
(a) Prove the associative law: $L_1(L_2L_3) = (L_1L_2)L_3$.
(b) Prove the distributive law: $L_1(L_2 + L_3) = L_1L_2 + L_1L_3$.

4. Find a particular solution by factoring the operator in each of the following equations:
(a) $(D - 1)^2y = e^x$,
(b) $(D^2 - 2D - 3)y = e^{5x}$,
(c) $(D^4 + 5D^2 + 4)y = \sin 3x$,
(d) $(D + 1)^5y = xe^{-x}$,
(e) $(D - 1)^2y = e^{e^x}(e^{2x} - e^x + 1)$,
(f) $(D^2 + 3D + 2)y = (2/x^3) - (3/x^2) + (2/x)$.

5. *Cauchy's linear equation.* This term is used for an equation of form

$$a_0x^ny^{(n)} + a_1x^{n-1}y^{(n-1)} + \cdots + a_{n-1}xy' + a_ny = Q(x),$$

where $a_0, a_1, \ldots, a_n$ are constants.

(a) Show that $y = x^r$ is a solution of the related homogeneous equation provided r satisfies the equation

$$a_0r(r - 1)\cdots(r - n + 1) + a_1r(r - 1)\cdots(r - n + 2) + \cdots + a_{n-1}r + a_n = 0.$$

If this equation has distinct real roots $r_1, \ldots, r_n$, obtain the general solution.

(b) Prove that the substitution $x = e^t$ reduces the equation to one with constant coefficients for y in terms of t. [*Hint:* Show first that if D stands for the operator d/dt, then

$$x\frac{dy}{dx} = Dy,$$

$$x^2\frac{d^2y}{dx^2} = D(D-1)y,$$

$$\vdots$$

$$x^k\frac{d^ky}{dx^k} = D(D-1)\dots(D-k+1)y;$$

the general case can be established by induction.]

6. Obtain the general solution of each of the following (see Prob. 5):

(a) $x^2\,(d^2y/dx^2) - 2x\,(dy/dx) + 2y = 0$,
(b) $x^2\,(d^2y/dx^2) + x\,(dy/dx) + 4y = 0$,
(c) $x^2\,(d^2y/dx^2) - x\,(dy/dx) + y = x$.

ANSWERS

1. (a) $2x^2D^2 + xD + x^2 - 2x$, (b) $2D^2 + 2$, (c) $D^3 - 1$, (d) $xD^2 + (2x-1)D - 2$, (e) $x^2e^xD^3 + (2x^2e^x + x^3)D^2 + (x^2e^x + 2x^2 - e^{2x})D - xe^x$.

4. (a) $x^2e^x/2$, (b) $e^{5x}/12$, (c) $(\sin 3x)/40$, (d) $x^6e^{-x}/720$, (e) e^{e^x}, (f) $1/x$.

6. (a) $y = c_1x + c_2x^2$, (b) $y = c_1\cos\{2\log|x|\} + c_2\sin\{2\log|x|\}$, (c) $y = c_1x + c_2x\log|x| + \frac{1}{2}x\log^2|x|$.

5–3 Inverse operators. Since the reciprocal of a polynomial is not a polynomial, we cannot interpret $1/(a_0D^n + \cdots)$ as a differential operator. Instead, we interpret it as the inverse of the operator; that is,

$$h(x) = \frac{1}{a_0D^n + \cdots + a_n}Q(x)$$

if

$$(a_0D^n + \cdots a_n)h(x) = Q(x).$$

In other words, $1/(a_0D^n + \cdots + a_n)$ applied to $Q(x)$ yields a solution $y(x)$ of the differential equation

$$(a_0D^n + \cdots a_n)y = Q(x).$$

Since there are many such solutions and we have not specified any initial conditions, the inverse operator is ambiguously defined. For example,

$$\frac{1}{D+2}e^x$$

stands for a solution of $(D + 2)y = e^x$. Possible choices are $e^x/3$, $(e^x/3) + e^{-2x}$, $(e^x/3) + 2e^{-2x}$, etc. We shall write, for example,

$$\frac{1}{D + 2} e^x = \frac{e^x}{3},$$

with the understanding that we have selected only one of many possible choices. We are interested mainly in obtaining particular solutions; other solutions are obtained by adding the complementary function.

Throughout we restrict attention to operators with *constant coefficients.* The following rules will simplify the evaluations:

$$\frac{1}{f(D)}[c_1Q_1(x) + c_2Q_2(x)] = c_1\frac{1}{f(D)}Q_1(x) + c_2\frac{1}{f(D)}Q_2(x), \tag{5–7}$$

$$\frac{1}{f(D)g(D)}Q(x) = \frac{1}{f(D)}\left[\frac{1}{g(D)}Q(x)\right] = \frac{1}{g(D)}\left[\frac{1}{f(D)}Q(x)\right]. \tag{5–8}$$

Equation (5–7) is simply the superposition principle (Section 4–4). Equation (5–8) follows from the definition of multiplication and from the commutative law (5–3); it is equivalent to the factorization method of Section 5–2.

EXAMPLE 1. Evaluate $[1/(D - a)]e^{ax}$. We must find a solution of the differential equation

$$(D - a)y = e^{ax}.$$

The method of undetermined coefficients leads to the trial function kxe^{ax}; k is found to be 1. Hence

$$\frac{1}{D - a} e^{ax} = xe^{ax}. \tag{5–9}$$

EXAMPLE 2. Evaluate $[1/f(D)]e^{ax}$, where $f(D) = a_0D^n + \cdots + a_n$, $f(a) \neq 0$. The differential equation is

$$f(D)y = e^{ax}.$$

Since $f(a) \neq 0$, we seek a solution of form ke^{ax}:

$$f(D)ke^{ax} = kf(a)e^{ax} = e^{ax}.$$

Hence $k = 1/f(a)$ and

$$\frac{1}{f(D)} e^{ax} = \frac{e^{ax}}{f(a)} \qquad [f(a) \neq 0]. \tag{5–10}$$

EXAMPLE 3. Evaluate $[1/(D - a)^m]e^{ax}$, where $m = 1, 2, 3, \ldots$ We are led to the equation

$$(D - a)^m y = e^{ax}$$

and the trial function $kx^m e^{ax}$. Now

$$(D - a)x^m e^{ax} = mx^{m-1}e^{ax},$$
$$(D - a)^2 x^m e^{ax} = m(m - 1)x^{m-2}e^{ax},$$
$$\vdots$$
$$(D - a)^m x^m e^{ax} = m!e^{ax}.$$

Hence $k = 1/m!$ and

$$\frac{1}{(D - a)^m} e^{ax} = \frac{x^m e^{ax}}{m!}. \tag{5-11}$$

EXAMPLE 4. Show that

$$\frac{1}{(D - a)^m f(D)} e^{ax} = \frac{x^m e^{ax}}{m! f(a)}, \qquad [f(a) \neq 0], \tag{5-12}$$

where $m = 1, 2, 3, \ldots$ We can reason:

$$\frac{1}{(D - a)^m f(D)} e^{ax} = \frac{1}{(D - a)^m}\left[\frac{1}{f(D)} e^{ax}\right]$$
$$= \frac{1}{(D - a)^m} \frac{e^{ax}}{f(a)} = \frac{x^m e^{ax}}{m! f(a)},$$

by (5-10) and (5-11) above. The first step is based on (5-8).

EXAMPLE 5. Evaluate $[1/(D^2 + a^2)] \sin bx$, $a \neq b$. The differential equation $(D^2 + a^2)y = \sin bx$ can be solved by undetermined coefficients. An alternative procedure is to find a solution y of the equation $(D^2 + a^2)y = e^{bix}$; the *imaginary part* of y will then satisfy the equation with $\sin bx = \text{Im}\,(e^{bix})$ on the right. (See Probs. 5, 6 following Section 4-9.) Hence, by Example 2,

$$\frac{1}{D^2 + a^2} \sin bx = \text{Im}\left(\frac{1}{D^2 + a^2} e^{ibx}\right) = \text{Im}\left(\frac{e^{ibx}}{a^2 - b^2}\right),$$

$$\frac{1}{D^2 + a^2} \sin bx = \frac{\sin bx}{a^2 - b^2} \qquad (a \neq b). \tag{5-13}$$

In the same way we show that

$$\frac{1}{D^2 + a^2} \cos bx = \frac{\cos bx}{a^2 - b^2} \qquad (a \neq b). \tag{5-14}$$

The rules thus far established permit us to obtain solutions of particular equations with great ease.

EXAMPLE 6. $(3D^2 - 2D + 5)y = e^{2x}$. By (5–10) a particular solution is

$$y = \frac{1}{3D^2 - 2D + 5} e^{2x} = \frac{e^{2x}}{13}.$$

EXAMPLE 7. $(D^3 - D)y = e^x$. By (5–12) a particular solution is

$$y = \frac{1}{(D - 1)(D^2 + D)} e^x = \frac{xe^x}{2}.$$

5–4 A table of inverse operators. Table 5–1 systematically lists rules for inverse operators. Rules 1 through 4 and 10 through 11 are established in the preceding section, and Rules 5 through 9 are obtained by similar methods. The remaining rules require discussion.

Rule 12 merely states that integration is the inverse of differentiation. Rule 13 is the expression for a solution of the first order linear equation

$$(D - a)y = Q(x)$$

(see Section 2–8).

Rule 14 is a rearrangement of the result of repeated application of Rule 13. First, we make a special choice of the indefinite integral in Rule 13:

$$\frac{1}{D - a} Q(x) = e^{ax} \int_c^x e^{-au} Q(u)\, du;$$

here c is any convenient value within the interval in which $Q(x)$ is given (and continuous). Next, by Rule 11

$$\frac{1}{(D - a)^2} Q(x) = \frac{1}{D - a} P(x), \qquad P(x) = e^{ax} \int_c^x e^{-au} Q(u)\, du,$$

$$\frac{1}{(D - a)^2} Q(x) = e^{ax} \int_c^x e^{-av} P(v)\, dv = e^{ax} \int_c^x \int_c^v e^{-au} Q(u)\, du\, dv$$

$$= e^{ax} \int_c^x \int_u^x e^{-au} Q(u)\, dv\, du$$

$$= e^{ax} \int_c^x e^{-au} Q(u)(x - u)\, du.$$

A similar procedure justifies the rule for general m.

TABLE 5–1

RULES FOR INVERSE OPERATORS

No.	Expression	Value (one choice)
1	$\frac{1}{f(D)} e^{ax}$	$\frac{e^{ax}}{f(a)}$ $[f(a) \neq 0]$
2	$\frac{1}{(D-a)^m} e^{ax}$	$\frac{x^m e^{ax}}{m!}$ $(m = 1, 2, \ldots)$
3	$\frac{1}{(D-a)^m f(D)} e^{ax}$	$\frac{x^m e^{ax}}{m! f(a)}$ $[m = 1, 2, \ldots, f(a) \neq 0]$
4	$\frac{1}{D^2+a^2} \sin bx$	$\frac{\sin bx}{a^2-b^2}$ $(a \neq b)$
5	$\frac{1}{D^2+a^2} \sin ax$	$\frac{-x \cos ax}{2a}$
6	$\frac{1}{D^2+a^2} \cos bx$	$\frac{\cos bx}{a^2-b^2}$ $(a \neq b)$
7	$\frac{1}{D^2+a^2} \cos ax$	$\frac{x \sin ax}{2a}$
8	$\frac{1}{aD^2+bD+c} \sin \omega x$	$\frac{(c-a\omega^2) \sin \omega x - b\omega \cos \omega x}{(c-a\omega^2)^2 + b^2\omega^2}$ (denom $\neq 0$)
9	$\frac{1}{aD^2+bD+c} \cos \omega x$	$\frac{(c-a\omega^2) \cos \omega x + b\omega \sin \omega x}{(c-a\omega^2)^2 + b^2\omega^2}$ (denom $\neq 0$)
10	$\frac{1}{f(D)} [c_1 Q_1(x) + c_2 Q_2(x)]$	$c_1 \frac{1}{f(D)} Q_1(x) + c_2 \frac{1}{f(D)} Q_2(x)$
11	$\frac{1}{f(D)g(D)} Q(x)$	$\frac{1}{f(D)} \left[\frac{1}{g(D)} Q(x) \right]$ or $\frac{1}{g(D)} \left[\frac{1}{f(D)} Q(x) \right]$
12	$\frac{1}{D} Q(x)$	$\int Q(x)\, dx$

(continued)

No.	Expression	Value (one choice)
13	$\dfrac{1}{D-a}Q(x)$	$e^{ax}\int e^{-ax}Q(x)\,dx$
14	$\dfrac{1}{(D-a)^m}Q(x)$ $(m = 1, 2, \ldots)$	$\dfrac{e^{ax}}{(m-1)!}\int_c^x e^{-au}(x-u)^{m-1}\,Q(u)\,du$ (c is arbit.)
15	$\dfrac{1}{(D-a)^2+b^2}Q(x)$ $(b \neq 0)$	$\dfrac{e^{ax}}{b}\int_c^x e^{-au}\sin b(x-u)\,Q(u)\,du$ (c is arbit.)
16	$\dfrac{1}{f(D)}e^{ax}Q(x)$	$e^{ax}\dfrac{1}{f(D+a)}Q(x)$
17	$\dfrac{1}{f(D)}e^{ax}P(x)$ [$f(a) \neq 0$, $P(x)$ a polyn. of deg. N]	$e^{ax}\left[g(a)P(x)+\dfrac{g'(a)}{1!}P'(x)+\cdots+\dfrac{g^{(N)}(a)}{N!}P^{(N)}(x)\right]$ [$g(r) = 1/f(r)$]
18	$\dfrac{1}{(D-a)^m f(D)}e^{ax}P(x)$ [$f(a) \neq 0$, $m = 1, 2, \ldots,$ P a polyn. of deg. N]	$e^{ax}\left[g(a)Q(x)+\dfrac{g'(a)}{1!}Q'(x)+\cdots+\dfrac{g^{(N)}(a)}{N!}Q^{(N)}(x)\right]$ [$g(r) = 1/f(r)$, $Q(x) = (1/D^m)P(x)$]
19	$\dfrac{1}{f(D)}Q(x)$ [$f(r) = a_0(r-r_1)\ldots(r-r_n)$, $r_1, \ldots, r_n$ distinct]	$\sum_{k=1}^{n}\dfrac{1}{f'(r_k)}\dfrac{1}{D-r_k}Q(x)$
20	$\dfrac{1}{f(D)}Q(x)$	$\int_c^x Q(u)W(x-u)\,du$, where $y = W(x)$ is solution of $f(D)y \equiv (a_0D^n+\cdots)y = 0$ such that $W(0) = 0$, $W'(0) = 0, \ldots, W^{(n-2)}(0) = 0$, $W^{(n-1)}(0) = 1/a_0$
21	$\dfrac{1}{f(D)}Q(x-x_0)$	$\phi(x-x_0)$, where $\phi(x) = \dfrac{1}{f(D)}Q(x)$

The proofs of Rules 15 and 16 are left as exercises (Probs. 5, 6 below). Rule 16 is known as the *exponential shift*, and we can illustrate it by an example:

$$\frac{1}{D^2+2D+5}e^{-x}\sin 2x = e^{-x}\frac{1}{(D-1)^2+2(D-1)+5}\sin 2x$$

$$= e^{-x}\frac{1}{D^2+4}\sin 2x = \frac{-xe^{-x}\cos 2x}{4}.$$

For the last step, Rule 5 is applied.

To obtain Rule 17, we can reason as follows. We first assert that if

$$\frac{1}{f(D)}Q(x, a) = y(x, a),$$

then

$$\frac{1}{f(D)}\frac{\partial Q}{\partial a} = \frac{\partial y}{\partial a} \tag{5-15}$$

(all derivatives concerned are assumed continuous). For if

$$f(D)y(x, a) = Q(x, a),$$

then

$$f(D)\frac{\partial y}{\partial a} = (a_0D^n + \cdots + a_n)\frac{\partial y}{\partial a} = a_0\frac{\partial^{n+1}y}{\partial x^n\partial a} + \cdots$$

$$= \frac{\partial}{\partial a}(a_0D^ny + \cdots) = \frac{\partial}{\partial a}f(D)y = \frac{\partial Q}{\partial a},$$

by interchange of order of differentiation. We now apply (5-15) with $Q = e^{ax}$:

$$\frac{1}{f(D)}e^{ax} = \frac{e^{ax}}{f(a)} = g(a)e^{ax},$$

$$\frac{1}{f(D)}xe^{ax} = \frac{\partial}{\partial a}[g(a)e^{ax}] = e^{ax}[xg(a) + g'(a)],$$

and by repeated differentiation with respect to a (with the aid of Leibnitz' rule—see Prob. 5(a) following Section 4-5), we obtain

$$\frac{1}{f(D)}x^me^{ax} = e^{ax}\left[x^mg(a) + mx^{m-1}\frac{g'(a)}{1!} + \cdots + m!\frac{g^{(m)}(a)}{m!}\right].$$

This shows the correctness of Rule 17 when $P(x) = x^m$. By the superposition principle (Rule 10) we obtain the rule for a general polynomial.

Rule 18 can be deduced from Rule 17 and Rules 11 and 16. For

$$\frac{1}{(D-a)^m f(D)} e^{ax} P(x) = \frac{1}{(D-a)^m}\left[\frac{1}{f(D)} e^{ax} P(x)\right]$$

$$= \frac{1}{(D-a)^m} e^{ax}\left[g(a)P(x) + g'(a)P'(x) + \cdots + \frac{g^{(N)}(a)}{N!} P^{(N)}(x)\right]$$

$$= e^{ax}\frac{1}{D^m}[g(a)P(x) + g'(a)P'(x) + \cdots]$$

$$= e^{ax}\left[g(a)Q(x) + g'(a)Q'(x) + \cdots + \frac{g^{(N)}(a)}{N!} Q^{(N)}(x)\right],$$

where $Q(x) = (1/D^m)P(x)$ is an m-fold integral of $P(x)$.

EXAMPLE A.

$$\frac{1}{D^2+5}[(2x+1)e^{3x}] = e^{3x}\left[\frac{2x+1}{14} - \frac{3}{49}\right].$$

Here $a = 3$, $g(r) = (r^2+5)^{-1}$, $g'(r) = -2r(r^2+5)^{-2}$, $P(x) = 2x+1$.

EXAMPLE B.

$$\frac{1}{D^2-9}[(2x+1)e^{3x}] = e^{3x}\left[\frac{x^2+x}{6} - \frac{2x+1}{36}\right].$$

Here Rule 18 applies: $f(D) = D+3$, $g(r) = (r+3)^{-1}$, $a = 3$, $P(x) = 2x+1$, $Q(x) = x^2+x$.

By allowing a to be complex (that is, $a = \alpha + \beta i$) Rules 17 and 18 can be extended to functions $e^{\alpha x}\cos\beta x\, P(x)$, $e^{\alpha x}\sin\beta x\, P(x)$. *Hence Rules* 17 *and* 18 *completely replace the method of undetermined coefficients.*

Rule 19 is known as the *Heaviside expansion.* It is equivalent to the statement that (when the characteristic roots are distinct) $1/f(D)$ can be replaced by its *partial-fraction* expansion; for example,

$$\frac{1}{(D-2)(D-3)} = \frac{1}{D-3} - \frac{1}{D-2}.$$

In the general case, $1/f(r)$ has the partial-fraction expansion

$$\frac{1}{f(r)} = \sum_{k=1}^{n}\frac{A_k}{r-r_k}.$$

Each A_k is equal to $1/f'(r_k)$. For if we multiply both sides by $r - r_k$ and then let $r \to r_k$, the right-hand side has the limit A_k and the left-hand side has the limit

$$\lim_{r \to r_k} \frac{r - r_k}{f(r)} = \lim_{r \to r_k} \frac{r - r_k}{f(r) - f(r_k)} = \frac{1}{f'(r_k)},$$

since $f(r_k) = 0$. Hence Rule 19 is simply a partial-fraction expansion of the inverse operator.

To prove the validity of Rule 19, we apply induction. For $n = 1$ the rule is an identity. We can also verify it for $n = 2$ as follows. Since

$$\frac{1}{a_0(r - r_1)(r - r_2)} = \frac{1}{a_0}\left[\frac{1}{r_1 - r_2}\frac{1}{r - r_1} + \frac{1}{r_2 - r_1}\frac{1}{r - r_2}\right],$$

the rule states that

$$\frac{1}{a_0(D - r_1)(D - r_2)} Q$$

$$= \frac{1}{a_0}\left[\frac{1}{r_1 - r_2}\frac{1}{D - r_1} Q(x) + \frac{1}{r_2 - r_1}\frac{1}{D - r_2} Q(x)\right];$$

it can be proved to be correct by the method of variation of parameters (see Prob. 5 following Section 4-8). Now we suppose the rule to have been proved correct when $f(r)$ has degree n. We then proceed to prove it true when $f(r)$ has degree $n + 1$. We thus assume

$$\frac{1}{a_0(D - r_1) \cdots (D - r_n)} Q = \sum_{k=1}^{n} \frac{A_k}{D - r_k} Q(x),$$

where the A_k are the coefficients of the partial-fraction expansion. We apply the operator $1/(D - r_{n+1})$ to both sides:

$$\frac{1}{a_0(D - r_1) \cdots (D - r_n)(D - r_{n+1})} Q$$

$$= \sum_{k=1}^{n} \frac{A_k}{(D - r_{n+1})(D - r_k)} Q(x).$$

By the case $n = 2$ verified above, each term on the right can be replaced by its partial-fraction expansion. If this is done and terms are collected, the (unique) partial-fraction expansion of the left-hand side is obtained. Hence the rule is true for degree $n + 1$ and, by induction, for all n.

Remark. We can prove in the same way that $1/f(D)$ can be replaced by its partial-fraction expansion even when the characteristic roots are not distinct.

Rule 20 gives the solution of the nonhomogeneous equation with $y = 0$, $y' = 0, \ldots, y^{(n-1)} = 0$ for $x = c$. (For a full discussion see Reference 7, Chapter 2.) The rule can be proved by means of the partial-fraction expansion. For example, if $f(D) = a_0D^2 + a_1D + a_2$ and the roots r_1, r_2 are distinct, then, as above,

$$y = \frac{1}{a_0}\left[\frac{1}{r_1 - r_2}\,\frac{1}{D - r_1}Q + \frac{1}{r_2 - r_1}\,\frac{1}{D - r_2}Q\right]$$

$$= \frac{1}{a_0}\left[\frac{e^{r_1x}}{r_1 - r_2}\int_c^x e^{-r_1u}Q(u)\,du + \frac{e^{r_2x}}{r_2 - r_1}\int_c^x e^{-r_2u}Q(u)\,du\right]$$

$$= \int_c^x Q(u)\,\frac{e^{r_1(x-u)} - e^{r_2(x-u)}}{a_0(r_1 - r_2)}\,du.$$

Since

$$W(x) = \frac{e^{r_1x} - e^{r_2x}}{a_0(r_1 - r_2)}$$

is a solution of the homogeneous equation and $W(0) = 0$, $W'(0) = 1/a_0$, the rule is verified. A general proof is outlined in Prob. 9 below.

Rule 21 is a *principle of stationarity*. If $Q(x)$ is regarded as an input, then $[1/f(D)]\,Q(x)$ is an output. The principle states that delay of the input by "time" x_0 has the effect of delaying the output by the same time. For the validity of the principle it is crucial that the coefficients be *constant*. To justify the rule, we remark that

$$D\phi(x - x_0) = \phi'(x - x_0), \qquad D^2\phi(x - x_0) = \phi''(x - x_0), \qquad \ldots,$$

and hence that if $f(D)\phi(x) = Q(x)$,

$$f(D)\phi(x - x_0) = Q(x - x_0).$$

The operational rules listed and their elaborations are known as the *Heaviside calculus* (after Oliver Heaviside (1850–1925); see Reference 5 at the end of this chapter). The most striking characteristic is the correctness of the results obtained by manipulating operational expressions as though D were a numerical variable. The procedure is not infallible and every new rule must be tested to establish its validity. An alternative method, the results of which parallel those of Heaviside, is based on the *Laplace transform*, which is described briefly in the next section.

PROBLEMS

1. Find a particular solution of each of the following equations, with the aid of the operational rules (numbers of rules suggested are given in parentheses):

(a) $(D^2 - 7D + 2)y = e^{5x}$ (1),
(b) $(D^2 - 3D + 2)y = e^{2x}$ (3),
(c) $(D^2 - 3D + 2)y = \cos 4x$ (1 or 9),
(d) $(D^3 + 4D)y = \sin 3x$ (11, 12, 6)
(e) $(D - 2)(D^2 + 3D + 2)y = e^{2x} \cos 3x$ (1 alone or 11, 16, 12, 8),
(f) $(D^3 + D + 1)y = e^{4x}(2x + 3)$ (17),
(g) $(D^3 + D^2 + 1)y = (x^2 - 1) \cos x$ (17),
(h) $(D - 1)^2(D^3 + D^2 + 1)y = xe^x$ (18),
(i) $(D - 2)^4y = e^{2x}x^3$ (14 or 18),
(j) $(D^2 - 3D + 2)y = \log x$ (19, 13),
(k) $(D^2 + 2D + 2)y = 1/(1 + x^2)$ (15).

2. (a) ... (j). With the aid of operational rules, find a particular solution of each of the equations of Prob. 1 following Section 4–9.

3. (a) ... (e). With the aid of operational rules, find a particular solution of each of the equations of Prob. 2 following Section 4–9.

4. Extend the proof of Rule 14 to the operator $1/(D - a)^3$.

5. Prove Rule 15. [*Hint:* Write the result as $y(x) = (e^{ax}/b)[p(x) \sin bx - q(x) \cos bx]$, where

$$p(x) = \int_c^x \cos bu\, e^{-au}Q(u)\, du, \qquad q(x) = \int_c^x \sin bu\, e^{-au}Q(u)\, du,$$

so that $p'(x) = \cos bx\, e^{-ax}Q(x)$, $q'(x) = \sin bx\, e^{-ax}Q(x)$. Show that $y(x)$ satisfies the differential equation $[(D - a)^2 + b^2]y = Q(x)$.]

6. (a) Prove: $[1/(D - b)]e^{ax}Q(x) = e^{ax}[1/(D + a - b)]Q(x)$. [*Hint:* Apply Rule 13 to both sides.]

(b) Prove Rule 16. [*Hint:* Write $f(D)$ in factored form and then apply the result of part (a) to shift e^{ax} past each factor in turn:

$$\frac{1}{a_0(D - r_1)\cdots(D - r_n)} e^{ax}Q(x)$$

$$= \frac{1}{a_0(D - r_1)\cdots(D - r_{n-1})} e^{ax}\left[\frac{1}{(D + a - r_n)} Q(x)\right]$$

$$= \frac{1}{a_0(D - r_1)\cdots(D - r_{n-2})} e^{ax}\left[\frac{1}{(D + a - r_{n-1})(D + a - r_n)} Q(x)\right]$$

$= \cdots$]

7. (a) Prove: $(D - b)[e^{ax}\phi(x)] = e^{ax}[(D + a - b)\phi(x)]$.

(b) Prove: $f(D)[e^{ax}\phi(x)] = e^{ax}[f(D + a)\phi(x)]$. [*Hint:* Proceed as in the proof of Rule 16 in Prob. 6.]

(c) Prove that Rule 16 follows from the result of part (b).

(d) Prove: $(D - a)^m[e^{ax}\phi(x)] = e^{ax}D^m\phi(x)$.

(e) Apply the rule of part (d) to show that if r is a root of multiplicity k of the equation $f(r) = 0$, then $e^{rx}, xe^{rx}, \ldots, x^{k-1}e^{rx}$ are solutions of the equation $f(D)y = 0$. [*Hint:* $f(D) = (D - r)^k g(D)$.]

8. Let $f(r) = a_0 r^n + \cdots$, $g(r) = 1/f(r)$. If $f(a) \neq 0$, then $g(r)$ can be expanded in a Taylor series about $r = a$:

$$\frac{1}{f(r)} = g(r) = g(a) + g'(a)(r - a) + \cdots + \frac{g^{(m)}}{m!}(r - a)^m + \cdots$$

This suggests the operator identity

$$\frac{1}{f(D)} = g(a) + g'(a)(D - a) + \cdots + \frac{g^{(m)}(a)}{m!}(D - a)^m + \cdots \qquad (*)$$

Use this identity to evaluate $[1/f(D)]e^{ax}P(x)$, where $P(x)$ is a polynomial, and show, with the aid of the result of Prob. 7(d), that Rule 17 is obtained. [The identity (*) is valid only for operation on a restricted class of functions, which includes those of form $e^{ax}P(x)$.]

9. *Proof of Rule* 20. It is shown in advanced calculus (see, for example, Reference 6, pp. 218–222) that

$$\frac{\partial}{\partial x}\int_c^x F(x, u)\,du = F(x, x) + \int_c^x \frac{\partial F}{\partial x}(x, u)\,du,$$

provided F and $\partial F/\partial x$ are continuous. Apply this rule to

$$y = \int_c^x Q(u)W(x - u)\,du,$$

where $Q(x)$ is continuous for all x and $W(x)$ satisfies the conditions described in Rule 20. Conclude successively that

$$y' = \int_c^x Q(u)W'(x - u)\,du,$$

$$y'' = \int_c^x Q(u)W''(x - u)\,du, \qquad \ldots,$$

$$y^{(n-1)} = \int_c^x Q(u)W^{(n-1)}(x - u)\,du,$$

$$y^{(n)} = \frac{Q(x)}{a_0} + \int_c^x Q(u)W^{(n)}(x - u)\,du,$$

and hence that

$$\begin{aligned} f(D)y &= Q(x) + \int_c^x Q(u)[a_0 W^{(n)}(x-u) + \cdots + a_n W(x-u)]\, du \\ &= Q(x). \end{aligned}$$

Show also that $y(c) = 0, y'(c) = 0, \ldots, y^{(n-1)}(c) = 0$.

10. (a) Apply Rule 20 to evaluate $[1/(D-a)^m]Q(x)$ and show that Rule 14 is obtained.

(b) Apply Rule 20 to evaluate $[1/(D^2 - 2aD + a^2 + b^2)]Q(x)$, $b \neq 0$, and show that Rule 15 is obtained.

ANSWERS

1. (a) $-e^{5x}/8$, (b) xe^{2x}, (c) $(-7\cos 4x - 6\sin 4x)/170$, (d) $(\cos 3x)/15$, (e) $e^{2x}(\sin 3x - 7\cos 3x)/450$, (f) $e^{4x}(138x + 109)/4761$, (g) $(-6x - 22)\cos x - (x^2 + 4x - 5)\sin x$, (h) $e^x(x^3 - 5x^2)/18$, (i) $x^7e^{2x}/840$, (j) $e^{2x}\int e^{-2x}\log x\, dx - e^x\int e^{-x}\log x\, dx$, (k) $e^{-x}\int_0^x e^u \sin(x-u)(1+u^2)^{-1}\, du$.

5-5 Laplace transforms.

Let $f(x)$ be defined for $0 \leqq x < \infty$. The Laplace transform of $f(x)$ is defined as the function $F(s)$, where

$$F(s) = \int_0^\infty f(x)e^{-sx}\, dx. \tag{5-16}$$

We write $F(s) = \mathcal{L}[f]$ and consider $F(s)$ as the result of applying an operator $\mathcal{L}$ to f. Various assumptions on $f(x)$ will ensure that the integral has meaning for some values of s; in general, we allow s to be complex, so that $F(s)$ is a complex-valued function of a complex variable. Here we proceed formally in order to indicate briefly the properties of the Laplace transform and their utilization in solving differential equations. (For a detailed treatment the reader is referred to References 2 and 7 at the end of this chapter.)

If $f(x) \equiv 1$, then

$$\mathcal{L}[1] = F(s) = \int_0^\infty e^{-sx}\, dx = \frac{e^{-sx}}{-s}\bigg|_0^\infty = \frac{1}{s}. \tag{5-17}$$

The evaluation of the improper integral is correct if $s > 0$ or, if s is complex, when Re $(s) > 0$. If $f(x) \equiv x^n$, where n is a positive integer, then

$$\mathcal{L}[f] = F(s) = \int_0^\infty x^n e^{-sx}\, dx = \frac{x^n e^{-sx}}{-s}\bigg|_0^\infty + \frac{n}{s}\int_0^\infty x^{n-1}e^{-sx}\, dx,$$

and hence, for Re $(s) > 0$

$$\mathcal{L}[x^n] = \frac{n}{s}\,\mathcal{L}[x^{n-1}]. \tag{5–18}$$

Repeated application of this rule, together with (5–17), gives the conclusion

$$\mathcal{L}[x^n] = \frac{n!}{s^{n+1}} \qquad (n = 0, 1, 2, \ldots). \tag{5–19}$$

A similar analysis gives the rule

$$\mathcal{L}[x^n e^{ax}] = \frac{n!}{(s - a)^{n+1}} \qquad (n = 0, 1, 2, \ldots). \tag{5–20}$$

Further transform pairs $f(x)$, $F(s)$ can be obtained from some general rules. The Laplace transform is *linear:* if c_1, c_2 are constants, then

$$\mathcal{L}[c_1 f_1 + c_2 f_2] = c_1\mathcal{L}[f_1] + c_2\mathcal{L}[f_2]; \tag{5–21}$$

this follows directly from the definition. Under appropriate assumptions,

$$\begin{aligned}\mathcal{L}[f'(x)] = \int_0^\infty f'(x)e^{-sx}\,dx &= f(x)e^{-sx}\Big|_0^\infty + s\int_0^\infty f(x)e^{-sx}\,dx \\ &= -f(0) + s\mathcal{L}[f];\end{aligned}$$

$f(x)$ must, in particular, satisfy the condition $f(x)e^{-sx} \to 0$ as $x \to \infty$, for some values of s. By repeated application of the conclusion we obtain the general rules for *transformation of derivatives:*

$$\begin{aligned}\mathcal{L}[f'] &= s\mathcal{L}[f] - f(0), \\ \mathcal{L}[f''] &= s^2\mathcal{L}[f] - [f'(0) + sf(0)], \\ \mathcal{L}[f'''] &= s^3\mathcal{L}[f] - [f''(0) + sf'(0) + s^2 f(0)], \\ &\vdots \\ \mathcal{L}[f^{(n)}] &= s^n\mathcal{L}[f] - [f^{(n-1)}(0) + sf^{(n-2)}(0) + \cdots + s^{n-1}f(0)].\end{aligned} \tag{5–22}$$

Finally, a function f (under certain restrictions) is uniquely determined by its Laplace transform:

$$\mathcal{L}[f] = \mathcal{L}[g] \qquad \text{implies} \qquad f = g. \tag{5–23}$$

EXAMPLES.

$$\mathcal{L}[\sin ax] = \mathcal{L}\left[\frac{e^{aix} - e^{-aix}}{2i}\right] = \frac{1}{2i}\mathcal{L}[e^{aix}] - \frac{1}{2i}\mathcal{L}[e^{-aix}]$$

$$= \frac{1}{2i}\frac{1}{s - ai} - \frac{1}{2i}\frac{1}{s + ai} = \frac{a}{s^2 + a^2}. \tag{5–24}$$

Since $(\sin ax)' = a \cos ax$, we conclude from (5–22):

$$\mathcal{L}[\cos ax] = \frac{s}{s^2 + a^2}. \tag{5–25}$$

The Laplace transform can be used to obtain the solution for $x \geqq 0$ of a linear differential equation with constant coefficients, satisfying prescribed initial conditions at $x = 0$. We illustrate the procedure by an example. Given the equation with initial conditions

$$\frac{d^2y}{dx^2} + 4y = e^{3x}, \qquad y = a, \quad y' = b \quad \text{when} \quad x = 0,$$

we seek $\mathcal{L}[y]$. From the given equation,

$$\mathcal{L}[y'' + 4y] = \mathcal{L}[e^{3x}] = \frac{1}{s - 3}.$$

Hence by (5–22)

$$s^2\mathcal{L}[y] - (b + as) + 4\mathcal{L}[y] = \frac{1}{s - 3},$$

$$\mathcal{L}[y] = \frac{1}{(s^2 + 4)(s - 3)} + \frac{as + b}{s^2 + 4}$$

$$= \frac{1}{13}\frac{1}{s - 3} - \frac{1}{13}\frac{s + 3}{s^2 + 4} + \frac{as + b}{s^2 + 4}.$$

By Eqs. (5–20), (5–24), (5–25), and linearity we can write

$$\mathcal{L}[y] = \frac{1}{13}\mathcal{L}[e^{3x}] - \frac{1}{13}\mathcal{L}[\cos 2x] - \frac{3}{26}\mathcal{L}[\sin 2x]$$

$$+ a\mathcal{L}[\cos 2x] + \frac{b}{2}\mathcal{L}[\sin 2x]$$

$$= \mathcal{L}\left[\frac{e^{3x}}{13} - \frac{\cos 2x}{13} - \frac{3 \sin 2x}{26} + a \cos 2x + \frac{b}{2}\sin 2x\right],$$

$$y = \frac{e^{3x}}{13} - \frac{\cos 2x}{13} - \frac{3 \sin 2x}{26} + a \cos 2x + \frac{b}{2}\sin 2x.$$

The effectiveness of the method depends upon availability of a good table of transform pairs. Such tables closely resemble the table of inverse operators in the preceding section. For lists of Laplace transforms and inverse transforms see References 1, 3, 4, and 7.

PROBLEMS

1. Find the Laplace transforms of the following functions:

(a) $\cosh x$, (b) $\sinh x$,
(c) $x \sin x$, (d) $x^2 \sin x$,
(e) $f(x) = 1,\ 0 \leqq x < 1,\ f(x) = 0,\ x \geqq 1$,
(f) $f(x) = x^2 - x,\ 0 \leqq x \leqq 1,\ f(x) = 0,\ x > 1$,
(g) $e^{ax} \sin bx$, (h) $e^{ax} \cos bx$.

2. Find the Laplace transforms of the following functions, with the aid of results given above and linearity:

(a) $x^4 + 2$, (b) $xe^x - 1$,
(c) $\sin 3x - \cos 5x$, (d) $(1 - x^2)e^{2x}$.

3. With the aid of the Laplace transform, find the solutions that satisfy the given initial conditions:

(a) $y' + y = e^{-x};\ y = 1$ for $x = 0$;
(b) $(D^2 + 3D + 2)y = x$; for $x = 0$: $y = 1$ and $y' = -1$;
(c) $(D + 1)^3 y = e^{-x},\ y = 0$; for $x = 0$: $y' = 0,\ y'' = 0$;
(d) $(D^2 + 2D + 2)y = \sin x$; for $x = 0$: $y = 0,\ y' = 1$.
[*Hint:* For (d) use the results of Probs. 1(g) and 1(h).]

ANSWERS

1. (a) $\dfrac{s}{s^2 - 1}$, (b) $\dfrac{1}{s^2 - 1}$, (c) $\dfrac{2s}{(s^2 + 1)^2}$, (d) $\dfrac{2 - 6s^2}{(s^2 + 1)^3}$,
(e) $\dfrac{1 - e^{-s}}{s}$, (f) $\dfrac{1 + e^{-s}}{-s^2} + \dfrac{2}{s^2}(1 - e^{-s})$, (g) $\dfrac{b}{(s - a)^2 + b^2}$,
(h) $\dfrac{s - a}{(s - a)^2 + b^2}$.

2. (a) $\dfrac{24}{s^5} + \dfrac{2}{s}$, (b) $\dfrac{1}{(s - 1)^2} - \dfrac{1}{s}$, (c) $\dfrac{3}{s^2 + 9} - \dfrac{s}{s^2 + 25}$,
(d) $\dfrac{1}{s - 2} - \dfrac{2}{(s - 2)^3}$.

3. (a) $e^{-x}(x + 1)$, (b) $\frac{1}{4}(8e^{-x} - e^{-2x} - 3 + 2x)$, (c) $x^3 e^{-x}/6$,
(d) $\frac{1}{5}(-2 \cos x + \sin x + 2e^{-x} \cos x + 6e^{-x} \sin x)$.

SUGGESTED REFERENCES

1. *C. R. C. Standard Mathematical Tables*, 11th ed. Cleveland: Chemical Rubber Pub. Co., 1957.

2. CHURCHILL, RUEL V., *Modern Operational Mathematics in Engineering.* New York: McGraw-Hill, 1944.

3. ERDÉLYI, A., editor, *Tables of Integral Transforms*, Vol. I, compiled by the staff of the Bateman Manuscript Project. New York: McGraw-Hill, 1954.

4. GARDNER, M. F., and BARNES, J. L., *Transients in Linear Systems*, Vol. I. London: Chapman and Hall, 1942.

5. HEAVISIDE, OLIVER, *Electromagnetic Theory.* New York: Dover, 1950.

6. KAPLAN, WILFRED, *Advanced Calculus.* Reading, Mass.: Addison-Wesley, 1952.

7. KAPLAN, WILFRED, *Operational Methods for Linear Systems.* Reading, Mass.: Addison-Wesley, 1962.

CHAPTER 6

APPLICATIONS OF LINEAR DIFFERENTIAL EQUATIONS

6–1 Input-output analysis. In this chapter we consider the applications of the nth order linear equation, which we write in the form

$$(a_0D^n + \cdots + a_{n-1}D + a_n)x = F(t), \tag{6–1}$$

where $D = d/dt$. For most of the discussion, $a_0, \ldots, a_n$ will be constants.

In many applications one can consider Eq. (6–1), as in Section 3–2, as describing the output x of a mechanism in response to an input $F(t)$. This point of view is of value in mechanics, in electric circuit theory, and especially in the theory of control systems. When $a_n \neq 0$, as is normally the case, one can divide Eq. (6–1) by a_n and thereby reduce it to the form

$$(a_0D^n + \cdots + a_{n-1}D + 1)x = F(t). \tag{6–2}$$

If we now ignore the terms in derivatives, we obtain an approximate solution $x = F(t)$; that is, the output is approximately equal to the input. This approximation is very valuable as a first step in understanding the type of response to different inputs.

6–2 Stability. Transients. By the theory of Chapter 4 the general solution of Eq. (6–1) has the form

$$x = x^*(t) + c_1x_1(t) + \cdots + c_nx_n(t), \tag{6–3}$$

where $c_1, \ldots, c_n$ are arbitrary constants. The equation (6–1) is said to be *stable* if for every choice of $c_1, \ldots, c_n$, the complementary function

$$c_1x_1(t) + \cdots + c_nx_n(t)$$

approaches 0 as $t \to +\infty$. In other words, Eq. (6–1) is stable if every solution of the related homogeneous equation

$$[a_0D^n + \cdots + a_{n-1}D + a_n]x = 0 \tag{6–4}$$

approaches 0 as $t \to \infty$. In particular then, $x_1(t), \ldots, x_n(t)$ must approach 0 as $t \to +\infty$; conversely, if $x_1(t) \to 0, \ldots, x_n(t) \to 0$ as $t \to +\infty$, then every linear combination $c_1x_1(t) + \cdots + c_nx_n(t)$ must approach 0 as $t \to +\infty$, and the equation is stable. If at least one solution of the homo-

geneous equation fails to approach 0 as $t \to +\infty$, the equation (6–1) is said to be *unstable.*

The significance of stability is that there is effectively a unique output for a given input. For if the equation is stable, then any output $x(t)$ differs from any other [for example, $x^*(t)$] by a *transient,* that is, by a term which approaches 0 as $t \to \infty$. Indeed, from Eq. (6–3),

$$x(t) - x^*(t) = c_1x_1(t) + \cdots + c_nx_n(t) \to 0 \quad \text{as} \quad t \to \infty.$$

The choice of the particular solution $x^*(t)$ is irrelevant here. If $x^{**}(t)$ is any other particular solution, then it is also a possible output, so that $x^{**}(t) - x^*(t) \to 0$ as $t \to +\infty$; hence also

$$x(t) - x^{**}(t) = [x(t) - x^*(t)] + [x^*(t) - x^{**}(t)] \to 0.$$

Now let the coefficients $a_0, \ldots, a_n$ be *constants,* $(a_0 \neq 0)$. Then the nature of the solutions of Eq. (6–4) is determined by the characteristic equation

$$a_0r^n + \cdots + a_{n-1}r + a_n = 0. \tag{6–5}$$

The differential equation (6–1) *is stable if all roots of the characteristic equation have negative real parts; otherwise, the equation is unstable.* For if r_1 is a real root of multiplicity k of the characteristic equation, then e^{r_1t}, $te^{r_1t}, \ldots, t^{k-1}e^{r_1t}$ are solutions of the homogeneous differential equation (6–4); if $r_1 < 0$, then each of these solutions approaches 0 as $t \to +\infty$; if $r_1 \geqq 0$, then none of them approaches 0 as $t \to +\infty$. If $a \pm bi$ is a pair of complex roots of multiplicity k, then we have solutions of form $t^he^{at}\cos bt$, $t^he^{at}\sin bt$, $(h = 0, 1, \ldots, k - 1)$; if $a < 0$, all these solutions are transients; if $a \geqq 0$, none is a transient (Prob. 3 below). Hence when all roots have negative real parts, all solutions of the homogeneous equation are transients; when at least one root has positive or zero real part, a nontransient solution of the homogeneous equation exists.

Remarks. If $\pm bi$ is a pair of simple roots, the corresponding functions $\cos bt$, $\sin bt$ are not transients; however, they do not become arbitrarily large as $t \to +\infty$. We sometimes call an equation (6–1) stable if all solutions of the homogeneous equation are either transients or, at worst, remain *bounded* as $t \to +\infty$. With this definition, the output of a stable equation is not uniquely determined as above; however, if the initial conditions are confined to a narrow range, the possible outputs never differ greatly.

In mathematical literature one usually refers to a "stable solution" of a differential equation, rather than to a "stable differential equation." A solution $x = x^*(t)$, $(t_0 \leqq t < \infty)$, of a differential equation is termed *asymptotically stable* if for every solution $x(t)$ whose initial conditions are close enough to those of $x^*(t)$ when $t = t_0$, $\lim [x(t) - x^*(t)] = 0$ as $t \to +\infty$. A stable linear equation (5–1), as defined above, is simply an equation for which every solution is asymptotically stable for every choice of $F(t)$. The preceding remarks are somewhat oversimplified. For more details the reader is referred to References 2, 3, and 7, and to Chapter 11 of ODE.

6–3 Testing for stability. We shall consider only equations with constant coefficients. By the criterion of the preceding section, testing for stability requires examination of the roots of an algebraic equation and determination of whether there are roots with positive or zero real parts.

EXAMPLE 1. $\frac{2}{5}D^2x + \frac{3}{5}Dx + x = F(t)$. The characteristic equation is

$$2r^2 + 3r + 5 = 0.$$

The roots are

$$\frac{-3 \pm \sqrt{-31}}{4} = -\frac{3}{4} \pm \frac{\sqrt{31}}{4}i.$$

The real parts are equal to $-\frac{3}{4}$; the equation is stable.

The example suggests a general rule for the equation of second order,

$$(aD^2 + bD + c)x = F(t). \qquad (6\text{–}6)$$

The equation is stable if a, b, and c all have the same sign; it is unstable otherwise. This is equivalent to the statement that the roots of

$$ar^2 + br + c = 0$$

have negative real parts when $a > 0$, $b > 0$, $c > 0$ or $a < 0$, $b < 0$, $c < 0$, and not otherwise. The proof is left as an exercise (Prob. 4 below).

EXAMPLE 2. $(2D^3 + D^2 + D + 2)x = F(t).$

The characteristic equation is

$$2r^3 + r^2 + r + 2 = 0.$$

The roots are -1, $\frac{1}{4}(1 \pm \sqrt{15}i)$. The equation is unstable.

The second example shows that positiveness of the coefficients does not ensure stability for a third order equation. However, it can be shown that if the coefficients are not all of the same sign, then the equation is unstable.

Criteria have been developed for testing the stability of equations of arbitrary order with constant coefficients; see References 4, 5, and 6 at the end of this chapter.

PROBLEMS

1. Test the following equations for stability:

(a) $(3D^2 + 2D + 1)x = F(t)$, (b) $(D^3 + D^2 + D + 1)x = F(t)$,
(c) $(D^3 + 2D^2 + 2D + 1)x = F(t)$,
(d) $(D^3 + 5D^2 + D + 1)x = F(t)$.

2. For each of the following equations obtain the general solution and plot input and output for several choices of initial conditions:

(a) $(D^2 + 3D + 2)x = t^2 - t$, (b) $(D^2 + 2D + 2)x = t^2 - t$,
(c) $(D^2 - 3D + 2)x = t^2 - t$.

3. (a) Prove: if $a < 0$, $h = 1, 2, \ldots$, then $t^h e^{at} \to 0$ as $t \to +\infty$, but if $a \geqq 0$ then $t^h e^{at}$ does not approach 0 as $t \to +\infty$.

(b) Prove: if $a < 0$, then $f(t) = t^h e^{at} \cos bt \to 0$ and $g(t) = t^h e^{at} \sin bt \to 0$ as $t \to +\infty$. [*Hint:* $|f(t)| \leqq t^h e^{at}$, $|g(t)| \leqq t^h e^{at}$.]

(c) Prove: if $a \geqq 0$, $b > 0$, then the functions $f(t)$, $g(t)$ of part (b) do not approach 0 as $t \to +\infty$. [*Hint:* Consider the values of $f(t)$ for $bt = 2n\pi$ and of $g(t)$ for $bt = \frac{1}{2}\pi + 2n\pi$, $(n = 1, 2, \ldots)$.]

4. Prove: if $a > 0$, then the roots of the quadratic equation $ar^2 + br + c = 0$ have negative real parts if and only if $b > 0$ and $c > 0$.

ANSWERS

1. (a) Stable, (b) unstable, (c) stable, (d) stable.

2. General solutions:

(a) $\frac{1}{2}(t^2 - 4t + 5) + c_1 e^{-t} + c_2 e^{-2t}$,
(b) $\frac{1}{2}(t^2 - 3t + 2) + e^{-t}(c_1 \cos t + c_2 \sin t)$,
(c) $\frac{1}{2}(t^2 + 2t + 2) + c_1 e^t + c_2 e^{2t}$.

6–4 Study of transients for second order equations. We consider a second order equation with constant coefficients:

$$a_0 D^2 x + a_1 Dx + a_2 x = F(t). \tag{6–7}$$

We assume that the equation is stable, so that we can assume

$$a_0 > 0, \qquad a_1 > 0, \qquad a_2 > 0, \tag{6–8}$$

and proceed to consider the output corresponding to *zero input.* The output is therefore a solution of the homogeneous equation

$$a_0 D^2 x + a_1 Dx + a_2 x = 0 \tag{6–9}$$

and is itself a *transient.* In effect, we are thus simply studying the transients of Eq. (6–7).

We introduce the new constants

$$h = \frac{1}{2}\frac{a_1}{a_0} > 0, \qquad \lambda = \sqrt{\frac{a_2}{a_0}} > 0. \tag{6–10}$$

Then Eq. (6–9) can be written

$$D^2x + 2hDx + \lambda^2 x = 0, \tag{6–11}$$

and the characteristic equation is

$$r^2 + 2hr + \lambda^2 = 0. \tag{6–12}$$

We now consider three cases:

Case 1. $0 < h < \lambda$. *Underdamped case.*

Case 2. $h = \lambda$. *Critically damped case.*

Case 3. $h > \lambda$. *Overdamped case.*

In Case 1 the characteristic roots are complex: $r = -h \pm i\sqrt{\lambda^2 - h^2}$. The solutions are

$$x = e^{-ht}(c_1 \cos \beta t + c_2 \sin \beta t), \qquad \beta = \sqrt{\lambda^2 - h^2}. \tag{6–13}$$

By trigonometry we can write

$$\begin{aligned} c_1 \cos \beta t + c_2 \sin \beta t &= A \sin (\beta t + \alpha), \\ A \cos \alpha = c_2, \qquad & A \sin \alpha = c_1. \end{aligned} \tag{6–14}$$

Thus A and α are polar coordinates of the point whose rectangular coordinates are c_2, c_1 (Fig. 6–1). The solution (6–13) becomes

$$x = Ae^{-ht} \sin (\beta t + \alpha). \tag{6–15}$$

Since $\sin (\beta t + \alpha)$ varies between -1 and $+1$, the solution varies between the two curves $x = Ae^{-ht}$, $x = -Ae^{-ht}$, touching these curves when $\beta t + \alpha$ is an odd multiple of $\pi/2$. The solution is called a *damped oscillation.* (See Fig. 6–2).

In Case 2 the characteristic roots are real and equal: $r = -h, -h$. The solutions are

$$x = c_1e^{-ht} + c_2te^{-ht}. \tag{6–16}$$

If $c_2 = 0$, this represents exponential decay (Section 3–2). If $c_2 \neq 0$, the solution approaches 0 as $t \to +\infty$, but is permitted one change of sign (*overshooting*), as in Fig. 6–3.

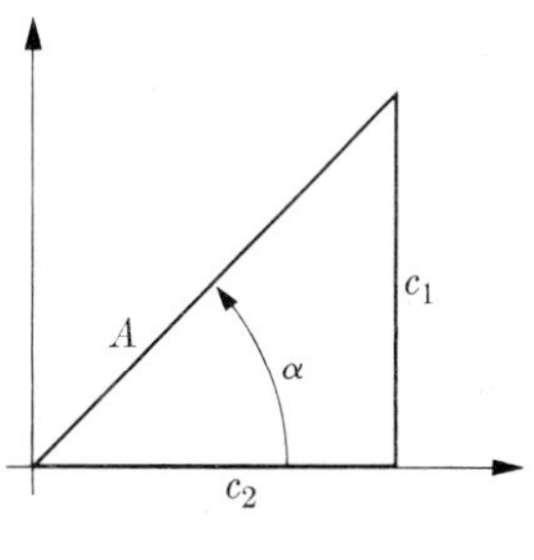

FIGURE 6–1

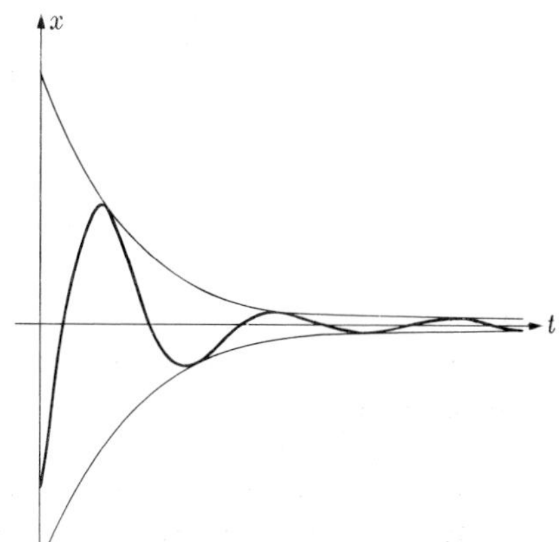

FIG. 6–2. Damped oscillation.

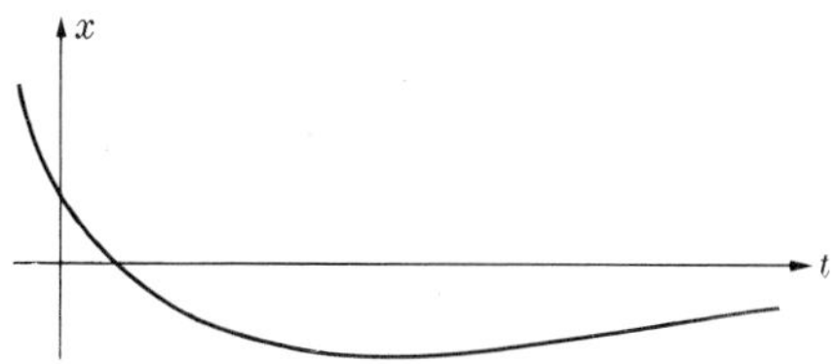

FIG. 6–3. Critical damping.

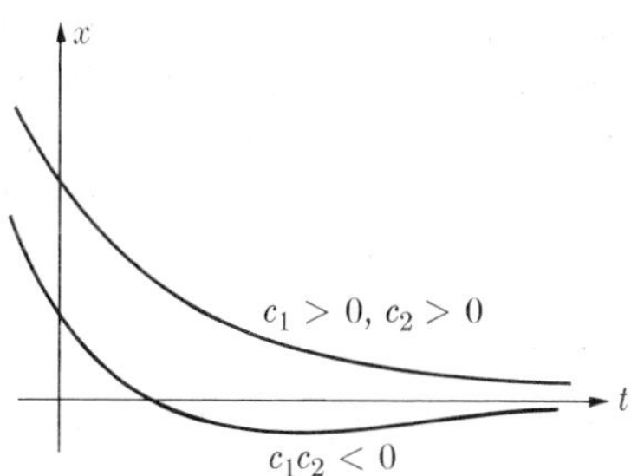

FIG. 6–4. Overcritical damping.

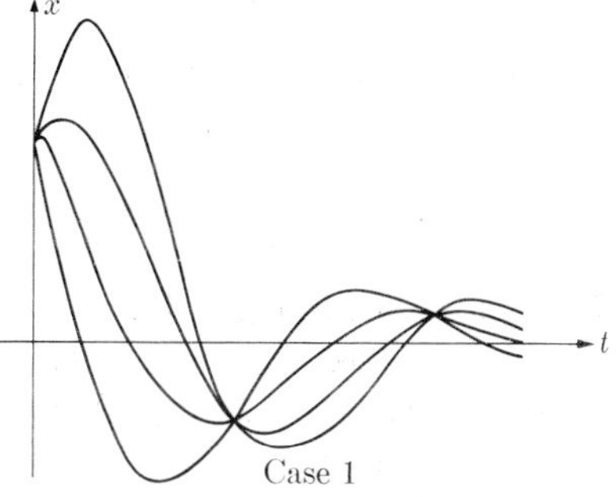

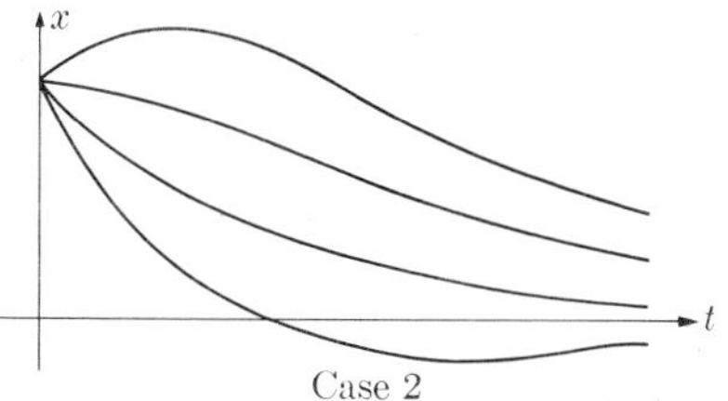

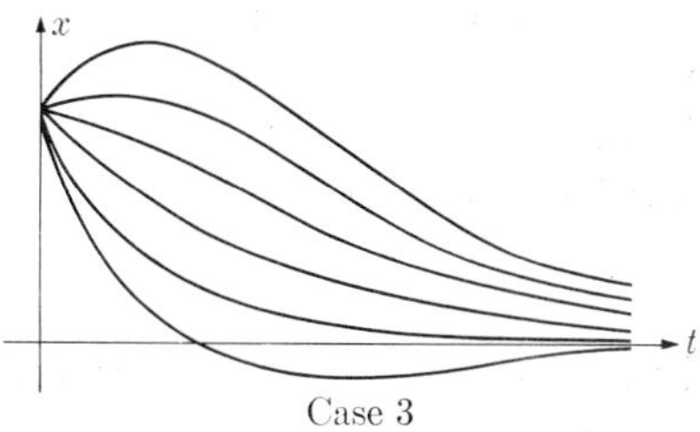

FIG. 6–5. Solutions with fixed initial value of x.

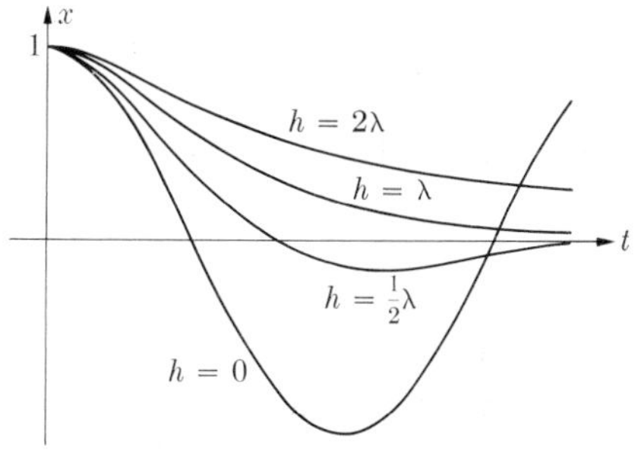

FIG. 6–6. Solutions with fixed λ.

In Case 3 the characteristic roots are distinct, real, and negative: $r = -h \pm \sqrt{h^2 - \lambda^2}$. The solutions are

$$\begin{gathered} x = c_1 e^{-at} + c_2 e^{-bt}, \\ -a = -h - \mu, \qquad -b = -h + \mu, \\ \mu = \sqrt{h^2 - \lambda^2} = \frac{a - b}{2}. \end{gathered} \tag{6-17}$$

Thus $-a$ and $-b$ are negative. If c_1 and c_2 have the same sign, x can be considered as an average of two exponential decay functions; when c_1 and c_2 have opposite signs, there is conflict between the two and a change of sign occurs. The two cases are illustrated in Fig. 6–4.

We can study the three cases in greater detail by considering the solutions with the initial values $x = x_0$, $D_t x = v_0$ when $t = 0$. The solutions are then found to be (Prob. 3 below) as follows:

$$\begin{aligned} &\textit{Case 1: } x = e^{-ht}\{x_0 \cos \beta t + [(v_0 + hx_0)/\beta] \sin \beta t\}, \\ &\textit{Case 2: } x = e^{-ht}[x_0 + (v_0 + hx_0)t], \\ &\textit{Case 3: } x = [1/(a - b)][(v_0 + ax_0)e^{-bt} - (v_0 + bx_0)e^{-at}]. \end{aligned} \tag{6-18}$$

If we now fix x_0 (e.g., at 1) and vary v_0, we obtain in each case a family of solutions, as shown in Fig. 6–5. These are drawn for a particular choice of x_0, h, β, and μ; however the appearance is similar for other values. Changing x_0, ($x_0 \neq 0$), while keeping h, β, μ fixed has the effect of changing the vertical scale. When $x_0 = 0$, the solutions are as follows:

$$\begin{aligned} &\textit{Case 1: } x = (v_0/\beta)e^{-ht} \sin \beta t, \\ &\textit{Case 2: } x = v_0 t e^{-ht}, \\ &\textit{Case 3: } x = [v_0/(a - b)](e^{-bt} - e^{-at}). \end{aligned} \tag{6-19}$$

These are easily pictured (Prob. 4 below); changing v_0 in (6–19) merely varies the vertical scale.

We can also compare the three cases by keeping λ fixed and letting h vary, ($0 < h < \infty$). Typical solutions for $x_0 = 1$, $v_0 = 0$ are shown in Fig. 6–6 for $t \geqq 0$. The figure also includes the limiting case $h = 0$, in which the solutions are

$$x = c_1 \cos \lambda t + c_2 \sin \lambda t,$$

i.e., pure sinusoidal oscillations. They are not transients but, as remarked at the end of Section 6–2, are sometimes included with transients in the definition of stability. Figure 6–6 clearly shows the effect of increasing h; the oscillations are slowed down and decreased in amplitude until they disappear and are replaced by exponential decay. In physical applications, h is a measure of friction or some similar loss of energy. When h is 0, the system is "conservative" and does not lose energy; when h is positive, a loss of energy occurs and slows down the motion.

PROBLEMS

1. Let $x = e^{-t} \sin 2t$. Make a careful graph, showing maximum and minimum points and points of contact with the curves $x = \pm e^{-t}$.

2. Graph the solutions of $(D^2 + 3D + 2)x = 0$ for which $x = 1$ when $t = 0$. For what initial values of $v = dx/dt$ does the solution never cross the t-axis for $-\infty < t < \infty$?

3. Verify that (6–18) provides the solution of (6–11) with prescribed initial values in (a) Case 1, (b) Case 2, (c) Case 3.

4. Describe the graphs of the functions (6–19) in (a) Case 1, (b) Case 2, (c) Case 3.

5. Show that the following equations are unstable and graph typical solutions: (a) $(D^2 + 2D - 3)x = 0$, (b) $(D^2 - D + 2)x = 0$.

ANSWERS

1. Max. at $t = 0.55 + n\pi$, min. at $t = 2.12 + n\pi$, contact at $t = 0.79 + n\pi/2$, $(n = 0, \pm 1, \ldots)$. 2. No crossing if $-2 \leqq v_0 \leqq -1$.

6–5 Response of second order equation to constant, ramp, and step-function inputs. We consider the stable second order equation with constant coefficients,

$$(a_0 D^2 + a_1 D + 1)x = F(t), \tag{6–20}$$

and consider the outputs x that correspond to various types of inputs $F(t)$. The output will also be composed of a particular solution plus a transient. We are interested mainly in the appearance of the particular solution for large t, after the effects of initial conditions have become negligible. For extension of the theory to equations of higher order and to other inputs, one is referred to Chapter 5 of ODE.

Constant input. If $F(t) \equiv F_0$, where F_0 is constant, then $x = F_0$ is a particular solution, and hence the general output is

$$x = F_0 + \text{transient}. \tag{6–21}$$

The form of the transient depends on the nature of the homogeneous equa-

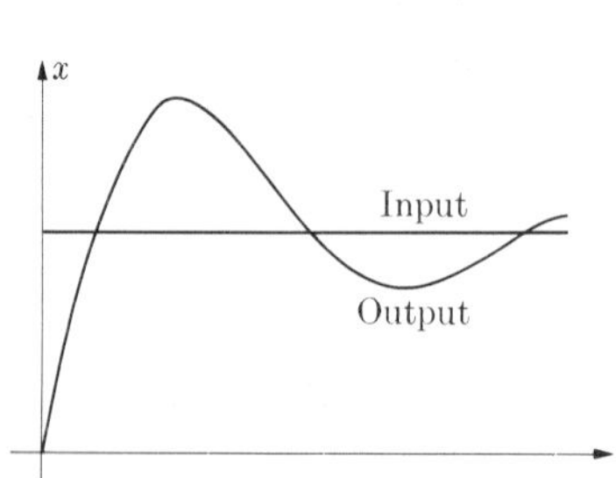

Fig. 6–7. Response to constant input.

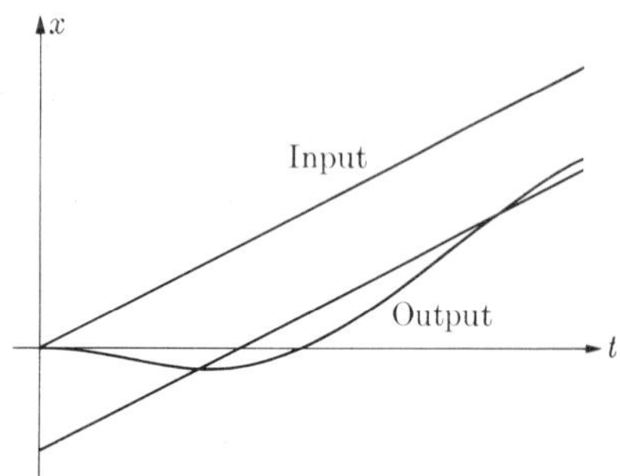

FIG. 6–8. Response to ramp input.

tion related to (6–20) (Section 6–4). For example, in the underdamped case the transient is a damped oscillation $Ae^{-ht}\sin(\beta t + \alpha)$ and the outputs (6–21) have the form of Fig. 6–7. The constant F_0 is an *equilibrium value* approached by x as t increases. In the overdamped case there is a similar conclusion, except that x approaches F_0 without oscillation.

Ramp input. If $F(t) = kt$, a linear function, then a particular solution is $x = k(t - a_1)$. The general output is

$$x = k(t - a_1) + \text{transient}. \tag{6–22}$$

When the transient is a damped oscillation, the solution has the appearance of Fig. 6–8. Hence for large t, the output effectively coincides with the linear function $k(t - a_1)$. The slope of the output coincides with that of the input, but output lags input by time a_1.

Step-function input. When $F(t)$ is continuous except for jumps, we can define the solutions of the differential equation as in Section 3–2. Each solution will be continuous and have a continuous derivative, but the second derivative will have a jump discontinuity at each such discontinuity of $F(t)$. Thus if $F(t)$ is continuous for $0 \leqq t < t_0$, with a jump at t_0, we can obtain the solution $x(t)$ with given initial values at $t = 0$ in the interval $0 \leqq t < t_0$; because $F(t)$ has a limit as $t \to t_0$ from the left, $x(t)$ and $x'(t)$ also have limits. The limiting values of x and x' serve as *initial values* at t_0 for the next interval $t_0 \leqq t < t_1$. Thus the solution can be prolonged in unique fashion past the discontinuities, and both $x(t)$ and $x'(t)$ remain continuous.

For example, let $F(t) = 0$ for $t \leqq 0$, $F(t) = 1$ for $0 < t \leqq 1$, and $F(t) = 0$ for $t > 1$. We consider the output for which $x = 0$, $x' = 0$ for $t = 0$. Since $x(t)$ satisfies the equation $(a_0D^2 + a_1D + 1)x = 0$ for $t \leqq 0$, we conclude that $x \equiv 0$ for $t \leqq 0$. For the interval $0 \leqq t \leqq 1$ the output satisfies the equation

$$(a_0D^2 + a_1D + 1)x = 1$$

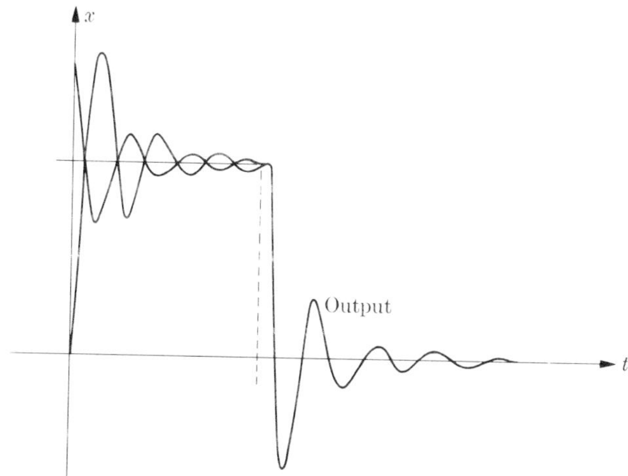

FIG. 6–9. Response to square pulse.

and has initial values $x = 0$, $x' = 0$ at $t = 0$. This is simply an output which corresponds to a constant input, e.g., as in Fig. 6–7; thus $x = 1 +$ transient, and x is approaching 1. At $t = 1$ the process is interrupted, and we then solve the equation

$$(a_0D^2 + a_1D + 1)x = 0$$

with initial values of x, x' at $t = 1$ equal to the values obtained from the previous solution. Hence for $t \geqq 1$, x has the form of a pure transient. A typical solution is shown in Fig. 6–9.

If the initial conditions at $t = 0$ are changed, the particular solution is modified only by addition of a transient. Hence for large t the solutions effectively coincide, as shown in Fig. 6–9.

PROBLEMS

1. Graph the input and the output with initial values $x = 0$, $x' = 0$ at $t = 0$ for each of the following:

(a) $(2D^2 + 2D + 1)x = 3$, (b) $(5D^2 + 2D + 1)x = 5t$,
(c) $(D^2 + 2D + 1)x = t(t - 1)(t - 2)$, (d) $(D^2 + 3D + 2)x = e^{2t}$.

2. Verify that (6–22) is a general solution of (6–20) when $F(t) = kt$.

3. Let $F(t) = 0$ for $t \leqq 0$, $F(t) = 2$ for $0 < t \leqq \pi$, $F(t) = -1$ for $t > \pi$. Find and graph the output with initial values $x = 0$, $x' = 0$ at $t = 0$ for the equation $(2D^2 + 2D + 1)x = F(t)$.

4. Let the equation $(2\gamma^2 D^2 + 2\gamma D + 1)x = t$ (where γ is a positive constant) be given.

(a) Find the solution such that $x = 0$ and $x' = 0$ when $t = 0$.

(b) In the solution of part (a) find the limiting value of x as $\gamma \to 0+$, for fixed positive t. Interpret the result in terms of the approximation: output $\sim$ input.

ANSWERS

1. Outputs: (a) $3 + e^{-t/2}\,(-3 \cos \frac{1}{2}t - 3 \sin \frac{1}{2}t)$,
(b) $5(t - 2) + e^{-t/5}(10 \cos \frac{2}{5}t - \frac{15}{2} \sin \frac{2}{5}t)$,
(c) $t^3 - 9t^2 + 32t - 46 + e^{-t}(46 + 14t)$,
(d) $(e^{2t} - 4e^{-t} + 3e^{-2t})/12$.

3. $x = 0$ for $t \leqq 0$, $\quad x = 2 - 2e^{-t/2}\,(\cos \frac{1}{2}t + \sin \frac{1}{2}t)$ for $0 \leqq t \leqq \pi$, $x = -1 + e^{-t/2}[(-2 - 3e^{\pi/2}) \cos \frac{1}{2}t + (3e^{\pi/2} - 2) \sin \frac{1}{2}t]$ for $t > \pi$.

4. (a) $t - 2\gamma + 2\gamma e^{-t/(2\gamma)} \cos\,[t/(2\gamma)]$, (b) limit is t.

6–6 Output of second order equation corresponding to sinusoidal input. With an input $A_i \sin \omega t$, $(\omega > 0)$, our equation becomes

$$(a_0 D^2 + a_1 D + 1)x = A_i \sin \omega t. \tag{6–23}$$

By the methods of Chapter 4 (Section 4–9, or Rule 8 in Table 5–1, Section 5–4) a particular output is found to be

$$x = A_i \frac{(1 - a_0\omega^2) \sin \omega t - a_1\omega \cos \omega t}{(1 - a_0\omega^2)^2 + a_1^2\omega^2} = A_o \sin(\omega t - \alpha), \tag{6–24}$$

where

$$A_o = \frac{A_i}{k}, \qquad \cos \alpha = \frac{1 - a_0\omega^2}{k}, \qquad \sin \alpha = \frac{a_1\omega}{k},$$
$$k = [(1 - a_0\omega^2)^2 + a_1^2\omega^2]^{1/2}. \tag{6–25}$$

Thus k and α are polar coordinates of the point whose rectangular coordinates are $1 - a_0\omega^2$, $a_1\omega$, as in Fig. 6–10.

Since our equation is assumed to be stable, the general output will effectively coincide with (6–24), after a transient period has elapsed. Thus, except for a transient, the output has form similar to the input. It is again sinusoidal, with the same *frequency* ω but with a new amplitude $A_o = A_i/k$; here A_i denotes input amplitude and A_o output amplitude, and there is a phase lag α. Since a_0, a_1 are positive, Fig. 6–10 shows that $0 < \alpha < \pi$.

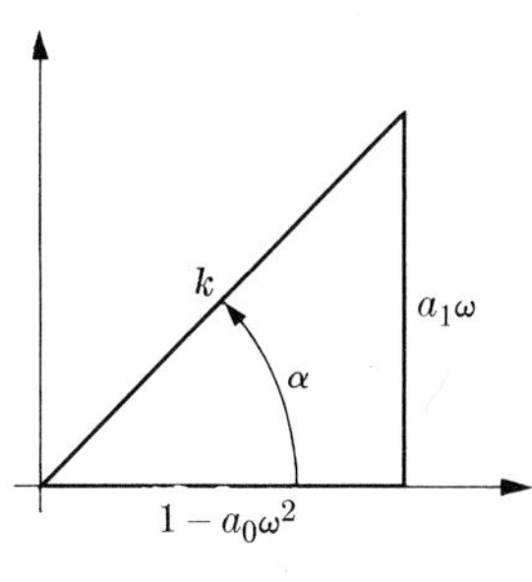

FIGURE 6–10

If we write $h = \frac{1}{2}a_1/a_0$, $\lambda = a_0^{-1/2}$, then we obtain

$$k = \left[\left(1 - \frac{\omega^2}{\lambda^2}\right)^2 + 4\frac{h^2}{\lambda^2}\frac{\omega^2}{\lambda^2}\right]^{1/2}. \qquad (6\text{–}26)$$

Thus the ratio of output amplitude to input amplitude depends only on the ratios ω/λ, h/λ:

$$\frac{A_o}{A_i} = \frac{1}{k} = \frac{1}{[(1 - \nu^2)^2 + 4\eta^2\nu^2]^{1/2}} \qquad (\nu = \omega/\lambda), \ (\eta = h/\lambda). \quad (6\text{–}27)$$

When $h = 0$, the solutions of the homogeneous equation are the undamped oscillations $c_1 \cos \lambda t + c_2 \sin \lambda t$. Hence λ is the frequency of the natural

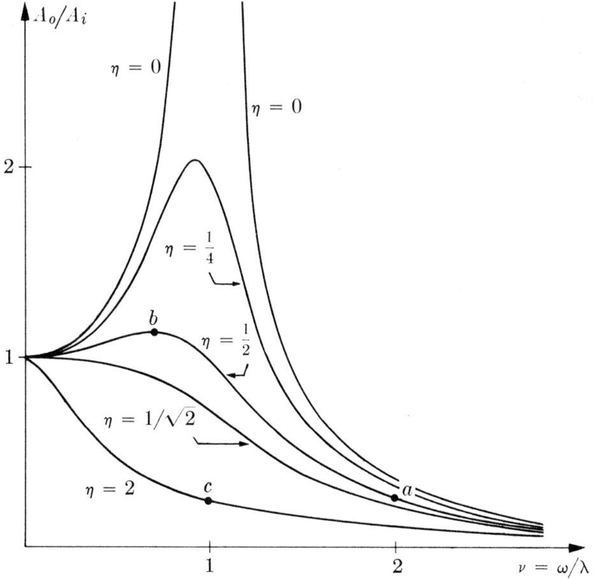

FIG. 6–11. Amplification for second order system.

undamped oscillations and $\nu = \omega/\lambda$ is the ratio of the frequency of the input to the frequency λ. The quantity η can be considered as a measure of the amount of damping, for fixed λ. The ratio A_o/A_i is called the *amplification factor* or simply the amplification. As we shall see, A_o/A_i can be both less than 1 and greater than 1.

To study the dependence of amplification on applied frequency and damping, we graph A_o/A_i against ν for different choices of η. The result is the family of curves shown in Fig. 6–11. The verification of this graph is left as an exercise (Prob. 2 below).

The borderline case $\eta = 0$ (that is, $h = 0$) is also shown. In this case, the amplification rises from 1 to ∞ as ν goes from 0 to 1. When $\nu = 1$, $\omega = \lambda$, and we are then considering the equation

$$(a_0D^2 + 1)x = A_i \sin \lambda t, \tag{6–28}$$

where $a_0 = 1/\lambda^2$. The output is no longer sinusoidal, but is given by

$$x = -A_i\frac{\lambda}{2}t\cos\lambda t + c_1\cos\lambda t + c_2\sin\lambda t.$$

The particular solution has a factor t, which leads to an oscillation of increasing amplitude, as shown in Fig. 6–12. The addition of the complementary function distorts this steady increase, but cannot prevent $|x|$ from rising to arbitrarily large values for large t. This phenomenon of excitation of large oscillations by matching of input and natural frequencies is known as *resonance*.

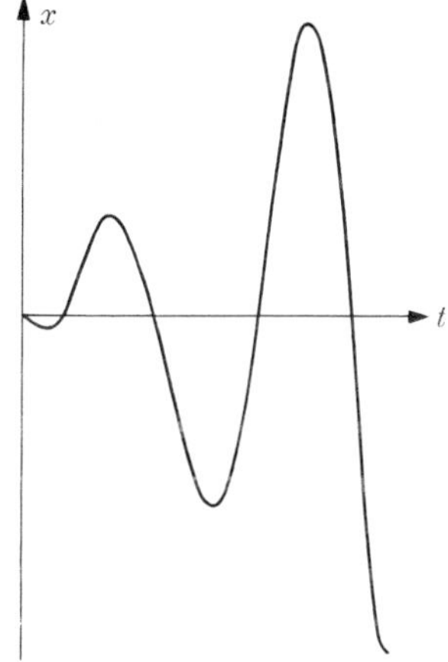

FIG. 6–12. Resonance.

When damping is present, so that h and η are positive, the complication disappears. The output is always sinusoidal (plus transient) and the output amplitude simply rises to a maximum and then falls as ν increases or, for large η, simply decreases steadily to 0 as ν increases. The maximum occurs for $0 < \eta < \sqrt{2}/2$, that is, for h between 0 and $\lambda/\sqrt{2}$; at each maximum point, $\nu = \sqrt{1 - 2\eta^2}$ and $A_o/A_i = (2\eta\sqrt{1 - \eta^2})^{-1}$ (Prob. 2 below). We term the value of ω at the maximum the *resonant frequency in presence of damping*. As the term suggests, the maximum is regarded as a form of resonance, even though for the corresponding solution $x(t)$ the amplitude does not increase as t increases.

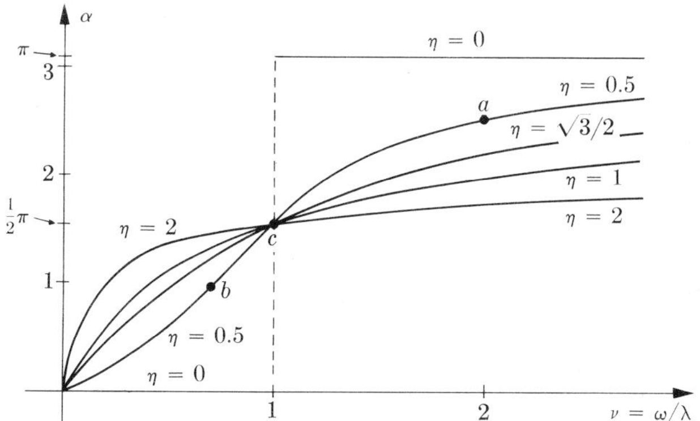

FIG. 6–13. Phase lag for second order system.

The dependence of phase lag α on η and ν can be analyzed similarly. From (6–25) and (6–27),

$$\begin{aligned} \alpha &= \tan^{-1} \frac{a_1 \omega}{1 - a_0 \omega^2} \\ &= \tan^{-1} \frac{2h\omega}{\lambda^2 - \omega^2} = \tan^{-1} \frac{2\eta\nu}{1 - \nu^2}. \end{aligned} \tag{6–29}$$

In Fig. 6–13 the angle α is graphed against ν for various values of η (Prob. 3 below). We see that for fixed η, α is increased if ν is increased.

Figure 6–14 shows graphs of input and output for three cases, corresponding to the points labeled a, b, c on Figs. 6–11 and 6–13.

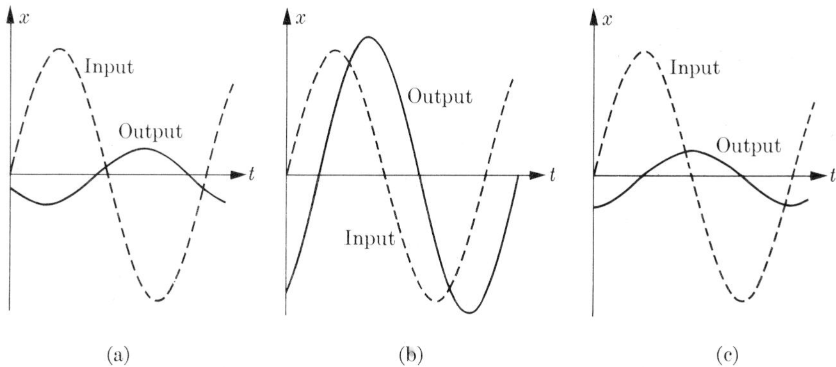

FIG. 6–14. Typical response to sinusoidal inputs.

PROBLEMS

1. For each of the following equations find ω, h, λ, ν, η and read the approximate values of amplification and phase lag from the graphs of Figs. 6–11 and 6–13:
(a) $(\frac{1}{9}D^2 + \frac{2}{9}D + 1)x = \sin 2t$, (b) $(4D^2 + 6D + 1)x = \sin t$,
(c) $(D^2 + 5D + 9)x = \sin 3t$.

2. To obtain the basic features of the graphs of Fig. 6–11, let $u = [(1 - \nu^2)^2 + 4\eta^2\nu^2]^{-1/2} = A_o/A_i$ and consider u as a function of ν for fixed η, ($\nu > 0$, $\eta > 0$).
(a) Show that as $\nu \to 0$, $u \to 1$. (b) Show that as $\nu \to +\infty$, $u \to 0$.
(c) Show that for $\eta \geqq \sqrt{2}/2$, $du/d\nu$ is always negative.
(d) Show that for $\eta < \sqrt{2}/2$, $du/d\nu$ is positive for $0 < \nu < \sqrt{1 - 2\eta^2}$ and negative for $\nu > \sqrt{1 - 2\eta^2}$, so that u has a maximum at $\nu = \sqrt{1 - 2\eta^2}$ and at the maximum, $u = (2\eta\sqrt{1 - \eta^2})^{-1}$.
(e) Show that for fixed ν, u decreases as η increases; as $\eta \to +\infty$, $u \to 0$; as $\eta \to 0$, $u \to |1 - \nu^2|^{-1}$.

3. To obtain the basic features of the graphs of Fig. 6–13, consider $\alpha = \tan^{-1}[2\eta\nu/(1 - \nu^2)]$ as a function of ν for fixed η, ($0 < \alpha < \pi$, $0 < \eta$, $0 < \nu$).
(a) Show that $\alpha(1) = \pi/2$.

(b) Show that $\dfrac{d\alpha}{d\nu} = \dfrac{2\eta(1 + \nu^2)}{(1 - \nu^2)^2 + 4\eta^2\nu^2}$.

(c) Show that $\dfrac{d^2\alpha}{d\nu^2} = \dfrac{-4\eta\nu(\nu^4 + 2\nu^2 + 4\eta^2 - 3)}{[(1 - \nu^2)^2 + 4\eta^2\nu^2]^2}$.

(d) Show that α increases as ν increases, that as $\nu \to 0$, $\alpha \to 0$, and as $\nu \to +\infty$, $\alpha \to \pi$.
(e) Show that for $\eta^2 \geqq \frac{3}{4}$ the graph of $\alpha(\nu)$ is concave down for all ν, but for $0 < \eta^2 < \frac{3}{4}$ the graph is concave up for $\nu < c_\eta$ and concave down for $\nu > c_\eta$, where $c_\eta = [-1 + 2(1 - \eta^2)^{1/2}]^{1/2}$, so that there is an inflection point at $u = c_\eta$.
(f) Show that for fixed ν, ($0 < \nu < 1$), α increases as η increases, and $\alpha \to 0$ as $\eta \to 0$, $\alpha \to \pi/2$ as $\eta \to +\infty$; show that for fixed ν, ($\nu > 1$), α decreases as η increases, and $\alpha \to \pi$ as $\eta \to 0$, $\alpha \to \pi/2$ as $\eta \to +\infty$.

ANSWERS

1. (a) $\omega = 2$, $h = 1$, $\lambda = 3$, $\nu = \frac{2}{3}$, $\eta = \frac{1}{3}$, $A_o/A_i = 1.4$, $\alpha = 0.67$; (b) $\omega = 1$, $h = \frac{3}{4}$, $\lambda = \frac{1}{2}$, $\nu = 2$, $\eta = \frac{3}{2}$, $A_o/A_i = 0.15$, $\alpha = 2.03$; (c) $\omega = 3$, $h = \frac{5}{2}$, $\lambda = 3$, $\nu = 1$, $\eta = \frac{5}{6}$, $A_o/A_i = \frac{3}{5}$, $\alpha = \pi/2$.

6–7 Applications of linear differential equations in mechanics. Here and in the following sections we shall give some examples of physical applications of linear differential equations.

A. *Forced vibrations of a spring-mass system.* A mass m is free to move along a line and is subject to a spring force $-k^2x$, a frictional force $-bv$

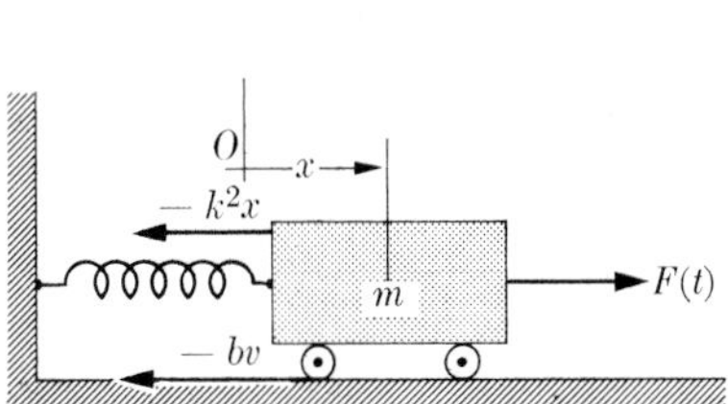

FIG. 6–15. Spring-mass system.

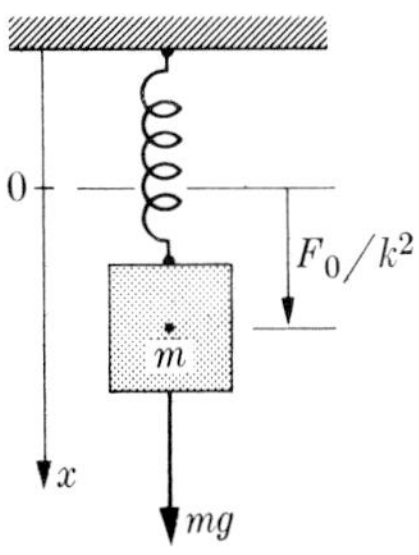

FIG. 6–16. Vertical spring-mass system.

(where $v = dx/dt$), and an external force $F(t)$, as shown in Fig. 6–15. The coordinate x measures the displacement of the mass from its equilibrium position under the spring force. Newton's second law gives the equation

$$m\frac{d^2x}{dt^2} = -k^2x - b\frac{dx}{dt} + F(t)$$

or

$$(mD^2 + bD + k^2)x = F(t). \tag{6–30}$$

We assume m, b, and k^2 to be positive constants. Accordingly, Eq. (6–30) is a linear differential equation of second order, to which the discussions of Sections 6–5 and 6–6 are applicable. The *input* is $F(t)/k^2$, and

$$h = \frac{1}{2}\frac{b}{m}, \qquad \lambda^2 = \frac{k^2}{m}, \qquad \eta = \frac{1}{2}\frac{b}{k\sqrt{m}}. \tag{6–31}$$

If, in particular, $h < \lambda$ and $F(t) = 0$, then the motions are the damped oscillations of Fig. 6–2; in the limiting case $h = 0$, the oscillations are purely sinusoidal and the mass moves in *simple harmonic motion*.

If $F(t)$ is constant, $F(t) \equiv F_0$, then the input is F_0/k^2 and the output is F_0/k^2 plus a transient. This is illustrated by the oscillations of a vertical spring (Fig. 6–16), in which the applied force F_0 is mg, the force of gravity. The constant force simply displaces the equilibrium point about which the oscillations take place.

If $F(t)$ is sinusoidal, ($F = B \sin \omega t$), then the input is $A_i \sin \omega t$, where $A_i = B/k^2$, and the output is $A_o \sin(\omega t - \alpha)$ plus a transient, as in Section 6–6. Here the oscillations of the mass are forced; such motions can be achieved physically in a variety of ways: for example, by forcing the wall to which the spring is attached (Fig. 6–15) to oscillate sinusoidally. If η is very small and ω/λ is properly chosen, the output amplitude can be very large; that is, we can achieve *resonance*, a very common phenomenon which is often called *sympathetic vibration.*

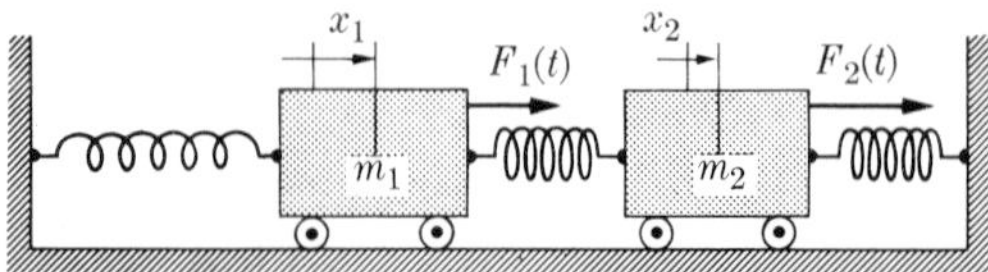

FIG. 6–17. Coupled springs.

B. *Coupled springs.* Equations of order higher than two arise in mechanics most often by elimination in a system of simultaneous second order equations. Consider the case of oscillations of two masses coupled by springs, as in Fig. 6–17. We assume that all three springs have natural length L and spring constant k^2. We let x_1, x_2 measure the displacements of m_1, m_2 from their equilibrium positions, at which the springs all have length L_1. The mass m_1 is subject to a spring force $-k^2(L_1 + x_1 - L)$ to the left and a spring force $+k^2(L_1 + x_2 - x_1 - L)$ to the right; we also assume a frictional force $-b_1\, dx_1/dt$ and an applied force $F_1(t)$. A similar analysis applies to m_2, and we obtain the differential equations

$$m_1 \frac{d^2x_1}{dt^2} = -k^2(L_1 + x_1 - L) + k^2(L_1 + x_2 - x_1 - L) - b_1 \frac{dx_1}{dt} + F_1(t),$$

$$m_2 \frac{d^2x_2}{dt^2} = -k^2(L_1 + x_2 - x_1 - L) + k^2(L_1 - x_2 - L) - b_2 \frac{dx_2}{dt} + F_2(t),$$

which can be written

$$\begin{aligned}(m_1D^2 + b_1D + 2k^2)x_1 - k^2x_2 &= F_1(t),\\ (m_2D^2 + b_2D + 2k^2)x_2 - k^2x_1 &= F_2(t).\end{aligned} \tag{6–32}$$

Hence we have a system of two simultaneous second order differential equations.

We now obtain a single equation for x_1 by solving the first equation for x_2 and substituting in the second equation:

$$x_2 = (1/k^2)[(m_1D^2 + b_1D + 2k^2)x_1 - F_1(t)], \tag{6–33}$$

$$(1/k^2)(m_2D^2 + b_2D + 2k^2)[(m_1D^2 + b_1D + 2k^2)x_1 - F_1(t)] - k^2x_1 = F_2(t). \tag{6–34}$$

We thus obtain a fourth order equation for x_1:

$$(a_0D^4 + a_1D^3 + a_2D^2 + a_3D + a_4)x_1 = F(t), \qquad (6\text{–}35)$$

$$a_0 = m_1m_2, \qquad a_1 = m_1b_2 + m_2b_1,$$
$$a_2 = b_1b_2 + 2k^2(m_1 + m_2), \qquad a_3 = 2k^2(b_1 + b_2), \qquad a_4 = 3k^4, \qquad (6\text{–}36)$$
$$F(t) = (m_2D^2 + b_2D + 2k^2)F_1(t) + k^2F_2(t).$$

When $x_1(t)$ has been found from (6–35), then $x_2(t)$ can be obtained from (6–33).

It can be proved that (6–35) is always stable; we verify this for the case where $m_1 = m_2$ and $b_1 = b_2$. Then (6–34) can be written

$$[(m_1D^2 + b_1D + 2k^2)^2 - k^4]x_1 = F(t).$$

Hence the characteristic equation is

$$(m_1r^2 + b_1r + 2k^2)^2 - k^4 = 0$$

or

$$(m_1r^2 + b_1r + 3k^2)(m_1r^2 + b_1r + k^2) = 0. \qquad (6\text{–}37)$$

Since m_1, b_1, and k^2 are assumed to be positive, the characteristic roots must have negative real parts.

Equation (6–35) is, then, stable, and we can discuss the relationship between inputs and outputs as in Sections 6–5, 6–6. In particular, if $F_1(t) = B \sin \omega t$ and $F_2(t) \equiv 0$, then $x_1(t)$ will follow a sinusoidal oscillation $A_o \sin \omega(t - \alpha)$, and a similar expression is obtained for $x_2(t)$.

C. *Simple pendulum.* For a simple pendulum (Fig. 6–18) we measure the position of the swinging arm by an angular coordinate θ. The angular component of acceleration is then $Ld^2\theta/dt^2$, and the component of gravitational force in the same direction is $-mg \sin \theta$. If we ignore other forces, we obtain the differential equation

$$mL \frac{d^2\theta}{dt^2} = -mg \sin \theta. \qquad (6\text{–}38)$$

This equation is nonlinear but can be reduced to a first order equation and solved explicitly (Prob. 4 following Section 3–4). Here we are considering *small oscillations* of the pendulum, that is, motions in which θ remains small. Thus we can make the approximation $\sin \theta = \theta$ and replace (6–38) by the linear equation

$$mL \frac{d^2\theta}{dt^2} + mg\theta = 0. \qquad (6\text{–}39)$$

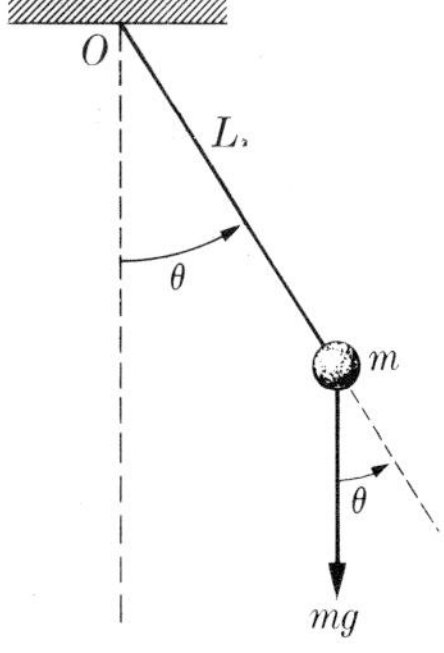

FIG. 6–18. Simple pendulum.

Here $h = 0$ and $\lambda^2 = g/L$, so that the solutions are sinusoidal:

$$\theta = c_1 \cos \lambda t + c_2 \sin \lambda t, \tag{6–40}$$

and have period

$$T = \frac{2\pi}{\lambda} = 2\pi \sqrt{\frac{L}{g}}. \tag{6–41}$$

If we add frictional and driving forces, we obtain the same type of equation as for the forced vibrations of a spring-mass system.

6–8 Applications in elasticity. The problems of elasticity lead, in general, to fourth order *partial* differential equations. In special circumstances these equations can be replaced by ordinary differential equations, as the following examples illustrate.

A. *Beam on elastic foundation.* Consider a beam whose axis is the x-axis and subject to deflections y in the y-direction (Fig. 6–19). We assume the beam to be subject to a load $F(x)$ (force per unit length) and to rest on an elastic foundation which exerts spring-type restoring forces proportional to deflection; the restoring force per unit length is $-k^2y$. In the theory of elasticity it is shown that when the beam is in equilibrium, the deflection $y(x)$ satisfies the differential equation

$$EI \frac{d^4y}{dx^4} + k^2y = F(x), \tag{6–42}$$

where E is a constant, *Young's modulus*, and I is the moment of inertia about the x-axis of a cross section of the beam perpendicular to that axis. We assume I also to be constant.

Although Eq. (6–42) suggests the input-output interpretation, there is a basic difference between this equation and those previously discussed. Here particular solutions are specified not by initial conditions but by boundary conditions. For example, if the beam is clamped at two points x_1, x_2, then at these points $y = dy/dx = 0$.

For derivation of Eq. (6–42) and discussion of its applications, the reader is referred to pp. 267–273 of Reference 9 at the end of this chapter.

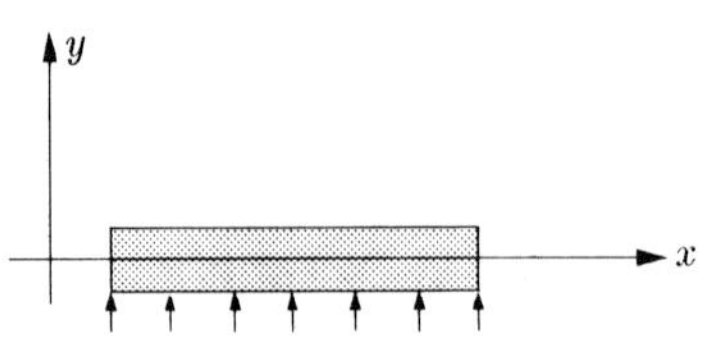

FIG. 6–19. Beam on elastic foundation.

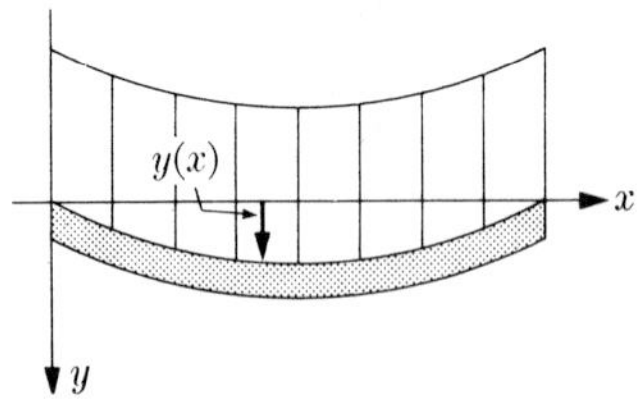

FIG. 6–20. Suspension bridge.

B. *The suspension bridge* can be considered as a beam partly supported by a cable (Fig. 6–20). Under various simplifying assumptions the following differential equation is obtained:

$$EI\frac{d^4y}{dx^4} - (H + h)\frac{d^2y}{dx^2} = F(x) - G(x)\frac{h}{H} \tag{6–43}$$

(see pp. 277–279 of Reference 9). In Eq. (6–43) H is the horizontal tension in the cable due to dead weight, h is the extra tension caused by addition of a live load $F(x)$, and $G(x)$ is the dead load of the system. The constants E, I, H are considered known, whereas h must be chosen to satisfy an auxiliary condition. If the cable is considered to be inextensible, the auxiliary condition takes the form

$$\int_0^L G(x)y(x)\,dx = 0. \tag{6–44}$$

In addition, boundary conditions must be imposed at the ends of the beam.

PROBLEMS

1. A 50-gm mass can stretch a spring 2 cm under its own weight. With what frequency will the spring oscillate when supporting the weight (ignore friction)?

2. If the spring-mass system of Prob. 1 is oscillating with an amplitude of 4 cm, find the maximum velocity.

3. In a frictionless spring-mass system the mass is 100 gm and the natural frequency is 2 rad/sec. The system is at rest at time $t = 0$ and a force $500 \cos 2t$ dynes (t in sec) is applied. For what value of t will the displacement first equal 1 cm?

4. In a system of coupled masses (Fig. 6–17) neglect friction and assume no outside forces are applied.

(a) Show that the characteristic roots of Eq. (6–35) are pure imaginary. [*Hint:* Show that the roots satisfy the condition

$$r^2 = \frac{k^2}{m_1m_2}\left(-(m_1 + m_2) \pm \sqrt{(m_1 - m_2)^2 + m_1m_2}\right)$$

and that the quantity on the right is negative.]

(b) Let $\pm\lambda_1 i$, $\pm\lambda_2 i$ be the characteristic roots obtained in part (a). Let $x_1 = \sin \lambda_1 t$ and find x_2. Describe the resulting motion.

5. The motion of a particle in the xy-plane under the influence of a central force *proportional to distance* leads to the differential equations

$$m\frac{d^2x}{dt^2} = -k^2x, \qquad m\frac{d^2y}{dt^2} = -k^2y.$$

Show that (except for certain degenerate cases) the particle moves in an ellipse with center at the origin.

6. Find the deflection of a beam on an elastic foundation, clamped at $x = -L$ and $x = L$ and subject to a load $F(x) = F_0 \cos(\pi x/L)$.

ANSWERS

1. 22.1 rad/sec. 2. 88.5 cm/sec. 3. 0.8 sec. 4. (b) $x_2 = \text{const} \times \sin \lambda_1 t$, so that the two masses oscillate either in phase or in opposite phase. It can be shown that for λ_1 one case arises and for λ_2 the other arises. (See Section 7–11.)

6. $y = [A/(ab + cd)]$
$\times [(ab + cd) \cos \alpha x + (ad + bc) \cosh \delta x \cos \delta x + (bc - ad) \sinh \delta x \sin \delta x],$

where $A = F_0/[EI(\beta^4 + \alpha^4)]$, $\beta = (k^2/EI)^{1/4}$, $\alpha = \pi/L$, $\delta = \beta/\sqrt{2}$, $a = \sinh \epsilon$, $b = \cosh \epsilon$, $c = \sin \epsilon$, $d = \cos \epsilon$, $\epsilon = \delta L = \beta L/\sqrt{2}$.

6–9 Applications to electric circuits. We consider a simple L-R-C circuit; that is, a circuit containing an inductance L (measured in henries), resistance R (ohms), capacitance C (farads), and a driving electromotive force $\mathcal{E}$ (volts). See Fig. 6–21. The current I is measured in amperes, the charge q on the capacitor in coulombs, and $\mathcal{E}$, q, and I are all considered to be functions of time t (sec).

The differential equation which governs the circuit is based on *Kirchhoff's law:* the total potential drop around a closed circuit is zero. The drop across the inductor is $L(dI/dt)$, across the resistor is RI, across the capacitor is q/C, across the driving emf is $-\mathcal{E}$; all potential drops are measured in volts, and with respect to the direction in which I is measured positively. The equation obtained is the following:

$$L\frac{dI}{dt} + RI + \frac{q}{C} = \mathcal{E}. \qquad (6\text{–}45)$$

In addition, the current I is equal to the rate of change of q:

$$\frac{dq}{dt} = I. \qquad (6\text{–}46)$$

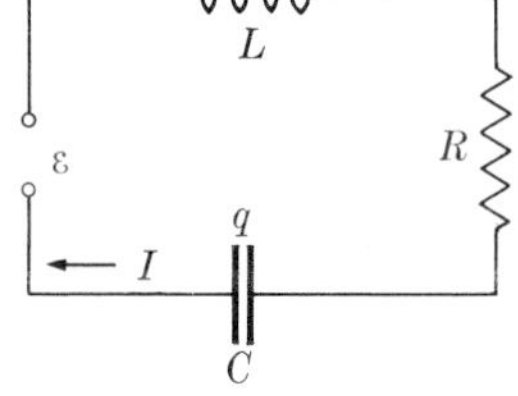

FIG. 6–21. L-R-C circuit.

The coefficients L, R, C are all assumed to be positive constants. We can eliminate q by differentiating (6–45) and using (6–46):

$$L\frac{d^2I}{dt^2} + R\frac{dI}{dt} + \frac{I}{C} = \frac{d\mathcal{E}}{dt}. \qquad (6\text{–}47)$$

We can also substitute $I = dq/dt$ in (6–45) to obtain a differential equation for q:

$$L\frac{d^2q}{dt^2} + R\frac{dq}{dt} + \frac{q}{C} = \mathcal{E}. \qquad (6\text{–}48)$$

Either (6–47) or (6–48) can be taken as the basic differential equation of the circuit.

Most commonly, initial conditions are given in the form of values of q and I at time t_0; by virtue of (6–46) this is the same as giving initial values of q and dq/dt; by (6–45) we can also find the initial value of dI/dt from the given values of q and I and knowledge of $\mathcal{E}$ as a function of t.

Equations (6–47) and (6–48) are of the form of second order equations with variable input, and hence the results of Sections 6–4 through 6–6 are applicable. Since all coefficients are positive, the equations are stable, and for both equations,

$$h = \frac{R}{2L}, \qquad \lambda^2 = \frac{1}{CL}, \qquad \eta = \frac{h}{\lambda} = \frac{R}{2}\sqrt{\frac{C}{L}} = \sqrt{\frac{CR^2}{4L}}. \tag{6–49}$$

Accordingly, the transients are

$$\begin{array}{llll} \text{damped oscillations when} & \eta < 1 & \text{or} & CR^2 < 4L, \\ \text{critically damped when} & \eta = 1 & \text{or} & CR^2 = 4L, \\ \text{overcritically damped when} & \eta > 1 & \text{or} & CR^2 > 4L. \end{array}$$

If the emf $\mathcal{E}$ is constant and the capacitor is removed ($1/C$ replaced by 0), then Eq. (6–45) has the steady-state solution

$$I = \mathcal{E}/R \qquad \text{(Ohm's law)}. \tag{6–50}$$

When the capacitor is reinserted, we use Eq. (6–48); in the steady state, $q = C\mathcal{E} = \text{const}$ and $I = dq/dt = 0$; the driving emf is simply balanced by a corresponding drop in potential across the capacitor.

If the emf $\mathcal{E}$ equals kt (ramp input), then we apply Eq. (6–48). In the notation of Section 6–5 the input is kCt and $a_1 = CR$. Hence the steady-state output q is $kC(t - CR)$, while the steady-state current I is $dq/dt = kC$.

If $\mathcal{E} = \mathcal{E}_0 \sin \omega t$, then we apply the results of Section 6–6. The input in Eq. (6–48) is $\mathcal{E}_0 C \sin \omega t$ and the steady-state output is $q = A_o \sin(\omega t - \alpha)$, where

$$\frac{A_o}{A_i} = \frac{A_o}{\mathcal{E}_0 C} = \frac{1}{[(1 - \nu^2)^2 + 4\eta^2\nu^2]^{1/2}}, \qquad \alpha = \tan^{-1}\frac{2\eta\nu}{1 - \nu^2}, \qquad \nu = \frac{\omega}{\lambda} = \omega\sqrt{CL}. \tag{6–51}$$

The steady-state current is

$$I = \frac{dq}{dt} = \omega A_o \cos(\omega t - \alpha) = \omega A_o \sin\left(\omega t - \alpha + \frac{\pi}{2}\right). \tag{6–52}$$

From (6–51) and (6–49)

$$\omega A_o = \frac{\omega \mathcal{E}_0 C}{[(1 - \omega^2 CL)^2 + R^2 C^2 \omega^2]^{1/2}} \tag{6–53}$$

$$= \frac{\mathcal{E}_0}{[\{(\omega C)^{-1} - L\omega\}^2 + R^2]^{1/2}}.$$

The quantity

$$Z = \left[\left(\frac{1}{\omega C} - L\omega\right)^2 + R^2\right]^{1/2} \tag{6–54}$$

is known as the *impedance*. From Eqs. (6–52) through (6–54)

$$I = \frac{\mathcal{E}_0}{Z} \sin\left(\omega t - \alpha + \frac{\pi}{2}\right). \tag{6–55}$$

Thus the oscillatory emf of amplitude $\mathcal{E}_0$ leads to an oscillatory current of amplitude $\mathcal{E}_0/Z$. This can be regarded as a generalization of Ohm's law (Eq. 6–50), with the impedance Z replacing the resistance R. The current also lags the emf in phase; the lag is

$$\beta = \alpha - \frac{\pi}{2} = \tan^{-1}\frac{2\eta\nu}{1 - \nu^2} - \frac{\pi}{2} = \tan^{-1}\frac{\nu^2 - 1}{2\eta\nu}.$$

Since $0 < \alpha < \pi$, β lies between $-\pi/2$ and $\pi/2$; in particular, β can be zero (current and emf *in phase*) and negative (current *leading* the emf). From Eqs. (6–49) and (6–51) we can write

$$\beta = \tan^{-1}\frac{\omega^2 CL - 1}{RC\omega} = \tan^{-1}\frac{L\omega - (C\omega)^{-1}}{R}. \tag{6–56}$$

The fact that the spring-mass system of Section 6–7 and the *L-R-C* circuit are governed by the same type of second order differential equation enables us to study one problem by means of the other. For example, the behavior of a given spring-mass system can be studied experimentally by designing an analogous electric circuit. The principle involved here has been generalized widely in the form of the electronic analog computer, which is a very flexible electric system capable of imitating a wide variety of physical systems.

PROBLEMS

1. In the *L-R-C* circuit of Fig. 6–21 let $L = 10$ henries, $R = 100$ ohms, $C = (500)^{-1}$ farad, $\mathcal{E} = 1$ volt (const). If $I = 0$ and $q = 0$ for $t = 0$, find (a) I and q as functions of t, (b) the maximum values of I and q for $t > 0$.

2. In Prob. 1 we can consider the circuit to be functioning for all t, with $\mathcal{E} = 0$ for $t < 0$ and $\mathcal{E} = 1$ for $t \geqq 0$, so that $\mathcal{E}$ has a jump discontinuity at $t = 0$. Equation (6–47) is then meaningless, since $d\mathcal{E}/dt = 0$ for $t < 0$ and $t > 0$, but $d\mathcal{E}/dt = \infty$ for $t = 0$. However, Eq. (6–48) can be solved for q, with initial values $q = 0$ and $dq/dt = 0$ for $t = 0$: $q = 0$ for $t < 0$ and $q = [1 - e^{-5t}(\cos 5t + \sin 5t)]/500$ for $t \geqq 0$ (as in Prob. 1). Show that $dq/dt = I$ is well defined and continuous, even at $t = 0$, that $d^2q/dt^2 = dI/dt$ has a jump discontinuity at $t = 0$, and that $d^3q/dt^3 = d^2I/dt^2 = \infty$ at $t = 0$. (The function $I(t)$ can be interpreted as a solution of Eq. (6–47) in which the right member is $\delta(t)$, the *Dirac delta function* or *unit impulse function.*)

3. In the L-R-C circuit of Fig. 6–21 let $\mathcal{E} = \mathcal{E}_0 e^{i\omega t}$. (a) Obtain the steady-state current in the form $I_0 e^{i(\omega t - \beta)}$. The ratio $\mathcal{E}/I = Z = (\mathcal{E}_0/I_0)e^{i\beta}$ is known as the *complex impedance.* (b) Show that the impedance of Eq. (6–54) is the absolute value of the complex impedance, $|x + iy| = (x^2 + y^2)^{1/2}$.

ANSWERS

1. (a) $q = [1 - e^{-5t}(\cos 5t + \sin 5t)]/500$, $I = (e^{-5t} \sin 5t)/50$; (b) max q is 2.08×10^{-3} coulomb, max I is 6.5×10^{-3} amp.

3. (a) $I = \mathcal{E}_0 e^{i\omega t}/\{R + [L\omega - (C\omega)^{-1}]i\} = I_0 e^{i(\omega t - \beta)}$, $I_0 = \mathcal{E}_0 \div \{R^2 + [L\omega - (C\omega)^{-1}]^2\}^{1/2}$, β = polar angle of $Z = R + [L\omega - (C\omega)^{-1}]i$.

SUGGESTED REFERENCES

1. ANDRONOW, A., and CHAIKIN, C. E., *Theory of Oscillations.* Princeton, N. J.: Princeton University Press, 1949.

2. BELLMAN, RICHARD, *Stability Theory of Differential Equations.* New York: McGraw-Hill, 1953.

3. CODDINGTON, EARL A., and LEVINSON, NORMAN, *Theory of Ordinary Differential Equations.* New York: McGraw-Hill, 1955.

4. DRAPER, CHARLES S., MCKAY, WALTER, and LEES, SIDNEY, *Instrument Engineering*, Vol. 2. New York: McGraw-Hill, 1953.

5. GUILLEMIN, E. A., *Mathematics of Circuit Analysis.* New York: John Wiley and Sons, Inc., 1949.

6. KAPLAN, WILFRED, *Operational Methods for Linear Systems.* Reading, Mass.: Addison-Wesley, 1962.

7. KAPLAN, WILFRED, "Stability Theory," *Proceedings of the Symposium on Non-linear Circuit Analysis*, Vol. VI, pp. 3–21. New York: Polytechnic Institute of Brooklyn, 1957.

8. LAWDEN, DEREK F., *Mathematics of Engineering Systems.* New York: John Wiley and Sons, Inc., 1954.

9. VON KÁRMÁN, T., and BIOT, M. A., *Mathematical Methods in Engineering.* New York: McGraw-Hill, 1940.

CHAPTER 7

SIMULTANEOUS LINEAR DIFFERENTIAL EQUATIONS

7–1 General principles. In this chapter we consider systems of n first order linear differential equations in n unknowns. First we consider them in a special *basic form*, which we illustrate for $n = 2$:

$$\begin{aligned} \frac{dx}{dt} &= a_1x + b_1y + f_1(t), \\ \frac{dy}{dt} &= a_2x + b_2y + f_2(t); \end{aligned} \tag{7–1}$$

and for $n = 3$:

$$\begin{aligned} \frac{dx}{dt} &= a_1x + b_1y + c_1z + f_1(t), \\ \frac{dy}{dt} &= a_2x + b_2y + c_2z + f_2(t), \\ \frac{dz}{dt} &= a_3x + b_3y + c_3z + f_3(t). \end{aligned} \tag{7–2}$$

For n equations the unknowns can be denoted by $x_1, \ldots, x_n$, and the equations have the form

$$\frac{dx_i}{dt} = a_{i1}x_1 + \cdots + a_{in}x_n + f_i(t) \qquad (i = 1, \ldots, n). \tag{7–3}$$

More general systems can also be reduced to this form.

The coefficients $a_1, b_1, \ldots, a_{i1}, \ldots a_{in}$ may depend on t, but for most of this chapter they will be *constant.*

Systems of equations are discussed in Section 1–7. Let us recall the basic facts as they relate to the systems (7–1), (7–2), or (7–3). A *solution* of (7–1) is a *pair* of functions $x(t)$, $y(t)$ which together satisfy the equations identically over some interval; if the coefficients a_1, b_1, a_2, b_2 and the functions $f_1(t)$, $f_2(t)$ are continuous over an interval $t_1 < t < t_2$, then there is a unique solution $x(t)$, $y(t)$ with prescribed initial values $x(t_0) = x_0$, $y(t_0) = y_0$ at $t = t_0$, where $t_1 < t_0 < t_2$. Similarly, a solution of (7–2) is a *triple* of functions $x(t)$, $y(t)$, $z(t)$ which satisfy the equations, and a solution of (7–3) is an n-tuple of functions $x_1(t), \ldots, x_n(t)$ which satisfy the equations; when the coefficients and the $f_i(t)$ are continuous, a unique solution satisfying prescribed initial conditions exists.

For the remainder of this section we assume that $n = 3$, and hence consider only the equations (7–2); the extension of the results to general values of n will be evident.

If the functions $f_1(t), f_2(t), f_3(t)$ are identically 0, the equations (7–2) are termed *homogeneous;* otherwise they are *nonhomogeneous.* If the equations

(7–2) are nonhomogeneous, we can replace the $f_i(t)$ by 0 and obtain the *related homogeneous system*

$$\frac{dx}{dt} = a_1x + b_1y + c_1z,$$
$$\frac{dy}{dt} = a_2x + b_2y + c_2z, \tag{7-4}$$
$$\frac{dz}{dt} = a_3x + b_3y + c_3z.$$

A set of k solutions of (7–4) is said to be *linearly independent* over an interval if no linear combination of the solutions, with coefficients not all 0, is identically 0 over the interval. We can denote the k solutions (which form k *triples*) by the following: $x_1(t)$, $y_1(t)$, $z_1(t)$; $x_2(t)$, $y_2(t)$, $z_2(t)$; . . . ; $x_k(t)$, $y_k(t)$, $z_k(t)$. The linear combination is then itself a triple: $C_1x_1(t) + C_2x_2(t) + \cdots + C_kx_k(t)$, $C_1y_1 + \cdots + C_ky_k$, $C_1z_1 + \cdots + C_kz_k$. Linear independence of the solutions is equivalent to the condition: if

$$C_1x_1(t) + \cdots + C_kx_k(t) \equiv 0,$$
$$C_1y_1(t) + \cdots + C_ky_k(t) \equiv 0, \tag{7-5}$$
$$C_1z_1(t) + \cdots + C_kz_k(t) \equiv 0$$

over the given interval, then $C_1 = 0, C_2 = 0, \ldots, C_k = 0$.

The fact that the triples are solutions of (7–4) is not essential to the above definitions; it applies equally well to any set of k triples. However, if the triples are solutions of (7–4), then each linear combination

$$x(t) = C_1x_1(t) + \cdots + C_kx_k(t), \qquad y(t) = C_1y_1(t) + \cdots,$$
$$z(t) = C_1z_1(t) + \cdots \tag{7-6}$$

forms a new triple which is itself a solution of (7–4). For example, since

$$\frac{dx_i}{dt} = a_1x_i + b_1y_i + c_1z_i$$

for $i = 1, \ldots, k$, we conclude from (7–6) that

$$\begin{aligned}\frac{dx}{dt} &= C_1\frac{dx_1}{dt} + \cdots + C_k\frac{dx_k}{dt}\\ &= C_1(a_1x_1 + b_1y_1 + c_1z_1) + \cdots + C_k(a_1x_k + b_1y_k + c_1z_k)\\ &= a_1(C_1x_1 + \cdots + C_kx_k) + b_1(C_1y_1 + \cdots) + c_1(C_1z_1 + \cdots)\\ &= a_1x + b_1y + c_1z.\end{aligned}$$

Similarly, the other two equations are satisfied.

Let us suppose we have found *three* linearly independent solutions of (7–4). We then see that the corresponding linear combinations

$$\begin{aligned} x(t) &= C_1x_1(t) + C_2x_2(t) + C_3x_3(t), \\ y(t) &= C_1y_1(t) + C_2y_2(t) + C_3y_3(t), \\ z(t) &= C_1z_1(t) + C_2z_2(t) + C_3z_3(t) \end{aligned} \tag{7–7}$$

provide the *general solution* of (7–4) over the interval for which the solutions exist. If initial values x_0, y_0, z_0 at t_0 are given, then to determine the C's, we are led to the equations

$$\begin{aligned} x_0 &= C_1x_1(t_0) + C_2x_2(t_0) + C_3x_3(t_0), \\ y_0 &= C_1y_1(t_0) + C_2y_2(t_0) + C_3y_3(t_0), \\ z_0 &= C_1z_1(t_0) + C_2z_2(t_0) + C_3z_3(t_0). \end{aligned}$$

These three equations in three unknowns C_1, C_2, C_3 can be solved for C_1, C_2, C_3, provided the determinant of coefficients is not zero. It turns out that linear independence implies that this determinant cannot be zero; hence the C's can always be chosen to satisfy initial conditions (Prob. 6 below).

We can now state a theorem that parallels the fundamental theorem of Section 4–3.

THEOREM 1. *Let the system* (7–2) *be given, with the related homogeneous system* (7–4). *Let the coefficients* $a_1(t)$, $b_1(t)$, ..., *and the functions* $f_1(t), f_2(t), f_3(t)$ *be continuous for* $t_1 < t < t_2$.

There exists a set of three linearly independent solutions of (7–4) *over the given interval. If* $x_i(t)$, $y_i(t)$, $z_i(t)$, $(i = 1, 2, 3)$, *is any such set of linearly independent solutions, then* (7–7) *provides the general solution of* (7–4) *over the interval.*

There exist solutions of the nonhomogeneous system (7–2) *over the interval. If* $x^*(t)$, $y^*(t)$, $z^*(t)$ *is one such solution, and* $x_i(t)$, $y_i(t)$, $z_i(t)$ *are chosen as above, then*

$$\begin{aligned} x &= x^*(t) + C_1x_1(t) + C_2x_2(t) + C_3x_3(t), \\ y &= y^*(t) + C_1y_1(t) + C_2y_2(t) + C_3y_3(t), \\ z &= z^*(t) + C_1z_1(t) + C_2z_2(t) + C_3z_3(t) \end{aligned} \tag{7–8}$$

is the general solution of (7–2) *over the given interval.*

The proof of this theorem is given in Chapter 12 of ODE. The following examples illustrate its applications.

EXAMPLE 1. Consider the homogeneous system

$$\frac{dx}{dt} = 4x - 9y + 5z, \qquad \frac{dy}{dt} = x - 10y + 7z, \qquad \frac{dz}{dt} = x - 17y + 12z.$$

One solution is given by

$$x_1 \equiv e^t, \qquad y_1 \equiv 2e^t, \qquad z_1 \equiv 3e^t,$$

for substitution in the differential equations yields the identities

$$e^t = 4e^t - 18e^t + 15e^t, \qquad 2e^t = e^t - 20e^t + 21e^t,$$
$$3e^t = e^t - 34e^t + 36e^t.$$

Similarly, the following triples are solutions:

$$x_2 \equiv e^{2t}, \qquad y_2 \equiv 3e^{2t}, \qquad z_2 \equiv 5e^{2t};$$
$$x_3 \equiv e^{3t}, \qquad y_3 \equiv -e^{3t}, \qquad z_3 \equiv -2e^{3t}.$$

The three triples are linearly independent for all t, for the relations (7–5) here become

$$\begin{aligned} C_1e^t + C_2e^{2t} + C_3e^{3t} &\equiv 0, \\ 2C_1e^t + 3C_2e^{2t} - C_3e^{3t} &\equiv 0, \\ 3C_1e^t + 5C_2e^{2t} - 2C_3e^{3t} &\equiv 0; \end{aligned}$$

since e^t, e^{2t}, e^{3t} are linearly independent, each relation by itself implies that $C_1 = C_2 = C_3 = 0$. Hence the general solution is given by

$$\begin{aligned} x &= C_1e^t + C_2e^{2t} + C_3e^{3t}, \\ y &= 2C_1e^t + 3C_2e^{2t} - C_3e^{3t}, \\ z &= 3C_1e^t + 5C_2e^{2t} - 2C_3e^{3t}. \end{aligned} \tag{7–9}$$

EXAMPLE 2. We now consider the nonhomogeneous system

$$\frac{dx}{dt} = 4x - 9y + 5z + 1 + 13t, \qquad \frac{dy}{dt} = x - 10y + 7z + 3 + 15t,$$
$$\frac{dz}{dt} = x - 17y + 12z + 2 + 26t.$$

The related homogeneous system is that of Example 1; hence the "complementary function" is given by the triple (7–9). We verify that a particular solution is given by the triple

$$x^* \equiv t, \qquad y^* \equiv 3t, \qquad z^* \equiv 2t.$$

Hence the general solution is given by

$$\begin{aligned} x &= C_1e^t + C_2e^{2t} + C_3e^{3t} + t, \\ y &= 2C_1e^t + 3C_2e^{2t} - C_3e^{3t} + 3t, \\ z &= 3C_1e^t + 5C_2e^{2t} - 2C_3e^{3t} + 2t. \end{aligned}$$

For equations with two unknowns such as (7–1) the general solution is constructed from *two* linearly independent solutions and depends on *two* arbitrary constants. For general n there are n constants and n linearly independent solutions. This is to be expected, since the system is of nth *order* (Section 1–7).

Methods for finding the linearly independent solutions of the homogeneous systems and for finding particular solutions of nonhomogeneous systems will be described later. As the above results indicate, there is a great similarity between the linear system of order n and the single linear equation of order n; this resemblance will continue to be evident in the methods described in the following sections.

PROBLEMS

1. (a) Verify that each of the pairs of functions $x = e^t$ and $y = e^t$, $x = 3e^{-t}$ and $y = 5e^{-t}$ is a solution of the system

$$\frac{dx}{dt} = 4x - 3y, \qquad \frac{dy}{dt} = 5x - 4y.$$

(b) Show that the two pairs of functions of part (a) are linearly independent for all t.

(c) With the aid of the results of parts (a) and (b), obtain the general solution of the system of part (a).

(d) Show that the pair $x = -\cos t - 4 \sin t$, $y = -5 \sin t$ is a solution of the system

$$\frac{dx}{dt} = 4x - 3y + 2 \sin t, \qquad \frac{dy}{dt} = 5x - 4y.$$

(e) With the aid of the results of parts (c) and (d), obtain the general solution of the system of part (d).

(f) Find a solution of the system of part (d) such that $x = 1$, $y = 0$, when $t = 0$.

2. (a) Verify that each of the triples of functions

$$x = 3, \qquad y = 1, \qquad z = 2,$$

$$x = 4 \sin t + 9 \cos t, \qquad y = \sin t + 3 \cos t, \qquad z = 2 \sin t + 7 \cos t,$$

$$x = 9 \sin t - 4 \cos t, \qquad y = 3 \sin t - \cos t, \qquad z = 7 \sin t - 2 \cos t$$

is a solution of the homogeneous system related to the system

$$\frac{dx}{dt} = -9x + 19y + 4z + 1, \qquad \frac{dy}{dt} = -3x + 7y + z,$$
$$\frac{dz}{dt} = -7x + 17y + 2z.$$

(b) Show that the three triples of functions of part (a) are linearly independent for all t.

(c) Show that the triple $x = -3t$, $y = -t$, $z = -2t - 1$ is a solution of the system of part (a), and obtain the general solution.

(d) Find a solution of the system of part (a) such that $x = 6$, $y = 2$, $z = 3$ for $t = 0$.

3. Test each of the following sets of triples of functions for linear independence:

(a) $x = t$, $y = t - 1$, $z = 3t$; $x = t + 2$, $y = 2t$, $z = 3 + t$; $x = 3t + 2$, $y = 4t - 2$, $z = 7t + 3$;

(b) $x = e^t$, $y = e^{2t}$, $z = e^{3t}$; $x = e^t$, $y = 2e^{2t}$, $z = 5e^{3t}$; $x = e^t$, $y = 5e^{2t}$, $z = 3e^{3t}$.

4. (a) Let the general solution of Eqs. (7–4) be given by Eqs. (7–7). Let $\alpha_1, \alpha_2, \alpha_3, \beta_1, \beta_2, \beta_3, \gamma_1, \gamma_2, \gamma_3$ be constants such that

$$\begin{vmatrix} \alpha_1 & \beta_1 & \gamma_1 \\ \alpha_2 & \beta_2 & \gamma_2 \\ \alpha_3 & \beta_3 & \gamma_3 \end{vmatrix} \neq 0.$$

Let functions $x_4(t), x_5(t), x_6(t), y_4(t), \ldots, z_4(t), \ldots$ be defined by the equations

$$\begin{aligned} x_{i+3}(t) &= \alpha_i x_1(t) + \beta_i x_2(t) + \gamma_i x_3(t), \\ y_{i+3}(t) &= \alpha_i y_1(t) + \beta_i y_2(t) + \gamma_i y_3(t), \\ z_{i+3}(t) &= \alpha_i z_1(t) + \beta_i z_2(t) + \gamma_i z_3(t), \end{aligned}$$

where $i = 1, 2, 3$. Show on the basis of Theorem 1 that the general solution of Eqs. (7–4) is also given by

$$\begin{aligned} x &= C_1 x_4(t) + C_2 x_5(t) + C_3 x_6(t), \\ y &= C_1 y_4(t) + C_2 y_5(t) + C_3 y_6(t), \\ z &= C_1 z_4(t) + C_2 z_5(t) + C_3 z_6(t). \end{aligned}$$

(b) Show on the basis of part (a) that the general solution of Example 1 in the text is given not only by (7–9) but also by

$$\begin{aligned} x &= C_1(e^t + e^{3t}) + C_2 e^{2t} + C_3(e^t - e^{2t}), \\ y &= C_1(2e^t - e^{3t}) + 3C_2 e^{2t} + C_3(2e^t - 3e^{2t}), \\ z &= C_1(3e^t - 2e^{3t}) + 5C_2 e^{2t} + C_3(3e^t - 5e^{2t}). \end{aligned}$$

5. Obtain for the following an equivalent system of first order equations of form (7–3):

(a) $\dfrac{d^2x}{dt^2} - 2x + y = \sin t, \qquad \dfrac{d^2y}{dt^2} - x - 2y = \cos t.$

[*Hint:* Set $x_1 = x$, $x_2 = dx/dt$, $x_3 = y$, $x_4 = dy/dt$.]

(b) $\dfrac{dx}{dt} - 2\dfrac{dy}{dt} + x - 3y = e^t, \qquad 2\dfrac{dx}{dt} + 3\dfrac{dy}{dt} - x + 4y = 2e^t.$

[*Hint:* Solve for dx/dt and dy/dt.]

6. Let the three triples $x_i(t)$, $y_i(t)$, $z_i(t)$, $(i = 1, 2, 3)$, be solutions of the system (7–2) for $t_1 < t < t_2$, and let

$$W(t) = \begin{vmatrix} x_1(t) & y_1(t) & z_1(t) \\ x_2(t) & y_2(t) & z_2(t) \\ x_3(t) & y_3(t) & z_3(t) \end{vmatrix}$$

Prove: if the triples are linearly independent for $t_1 < t < t_2$, then $W(t) \not\equiv 0$; if the triples are linearly dependent for $t_1 < t < t_2$, then $W(t) \equiv 0$. [*Hint:* Apply Theorem 1; cf. also the proof of Theorem 2 in Section 4–3.]

ANSWERS

1. (c) $x = C_1e^t + 3C_2e^{-t}$, $y = C_1e^t + 5C_2e^{-t}$; (e) $x = C_1e^t + 3C_2e^{-t} - \cos t - 4\sin t$, $y = C_1e^t + 5C_2e^{-t} - 5\sin t$; (f) $x = 5e^t - 3e^{-t} - \cos t - 4\sin t$, $y = 5e^t - 5e^{-t} - 5\sin t$.

2. (c) $x = 3C_1 + C_2(4\sin t + 9\cos t) + C_3(9\sin t - 4\cos t) - 3t$, $y = C_1 + C_2(\sin t + 3\cos t) + C_3(3\sin t - \cos t) - t$, $z = 2C_1 + C_2(2\sin t + 7\cos t) + C_3(7\sin t - 2\cos t) - 2t - 1$;
(d) $x = 6 - 3t$, $y = 2 - t$, $z = 3 - 2t$.

3. (a) dependent, (b) independent.

5. (a) $dx_1/dt = x_2$, $dx_2/dt = 2x_1 - x_3 + \sin t$, $dx_3/dt = x_4$, $dx_4/dt = x_1 + 2x_3 + \cos t$; (b) $dx/dt = (-x + y + 7e^t)/7$, $dy/dt = (3x - 10y)/7$.

7–2 Homogeneous linear systems with constant coefficients. Here we consider the typical case of a homogeneous system:

$$\begin{aligned} \frac{dx}{dt} &= a_1x + b_1y + c_1z, \\ \frac{dy}{dt} &= a_2x + b_2y + c_2z, \qquad (7\text{–}10) \\ \frac{dz}{dt} &= a_3x + b_3y + c_3z, \end{aligned}$$

and assume the coefficients to be constant. We seek particular solutions from which to construct the general solution. By analogy with the single equation of nth order, we try functions $e^{\lambda t}$, for constant λ. After experimenting, we discover that we must seek solutions of form

$$x = \alpha e^{\lambda t}, \qquad y = \beta e^{\lambda t}, \qquad z = \gamma e^{\lambda t}, \tag{7-11}$$

where α, β, γ are constants. Substitution of (7-11) in (7-10) leads to the equations

$$\begin{aligned} (a_1 - \lambda)\alpha + b_1\beta + c_1\gamma &= 0, \\ a_2\alpha + (b_2 - \lambda)\beta + c_2\gamma &= 0, \\ a_3\alpha + b_3\beta + (c_3 - \lambda)\gamma &= 0. \end{aligned} \tag{7-12}$$

These can be regarded as homogeneous linear equations for α, β, γ; solutions other than the trivial one $\alpha = 0$, $\beta = 0$, $\gamma = 0$ are obtainable precisely when the determinant of the coefficients is 0:

$$\begin{vmatrix} a_1 - \lambda & b_1 & c_1 \\ a_2 & b_2 - \lambda & c_2 \\ a_3 & b_3 & c_3 - \lambda \end{vmatrix} = 0. \tag{7-13}$$

When (7-13) is expanded, it appears as a cubic equation in λ. It is termed the *characteristic equation* associated with the system (7-10) and its roots are called *characteristic roots.*

Let us suppose that the roots λ_1, λ_2, λ_3 of (7-13) are *real and distinct.* Corresponding to the root λ_1, we can find a set of values α_1, β_1, γ_1 (not all 0) satisfying (7-12); then the triple

$$x_1 \equiv \alpha_1 e^{\lambda_1 t}, \qquad y_1 \equiv \beta_1 e^{\lambda_1 t}, \qquad z_1 \equiv \gamma_1 e^{\lambda_1 t}$$

is a solution of Eqs. (7-10). Similarly, each of the roots λ_2, λ_3 provides a solution. *The three triples are linearly independent, and the corresponding expressions*

$$\begin{aligned} x &= C_1\alpha_1 e^{\lambda_1 t} + C_2\alpha_2 e^{\lambda_2 t} + C_3\alpha_3 e^{\lambda_3 t}, \\ y &= C_1\beta_1 e^{\lambda_1 t} + C_2\beta_2 e^{\lambda_2 t} + C_3\beta_3 e^{\lambda_3 t}, \\ z &= C_1\gamma_1 e^{\lambda_1 t} + C_2\gamma_2 e^{\lambda_2 t} + C_3\gamma_3 e^{\lambda_3 t} \end{aligned} \tag{7-14}$$

provide the general solution of Eqs. (7-10). To verify linear independence, we need only show that the constants C_1, C_2, C_3 can be chosen so that x, y, z in (7-14) reduce identically to zero only if $C_1 = 0, C_2 = 0, C_3 = 0.$

If x, y, z do reduce to 0, then because of the linear independence of the functions $e^{\lambda_1 t}$, $e^{\lambda_2 t}$, $e^{\lambda_3 t}$, we conclude that

$$C_1\alpha_1 = 0, \quad C_2\alpha_2 = 0, \quad C_3\alpha_3 = 0, \quad C_1\beta_1 = 0, \quad \ldots, \quad C_3\gamma_3 = 0.$$

If $C_1 \neq 0$, then $\alpha_1 = 0$, $\beta_1 = 0$, $\gamma_1 = 0$, which is contrary to the way α_1, β_1, γ_1 were chosen; hence C_1 must equal 0. Similarly, $C_2 = 0$, $C_3 = 0$. Thus the triples are linearly independent.

EXAMPLE 1. We consider Example 1 of Section 7–1:

$$\frac{dx}{dt} = 4x - 9y + 5z, \qquad \frac{dy}{dt} = x - 10y + 7z, \qquad \frac{dz}{dt} = x - 17y + 12z.$$

The characteristic equation is

$$\begin{vmatrix} 4-\lambda & -9 & 5 \\ 1 & -10-\lambda & 7 \\ 1 & -17 & 12-\lambda \end{vmatrix} = 0.$$

When expanded, this becomes

$$\lambda^3 - 6\lambda^2 + 11\lambda - 6 = 0,$$

and the roots are found to be $\lambda_1 = 1$, $\lambda_2 = 2$, $\lambda_3 = 3$. The equations for α_1, β_1, γ_1 are

$$\begin{aligned} 3\alpha_1 - 9\beta_1 + 5\gamma_1 &= 0, \\ \alpha_1 - 11\beta_1 + 7\gamma_1 &= 0, \\ \alpha_1 - 17\beta_1 + 11\gamma_1 &= 0. \end{aligned} \tag{7–15}$$

These equations have as determinant of coefficients the above determinant, with λ replaced by $\lambda_1 = 1$; since the determinant has value 0 (that is precisely how λ_1 is chosen), we can solve (7–15) for two of the unknowns in terms of the third, or else (7–15) merely expresses one letter in terms of the other two. Subtraction of the second equation from the third gives

$$6\beta_1 - 4\gamma_1 = 0;$$

hence $\beta_1 = \frac{2}{3}\gamma_1$. Substitution in the second equation yields $\alpha_1 = \frac{1}{3}\gamma_1$. These values check in the first and third equations. We can write the solution as

$$\alpha_1 = k, \qquad \beta_1 = 2k, \qquad \gamma_1 = 3k,$$

where k is arbitrary. We want only one set of values, other than 0, 0, 0; hence we choose $k = 1$ and $\alpha_1 = 1$, $\beta_1 = 2$, $\gamma_1 = 3$.

Determination of α_2, β_2, γ_2 and of α_3, β_3, γ_3 is similar. We are led to the sets of equations

$$\begin{aligned} 2\alpha_2 - 9\beta_2 + 5\gamma_2 &= 0, \\ \alpha_2 - 12\beta_2 + 7\gamma_2 &= 0, \\ \alpha_2 - 17\beta_2 + 10\gamma_2 &= 0; \end{aligned} \tag{7–16a}$$

$$\begin{aligned} \alpha_3 - 9\beta_3 + 5\gamma_3 &= 0, \\ \alpha_3 - 13\beta_3 + 7\gamma_3 &= 0, \\ \alpha_3 - 17\beta_3 + 9\gamma_3 &= 0. \end{aligned} \tag{7–16b}$$

Solutions are found to be $\alpha_2 = 1$, $\beta_2 = 3$, $\gamma_2 = 5$, $\alpha_3 = 1$, $\beta_3 = -1$, $\gamma_3 = -2$. We thus obtain the three triples

$$\begin{aligned} x_1 &= e^t, & y_1 &= 2e^t, & z_1 &= 3e^t, \\ x_2 &= e^{2t}, & y_2 &= 3e^{2t}, & z_2 &= 5e^{2t}, \\ x_3 &= e^{3t}, & y_3 &= -e^{3t}, & z_3 &= -2e^{3t}, \end{aligned}$$

which were verified to be linearly independent solutions in Section 7–1. The general solution is given by Eqs. (7–9).

EXAMPLE 2. We consider the system of Prob. 1 following Section 7–1:

$$\frac{dx}{dt} = 4x - 3y, \qquad \frac{dy}{dt} = 5x - 4y.$$

The characteristic equation is

$$0 = \begin{vmatrix} 4 - \lambda & -3 \\ 5 & -4 - \lambda \end{vmatrix} = \lambda^2 - 1.$$

The characteristic roots are $\lambda_1 = 1$, $\lambda_2 = -1$. Corresponding to $\lambda_1 = 1$, we have the equations

$$3\alpha_1 - 3\beta_1 = 0, \qquad 5\alpha_1 - 5\beta_1 = 0,$$

for α_1, β_1; we see at once that $\alpha_1 = \beta_1 = k$, where k is arbitrary. We set $k = 1$ and obtain the solution $x_1 = e^t$, $y_1 = e^t$. Similarly, for $\lambda_2 = -1$ we have

$$5\alpha_1 - 3\beta_1 = 0, \qquad 5\alpha_1 - 3\beta_1 = 0;$$

hence $\alpha_1 = 3\beta_1/5$, or $\alpha_1 = 3k$, $\beta_1 = 5k$ (where k is arbitrary); we take $k = 1$ and obtain the solution $x_2 = 3e^{-t}$, $y_2 = 5e^{-t}$. The general solution is then

$$x = C_1e^t + 3C_2e^{-t}, \qquad y = C_1e^t + 5C_2e^{-t}.$$

7–3 Case of complex characteristic roots. If $\lambda = a \pm bi$ is a pair of complex roots of the characteristic equation, then we can write $\lambda_1 = a + bi$, $\lambda_2 = \bar{\lambda}_1 = a - bi$ (the bar denotes complex conjugate). The procedure of Section 7–2 can then be followed, but it leads to solutions $\alpha_1 e^{\lambda_1 t}$, $\beta_1 e^{\lambda_1 t}$, $\gamma_1 e^{\lambda_1 t}$ and $\alpha_2 e^{\lambda_2 t}$, $\beta_2 e^{\lambda_2 t}$, $\gamma_2 e^{\lambda_2 t}$, which are *complex* solutions of the differential equations, as in Section 4–6. However, since $\lambda_2 = \bar{\lambda}_1$, we can choose $\alpha_2 = \bar{\alpha}_1$, $\beta_2 = \bar{\beta}_1$, $\gamma_2 = \bar{\gamma}_1$. For since the coefficients $a_1, b_1, c_1, a_2, \ldots$ are assumed real, the equations

$$\begin{aligned} (a_1 - \lambda_1)\alpha_1 + b_1\beta_1 + c_1\gamma_1 &= 0, \\ a_2\alpha_1 + (b_2 - \lambda_1)\beta_1 + c_2\gamma_1 &= 0, \qquad \ldots, \end{aligned}$$

on taking conjugates, imply

$$\begin{aligned} (a_1 - \bar{\lambda}_1)\bar{\alpha}_1 + b_1\bar{\beta}_1 + c_1\bar{\gamma}_1 &= 0, \\ a_2\bar{\alpha}_1 + (b_2 - \bar{\lambda}_1)\bar{\beta}_1 + c_2\bar{\gamma}_1 &= 0, \qquad \ldots \end{aligned}$$

It follows that if $C_2 = \overline{C}_1$, then

$$C_1\alpha_1 e^{\lambda_1 t} + C_2\alpha_2 e^{\lambda_2 t} \qquad (\alpha_2 = \bar{\alpha}_1,\ \lambda_2 = \bar{\lambda}_1)$$

is real, and hence, as in Section 4–6, we obtain real solutions by writing

$$\begin{aligned} x &= C_1\alpha_1 e^{\lambda_1 t} + \overline{C}_1\bar{\alpha}_1 e^{\bar{\lambda}_1 t}, \\ y &= C_1\beta_1 e^{\lambda_1 t} + \overline{C}_1\bar{\beta}_1 e^{\bar{\lambda}_1 t}, \\ z &= C_1\gamma_1 e^{\lambda_1 t} + \overline{C}_1\bar{\gamma}_1 e^{\bar{\lambda}_1 t}. \end{aligned} \tag{7–17}$$

If we write $C_1 = C_1' + iC_1''$, $\overline{C}_1 = C_1' - iC_1''$, $\alpha_1 = \alpha_1' + i\alpha_1''$, $\bar{\alpha}_1 = \alpha_1' - i\alpha_1''$, $\beta_1 = \beta_1' + i\beta_1''$, ..., where C_1', C_1'', ... are real, then (7–17) can be expanded to give x, y, and z as linear combinations of $e^{at}\cos bt$, $e^{at}\sin bt$.

EXAMPLE. We take the system of Prob. 2(a) following Section 7–1:

$$\frac{dx}{dt} = -9x + 19y + 4z, \qquad \frac{dy}{dt} = -3x + 7y + z,$$
$$\frac{dz}{dt} = -7x + 17y + 2z.$$

The characteristic equation is

$$0 = \begin{vmatrix} -9-\lambda & 19 & 4 \\ -3 & 7-\lambda & 1 \\ -7 & 17 & 2-\lambda \end{vmatrix} = -\lambda^3 - \lambda = -\lambda(\lambda^2 + 1).$$

The roots are $\pm i$, 0. Corresponding to the root $\lambda_1 = i$, we obtain the equations for α_1, β_1, γ_1:

$$\begin{aligned}(-9 - i)\alpha_1 + 19\beta_1 + 4\gamma_1 &= 0,\\ -3\alpha_1 + (7 - i)\beta_1 + \gamma_1 &= 0,\\ -7\alpha_1 + 17\beta_1 + (2 - i)\gamma_1 &= 0.\end{aligned}$$

From the first and second equations we obtain

$$\begin{aligned}(3 - i)\alpha_1 + (-9 + 4i)\beta_1 &= 0,\\ \gamma_1 = 3\alpha_1 &- (7 - i)\beta_1.\end{aligned}$$

Hence if we take $\beta_1 = (3 - i)k$, then $\alpha_1 = (9 - 4i)k$ and $\gamma_1 = (7 - 2i)k$, where k is arbitrary. We choose $k = 1$, and hence

$$\alpha_1 = 9 - 4i, \qquad \beta_1 = 3 - i, \qquad \gamma_1 = 7 - 2i.$$

The equations for α_2, β_2, γ_2 are obtained from those for α_1, β_1, γ_1 by replacing i by $-i$, and we can verify that this simply replaces i by $-i$ in the results; that is, we can choose $\alpha_2 = \bar{\alpha}_1$, $\beta_2 = \bar{\beta}_1$, $\gamma_2 = \bar{\gamma}_1$ as remarked above:

$$\alpha_2 = 9 + 4i, \qquad \beta_2 = 3 + i, \qquad \gamma_2 = 7 + 2i.$$

Corresponding to the root $\lambda_3 = 0$, we obtain the equations

$$\begin{aligned}-9\alpha_3 + 19\beta_3 + 4\gamma_3 &= 0,\\ -3\alpha_3 + 7\beta_3 + \gamma_3 &= 0,\\ -7\alpha_3 + 17\beta_3 + 2\gamma_3 &= 0,\end{aligned}$$

for which we find the solution

$$\alpha_3 = 3, \qquad \beta_3 = 1, \qquad \gamma_3 = 2.$$

Accordingly, the general real solution is given by

$$\begin{aligned}x &= C_1(9 - 4i)e^{it} + \overline{C}_1(9 + 4i)e^{-it} + 3C_3,\\ y &= C_1(3 - i)e^{it} + \overline{C}_1(3 + i)e^{-it} + C_3,\\ z &= C_1(7 - 2i)e^{it} + \overline{C}_1(7 + 2i)e^{-it} + 2C_3.\end{aligned} \tag{7-18}$$

If we write $C_1 = \frac{1}{2}(c_1 + ic_2)$, $\overline{C}_1 = \frac{1}{2}(c_1 - ic_2)$, then

$$\begin{aligned}x &= C_1(9 - 4i)e^{it} + \overline{C}_1(9 + 4i)e^{-it} + 3C_3\\ &= 2\,\mathrm{Re}\,[C_1(9 - 4i)e^{it}] + 3C_3\\ &= \mathrm{Re}\,[(c_1 + ic_2)(9 - 4i)e^{it}] + 3C_3\\ &= c_1(9\cos t + 4\sin t) - c_2(9\sin t - 4\cos t) + 3C_3.\end{aligned}$$

Similarly, we find

$$y = c_1 (\sin t + 3 \cos t) - c_2(3 \sin t - \cos t) + C_3,$$
$$z = c_1(2 \sin t + 7 \cos t) + c_2(7 \sin t - 2 \cos t) + 2C_3.$$

Remark. As the example illustrates, we can obtain the solutions in real form by taking

$$x_1 = \text{Re}\,(\alpha_1 e^{\lambda_1 t}), \quad y_1 = \text{Re}\,(\beta_1 e^{\lambda_1 t}), \quad z_1 = \text{Re}\,(\gamma_1 e^{\lambda_1 t});$$
$$x_2 = \text{Im}\,(\alpha_1 e^{\lambda_1 t}), \quad y_2 = \text{Im}\,(\beta_1 e^{\lambda_1 t}), \quad z_2 = \text{Im}\,(\gamma_1 e^{\lambda_1 t});$$
$$x_3 = \alpha_3 e^{\lambda_3 t}, \quad y_3 = \beta_3 e^{\lambda_3 t}, \quad z_3 = \gamma_3 e^{\lambda_3 t}.$$

We can verify directly that these are three linearly independent solutions.

PROBLEMS

For each of the following systems of linear differential equations, obtain the general solution. Throughout, $D = d/dt$.

1. $Dx = 7x + 6y,\ Dy = 2x + 6y.$
2. $Dx = -x + y,\ Dy = -5x + 3y.$
3. $Dx = 16x + 14y + 38z,\ Dy = -9x - 7y - 18z,$
   $Dz = -4x - 4y - 11z.$
4. $Dx = -5x - 10y - 20z,\ Dy = 5x + 5y + 10z,\ Dz = 2x + 4y + 9z.$
5. $Dx = 3x - 5y + u,\ Dy = x - y,\ Dz = -3z - u,\ Du = 5z + u.$
6. $Dx = 2x,\ Dy = 4y.$
7. $Dx = 2x,\ Dy = 2y.$
8. $Dx = 7x + 6y,\ Dy = 2x + 6y,\ Dz = 7z + 6u,\ Du = 2z + 6u.$
[*Hint:* See Prob. 1.]

Remark. In each case the answer given provides *one form* of the general solution. As indicated in Prob. 4 following Section 7–1, other forms of the general solution are obtainable by means of a linear substitution with nonvanishing determinant, and it can be verified that all other forms are so obtainable. Hence if solution of a problem leads to an answer differing from the one given, one can check correctness in one of two ways: by verifying that the solution is constructed as in Theorem 1 from linearly independent solutions (Prob. 6 following Section 7–1 gives an easy test for linear independence); by showing that the answer in the text is obtainable from the one found by a linear substitution as in Prob. 4 following Section 7–1.

ANSWERS

1. $x = 2C_1e^{10t} + 3C_2e^{3t}$, $y = C_1e^{10t} - 2C_2e^{3t}$.

2. $x = e^t(C_1 \cos t + C_2 \sin t)$,
$y = e^t[C_1(2 \cos t - \sin t) + C_2(2 \sin t + \cos t)]$.

3. $x = C_1e^{2t} - 2C_2e^{-t} - 2C_3e^{-3t}$, $y = -C_1e^{2t} - 3C_2e^{-t}$, $z = 2C_2e^{-t} + C_3e^{-3t}$.

4. $x = -2C_1e^{5t} + e^{2t}[C_2(20 \cos t - 10 \sin t) + C_3(10 \cos t + 20 \sin t)]$,
$y = e^{2t}[C_2(15 \cos t + 5 \sin t) + C_3(15 \sin t - 5 \cos t)]$,
$z = C_1e^{5t} + e^{2t}[C_2(-14 \cos t + 2 \sin t) + C_3(-2 \cos t - 14 \sin t)]$.

5. $x = C_1(2 + i)e^{(1+i)t} + \overline{C}_1(2 - i)e^{(1-i)t} + C_2(3 - i)e^{(-1+i)t} + \overline{C}_2(3 + i)e^{(-1-i)t}$,
$y = C_1e^{(1+i)t} + \overline{C}_1e^{(1-i)t} + C_2(-1 - 3i)e^{(-1+i)t} + \overline{C}_2(-1 + 3i)e^{(-1-i)t}$,
$z = 8C_2e^{(-1+i)t} + 8\overline{C}_2e^{(-1-i)t}$,
$u = C_2(-16 - 8i)e^{(-1+i)t} + \overline{C}_2(-16 + 8i)e^{(-1-i)t}$.

6. $x = C_1e^{2t}$, $y = C_2e^{4t}$.

7. $x = C_1e^{2t}$, $y = C_2e^{2t}$.

8. $x = 2C_1e^{10t} + 3C_2e^{3t}$, $y = C_1e^{10t} - 2C_2e^{3t}$, $z = 2C_3e^{10t} + 3C_4e^{3t}$,
$u = C_3e^{10t} - 2C_4e^{3t}$.

7–4 Case of repeated roots. When the characteristic equation has repeated roots, the methods of the preceding sections appear to yield less than the required number of linearly independent solutions. We now show how the required additional solutions can be found. In essence, our method consists in adding terms which are linear combinations of $te^{\lambda t}$, $t^2e^{\lambda t}$, ..., $t^{k-1}e^{\lambda t}$, just as in the case of the single equation of order n. However, it can happen that for a root of multiplicity k, not all these terms are required; in fact, none of them may be needed, the solutions being built solely from the functions $e^{\lambda t}$.

After illustrating the method by examples, we shall formulate some general rules.

EXAMPLE 1. $dx/dt = 5x$, $dy/dt = 5y$. The characteristic equation is

$$0 = \begin{vmatrix} 5 - \lambda & 0 \\ 0 & 5 - \lambda \end{vmatrix} = (5 - \lambda)^2.$$

The roots are 5, 5. The substitution $x = \alpha e^{5t}$, $y = \beta e^{5t}$ leads to the equations

$$0\alpha + 0\beta = 0, \qquad 0\alpha + 0\beta = 0,$$

which are satisfied for all values of α and β. We obtain two linearly independent solutions by choosing $\alpha_1 = 1$, $\beta_1 = 0$ and $\alpha_2 = 0$, $\beta_2 = 1$:

$$x_1 = e^{5t}, \qquad y_1 = 0; \qquad\qquad x_2 = 0, \qquad y_2 = e^{5t}.$$

Hence the general solution is

$$x = C_1 e^{5t}, \qquad y = C_2 e^{5t}. \tag{7–19}$$

From the form of the given differential equations it is clear that (7–19) provides all solutions.

EXAMPLE 2. $dx/dt = x + y, \qquad dy/dt = -x + 3y.$

The characteristic equation is

$$0 = \begin{vmatrix} 1 - \lambda & 1 \\ -1 & 3 - \lambda \end{vmatrix} = \lambda^2 - 4\lambda + 4 = (\lambda - 2)^2.$$

The roots are 2, 2. The substitution $x = \alpha e^{2t}$, $y = \beta e^{2t}$ leads to the equations

$$-\alpha + \beta = 0, \qquad -\alpha + \beta = 0. \tag{7–20}$$

The solutions have the form $\alpha = k$, $\beta = k$, where k is arbitrary. With $k = 1$, we obtain the solution

$$x_1 = e^{2t}, \qquad y_1 = e^{2t},$$

but can obtain no second linearly independent solution of form αe^{2t}, βe^{2t}. To obtain the second solution, we set

$$x = e^{2t}(\alpha_1 t + \alpha_2), \qquad y = e^{2t}(\beta_1 t + \beta_2). \tag{7–21}$$

Substitution in the differential equations and cancellation of e^{2t} leads to the equations

$$\begin{aligned} 2\alpha_1 t + 2\alpha_2 + \alpha_1 &= (\alpha_1 + \beta_1)t + \alpha_2 + \beta_2, \\ 2\beta_1 t + 2\beta_2 + \beta_1 &= (3\beta_1 - \alpha_1)t + 3\beta_2 - \alpha_2. \end{aligned}$$

Since these are to be identities, we conclude that $2\alpha_1 = \alpha_1 + \beta_1, \ldots$; we thus obtain the four equations

$$-\alpha_1 + \beta_1 = 0, \qquad -\alpha_1 + \beta_1 = 0, \tag{7–22}$$

$$-\alpha_2 + \beta_2 = \alpha_1, \qquad -\alpha_2 + \beta_2 = \beta_1. \tag{7–23}$$

The first two result from comparison of terms in t, the second two from comparison of constant terms. We note that (7–22) has the same form as (7–20), so that its solutions are $\alpha_1 = k_1$, $\beta_1 = k_1$, where k_1 is arbitrary.

Equations (7–23) are then satisfied when $\alpha_2 = k_2$, $\beta_2 = k_1 + k_2$, where k_2 is arbitrary. We need only one set of values $\alpha_1, \beta_1, \alpha_2, \beta_2$, with α_1 and β_1 not both 0; hence we choose $k_1 = 1$, $k_2 = 0$, so that

$$\alpha_1 = 1, \qquad \beta_1 = 1, \qquad \alpha_2 = 0, \qquad \beta_2 = 1.$$

The desired solution (7–21) is

$$x_2 = e^{2t}(t), \qquad y_2 = e^{2t}(t+1),$$

and the general solution is

$$x = C_1e^{2t} + C_2te^{2t}, \qquad y = C_1e^{2t} + C_2(t+1)e^{2t}.$$

EXAMPLE 3. Consider the system of third order

$$\frac{dx}{dt} = 14x + 66y - 42z, \qquad \frac{dy}{dt} = 4x + 24y - 14z,$$

$$\frac{dz}{dt} = 10x + 55y - 33z.$$

The characteristic equation is

$$0 = \begin{vmatrix} 14-\lambda & 66 & -42 \\ 4 & 24-\lambda & -14 \\ 10 & 55 & -33-\lambda \end{vmatrix} = -(\lambda-2)^2(\lambda-1).$$

The roots are 2, 2, 1. The substitution $x = \alpha e^{2t}$, $y = \beta e^{2t}$, $z = \gamma e^{2t}$ leads to the equations

$$\begin{aligned} 12\alpha + 66\beta - 42\gamma &= 0, \\ 4\alpha + 22\beta - 14\gamma &= 0, \\ 10\alpha + 55\beta - 35\gamma &= 0. \end{aligned} \tag{7–24}$$

These can be reduced to the single equation

$$2\alpha + 11\beta - 7\gamma = 0;$$

hence the solutions can be written

$$\alpha = -11k_1 + 7k_2, \qquad \beta = 2k_1, \qquad \gamma = 2k_2,$$

in terms of *two* arbitrary constants k_1, k_2. We obtain two linearly independent solutions by choosing $k_1 = 1$, $k_2 = 0$, and then choosing $k_1 = 0$, $k_2 = 1$:

$$x_1 = -11e^{2t}, \qquad y_1 = 2e^{2t}, \qquad z_1 = 0;$$

$$x_2 = 7e^{2t}, \qquad y_2 = 0, \qquad z_2 = 2e^{2t}.$$

The simple root $\lambda_3 = 1$ leads to the equations

$$\begin{aligned} 13\alpha_3 + 66\beta_3 - 42\gamma_3 &= 0, \\ 4\alpha_3 + 23\beta_3 - 14\gamma_3 &= 0, \\ 10\alpha_3 + 55\beta_3 - 34\gamma_3 &= 0. \end{aligned}$$

These are satisfied when $\alpha_3 = 6k$, $\beta_3 = 2k$, $\gamma_3 = 5k$; with $k = 1$, we obtain the solution

$$x_3 = 6e^t, \qquad y_3 = 2e^t, \qquad z_3 = 7e^t.$$

Hence the general solution is

$$\begin{aligned} x &= -11C_1e^{2t} + 7C_2e^{2t} + 6C_3e^t, \\ y &= 2C_1e^{2t} + 2C_3e^t, \\ z &= 2C_2e^{2t} + 5C_3e^t. \end{aligned}$$

EXAMPLE 4. The system is

$$\frac{dx}{dt} = -8x + 47y - 8z, \qquad \frac{dy}{dt} = -4x + 18y - 2z,$$

$$\frac{dz}{dt} = -8x + 39y - 5z.$$

The characteristic equation is

$$0 = \begin{vmatrix} -8-\lambda & 47 & -8 \\ -4 & 18-\lambda & -2 \\ -8 & 39 & -5-\lambda \end{vmatrix} = -(\lambda - 2)^2(\lambda - 1).$$

As in Example 3, the roots are 2, 2, 1. The substitution $x = \alpha e^{2t}$, $y = \beta e^{2t}$, $z = \gamma e^{2t}$ leads to the equations

$$\begin{aligned} -10\alpha + 47\beta - 8\gamma &= 0, \\ -4\alpha + 16\beta - 2\gamma &= 0, \\ -8\alpha + 39\beta - 7\gamma &= 0. \end{aligned} \tag{7–25}$$

The solutions are $\alpha = 17k$, $\beta = 6k$, $\gamma = 14k$; hence, with $k = 1$,

$$x_1 = 17e^{2t}, \qquad y_1 = 6e^{2t}, \qquad z_1 = 14e^{2t}.$$

To obtain the second solution, we set

$$x = e^{2t}(\alpha_1 t + \alpha_2), \qquad y = e^{2t}(\beta_1 t + \beta_2), \qquad z = e^{2t}(\gamma_1 t + \gamma_2),$$

and as in Example 2 we are led to the equations

$$-10\alpha_1 + 47\beta_1 - 8\gamma_1 = 0, \qquad -4\alpha_1 + 16\beta_1 - 2\gamma_1 = 0, \qquad -8\alpha_1 + 39\beta_1 - 7\gamma_1 = 0, \tag{7–26}$$

and

$$\begin{aligned} -10\alpha_2 + 47\beta_2 - 8\gamma_2 &= \alpha_1, \\ -4\alpha_2 + 16\beta_2 - 2\gamma_2 &= \beta_1, \\ -8\alpha_2 + 39\beta_2 - 7\gamma_2 &= \gamma_1. \end{aligned} \tag{7–27}$$

The equations (7–26) are the same as (7–25) and are satisfied when $\alpha_1 = 17k_1$, $\beta_1 = 6k_1$, $\gamma_1 = 14k_1$, where k_1 is arbitrary. If we substitute these expressions in (7–27), then (7–27) becomes a set of three equations for α_2, β_2, γ_2, in terms of k_1. However, we verify that these are *dependent* equations (in particular, the third equation is obtained by subtracting one-half the second from the first). Hence we use only the first two equations; γ_2 can be chosen arbitrarily, $\gamma_2 = k_2$, and we solve for α_2, β_2:

$$\alpha_2 = \frac{17k_2 - 5k_1}{14}, \qquad \beta_2 = \frac{2k_1 + 3k_2}{7}, \qquad \gamma_2 = k_2.$$

Thus, as in Example 2, the solutions depend on two arbitrary constants k_1, k_2; we seek a solution for which α_1, β_1, γ_1 are not all 0. We find this by setting $k_1 = 14$, $k_2 = 0$; then $\alpha_1 = 238$, $\beta_1 = 84$, $\gamma_1 = 196$, $\alpha_2 = -5$, $\beta_2 = 4$, $\gamma_2 = 0$, and the solution is

$$x_2 = e^{2t}(238t - 5), \qquad y_2 = e^{2t}(84t + 4), \qquad z = e^{2t}(196t).$$

For the third solution we set $x = \alpha e^t$, $y = \beta e^t$, $z = \gamma e^t$ and find, without difficulty, $\alpha = 6k$, $\beta = 2k$, $\gamma = 5k$, so that we can choose

$$x_3 = 6e^t, \qquad y_3 = 2e^t, \qquad z_3 = 5e^t.$$

Then the general solution is

$$\begin{aligned} x &= e^{2t}[17C_1 + C_2(238t - 5)] + 6C_3e^t, \\ y &= e^{2t}[6C_1 + C_2(84t + 4)] + 2C_3e^t, \\ z &= e^{2t}[14C_1 + C_2(196t)] + 5C_3e^t. \end{aligned}$$

We now generalize the procedures indicated by the above examples. If λ_1 is a double root of the characteristic equation, we first seek solutions of form $x = \alpha e^{\lambda_1 t}$, $y = \beta e^{\lambda_1 t}$, ... At least one such solution can be found (with α, β, ... not all 0); it may also happen that two linearly independent solutions of this form can be found. If two independent solutions cannot be found, then the second solution is obtainable in the form

$$x = e^{\lambda_1 t}(\alpha_1 t + \alpha_2), \qquad y = e^{\lambda_1 t}(\beta_1 t + \beta_2), \ldots$$

For a triple root λ_1 we proceed similarly, obtaining first as many independent solutions of form $x = \alpha e^{\lambda_1 t}$, $y = \beta e^{\lambda_1 t}$, ... as possible (at most three), then as many independent solutions of form $x = e^{\lambda_1 t}(\alpha_1 t + \alpha_2)$, $y = e^{\lambda_1 t}(\beta_1 t + \beta_2)$, ... as possible, and finally (if one more solution is needed) a solution of form

$$x = e^{\lambda_1 t}(\alpha_1 t^2 + \alpha_2 t + \alpha_3), \qquad y = e^{\lambda_1 t}(\beta_1 t^2 + \beta_2 t + \beta_3), \qquad \ldots$$

For a root of multiplicity k we may have to use polynomial coefficients of degree $k - 1$ (but no higher).

Instead of gradually raising the degree of the coefficient of $e^{\lambda_1 t}$, we can obtain all the solutions associated with the characteristic root λ_1 by at once trying the polynomials of highest degree. Substitution in the differential equations leads to homogeneous linear equations for the coefficients in the polynomials. These equations can always be solved for some of the coefficients in terms of the others; when the multiplicity is k, the "others" are k in number. We can obtain k linearly independent solutions by in turn choosing one of the "others" to be 1 and the remaining ones to be 0. We illustrate this procedure by considering Examples 2 and 3 again.

For Example 2 the multiplicity is 2; we at once seek solutions of form (7–21) and are led to equations (7–22), (7–23), which can be solved for α_1, α_2 in terms of β_1, β_2:

$$\alpha_1 = \beta_1, \qquad \alpha_2 = \beta_2 - \beta_1.$$

When $\beta_1 = 1$, $\beta_2 = 0$, we obtain the solution

$$x_1 = e^{2t}(t - 1), \qquad y_1 = e^{2t}(t);$$

when $\beta_1 = 0$, $\beta_2 = 1$, we obtain the solution

$$x_2 = e^{2t}, \qquad y_2 = e^{2t}.$$

These are not the same two linearly independent solutions that we obtained in Example 2, but the general solution

$$x = C_1 e^{2t}(t - 1) + C_2 e^{2t}, \qquad y = C_1 t e^{2t} + C_2 e^{2t}$$

can be easily verified to be equivalent to the previous one.

For Example 3 the multiplicity is again 2, and we set

$$x = e^{2t}(\alpha_1 t + \alpha_2), \qquad y = e^{2t}(\beta_1 t + \beta_2), \qquad z = e^{2t}(\gamma_1 t + \gamma_2).$$

Substitution in the differential equations leads to the equations

$$\begin{aligned}
12\alpha_1 + 66\beta_1 - 42\gamma_1 &= 0,\\
4\alpha_1 + 22\beta_1 - 14\gamma_1 &= 0,\\
10\alpha_1 + 55\beta_1 - 35\gamma_1 &= 0;\\
12\alpha_2 + 66\beta_2 - 42\gamma_2 &= \alpha_1,\\
4\alpha_2 + 22\beta_2 - 14\gamma_2 &= \beta_1,\\
10\alpha_2 + 55\beta_2 - 35\gamma_2 &= \gamma_1.
\end{aligned}$$

From the second group of equations we conclude that

$$2\alpha_2 + 11\beta_2 - 7\gamma_2 = \frac{\alpha_1}{6} = \frac{\beta_1}{2} = \frac{\gamma_1}{5};$$

thus $\alpha_1 = 3\beta_1$, $\gamma_1 = 5\beta_1/2$. The first equation now gives $36\beta_1 + 66\beta_1 - 105\beta_1 = 0$, so that $\beta_1 = 0$, $\alpha_1 = 0$, and $\gamma_1 = 0$. The second group can then be reduced to the equation

$$2\alpha_2 + 11\beta_2 - 7\gamma_2 = 0;$$

hence, for example, β_2 and γ_2 can be chosen as the constants in terms of which all are expressed:

$$\alpha_2 = \frac{7\gamma_2 - 11\beta_2}{2}, \qquad \alpha_1 = 0,\ \beta_1 = 0,\ \gamma_1 = 0.$$

The choices $\beta_2 = 1$, $\gamma_2 = 0$ and $\beta_2 = 0$, $\gamma_2 = 1$ give us the two solutions

$$\begin{aligned}
x_1 &= -\tfrac{11}{2}e^{2t}, \qquad & y_1 &= e^{2t}, \qquad & z_1 &= 0;\\
x_2 &= \tfrac{7}{2}e^{2t}, & y_2 &= 0, & z_2 &= e^{2t}.
\end{aligned}$$

Except for a factor of 2, these are the same as those obtained in Example 3.

A proof that the method described does yield all solutions is given in Section 6–22 of ODE. The whole subject can be studied more systematically with the aid of matrices; see Sections 6–15 through 6–23 of ODE, and References 1 and 7 at the end of the chapter.

If λ_1 is a multiple complex root, we obtain complex solutions $x_1, y_1, \ldots, x_2, y_2 \ldots,$ as above. We can then obtain the general real solution by forming the terms

$$\begin{aligned}
&C_1x_1(t) + \overline{C}_1\overline{x}_1(t) + C_2x_2(t) + \overline{C}_2\overline{x}_2(t) + \cdots,\\
&C_1y_1(t) + \overline{C}_1\overline{y}_1(t) + C_2y_2(t) + \overline{C}_2\overline{y}_2(t) + \cdots, \qquad \ldots,
\end{aligned}$$

just as for simple roots. The justification is similar to that for the single differential equation of order n (Section 4–7). Equivalently, we can use the real solutions:

$$
\begin{array}{lll}
\text{Re}\,[x_1(t)], & \text{Re}\,[y_1(t)], & \ldots, \\
\text{Im}\,[x_1(t)], & \text{Im}\,[y_1(t)], & \ldots, \\
\text{Re}\,[x_2(t)], & \text{Re}\,[y_2(t)], & \ldots, \\
\text{Im}\,[x_2(t)], & \text{Im}\,[y_2(t)], & \ldots, \\
\ldots, & &
\end{array}
$$

as a set of linearly independent solutions which correspond to the root λ_1.

PROBLEMS

Find the general solution of the systems of Probs. 1–8. Throughout, $D = d/dt$.

1. $Dx = -x$, $Dy = -y$.
2. $Dx = -4x - y$, $Dy = x - 2y$.
3. $Dx = y$, $Dy = 4x + 3y - 4z$, $Dz = x + 2y - z$.
4. $Dx = -2x + 3z$, $Dy = 4y$, $Dz = -6x + 7z$.
5. $Dx = 2x + y + 2z$, $Dy = -x - 2z$, $Dz = z$.
6. $Dx = 3x + y - z$, $Dy = -x + 2y + z$, $Dz = x + y + z$.
7. $Dx = 3x$, $Dy = 3y$, $Dz = 3z$, $Du = 3u$.
8. $Dx = -7x - 4u$, $Dy = -13x - 2y - z - 8u$, $Dz = 6x + y + 4u$, $Du = 15x + y + 9u$.
9. Given a system $Dx_i = \sum_{j=1}^{n} a_{ij}x_j$, $(i = 1, \ldots, n)$, let λ_1 be a real root of multiplicity k and let Δ_1 represent the characteristic determinant, with λ replaced by λ_1, so that Δ_1 has value 0. Let Δ_1 have the property that every minor of order greater than $n - k$ is 0, but some minor of order $n - k$ is not 0 (so that Δ_1 has rank $n - k$). Show that k linearly independent solutions are obtainable in the form $x_i = \alpha_{il}e^{\lambda_1 t}$, $(i = 1, \ldots, n;\ l = 1, \ldots, k)$. Can Δ_1 have rank less than $n - k$?

ANSWERS

(See Remark preceding answers to problems after Section 7–3.)

1. $x = C_1e^{-t}$, $y = C_2e^{-t}$.
2. $x = e^{-3t}[C_1 + C_2(t - 1)]$, $y = e^{-3t}[-C_1 - C_2t]$.
3. $x = e^t[2C_1 + C_2(4t - 4)] + C_3$, $y = e^t(2C_1 + 4C_2t)$, $z = e^t[3C_1 + (6t - 5)C_2] + C_3$.
4. $x = C_1e^{4t} + C_2e^t$, $y = C_3e^{4t}$, $z = 2C_1e^{4t} + C_2e^t$.

5. $x = e^{2t}[-C_1 - 2C_2 + C_3(t+1)]$, $y = e^t(C_1 - tC_3)$, $z = C_2e^t$.

6. $x = e^{2t}[C_1 + (t+1)C_2 + (\frac{1}{2}t^2 + t)C_3]$, $y = e^{2t}[C_2 + C_3(t+2)]$,
$z = e^{2t}\{C_1 + C_2(t+1) + C_3[(t^2/2) + t + 1]\}$.

7. $x = C_1e^{3t}$, $y = C_2e^{3t}$, $z = C_3e^{3t}$, $u = C_4e^{3t}$.

8. $x = -4C_1e^{it} - 4\overline{C}_1e^{-it} - 4tC_2e^{it} - 4t\overline{C}_2e^{-it}$,
$y = (-4-2i)C_1e^{it} + (-4+2i)\overline{C}_1e^{-it} + C_2e^{it}[(-4-2i)t - 2 + 2i] + \overline{C}_2e^{-it}[(-4+2i)t - 2 - 2i]$,
$z = 2C_1e^{it} + 2\overline{C}_1e^{-it} + (2t+2)C_2e^{it} + (2t+2)\overline{C}_2e^{-it}$,
$u = C_1(7+i)e^{it} + \overline{C}_1(7-i)e^{-it} + C_2e^{it}[(7+i)t + 1] + \overline{C}_2e^{-it}[(7-i)t + 1]$.

7-5 Nonhomogeneous systems. Variation of parameters. We consider the nonhomogeneous system of third order

$$\begin{aligned} Dx &= a_1x + b_1y + c_1z + f_1(t), \\ Dy &= a_2x + b_2y + c_2z + f_2(t), \\ Dz &= a_3x + b_3y + c_3z + f_3(t), \end{aligned} \tag{7-28}$$

(where $D = d/dt$), and assume that the general solution of the related homogeneous system

$$\begin{aligned} Dx &= a_1x + b_1y + c_1z, \\ Dy &= a_2x + \cdots, \\ Dz &= a_3x + \cdots \end{aligned} \tag{7-29}$$

is known. Let this general solution be given in the form

$$\begin{aligned} x &= C_1x_1(t) + C_2x_2(t) + C_3x_3(t), \\ y &= C_1y_1(t) + C_2y_2(t) + C_3y_3(t), \\ z &= C_1z_1(t) + C_2z_2(t) + C_3z_3(t). \end{aligned} \tag{7-30}$$

We now replace the constants C_1, C_2, C_3 by variables v_1, v_2, v_3:

$$\begin{aligned} x &= v_1x_1(t) + v_2x_2(t) + v_3x_3(t), \\ y &= v_1y_1(t) + v_2y_2(t) + v_3y_3(t), \\ z &= v_1z_1(t) + v_2z_2(t) + v_3z_3(t). \end{aligned} \tag{7-31}$$

As in Section 4-8, the equations (7-31) are considered as describing a change of variables (x, y, z are replaced by v_1, v_2, v_3). If we substitute in (7-28), we obtain differential equations for v_1, v_2, v_3 in terms of t. Thus the first equation of (7–28) becomes

$$\begin{aligned} v_1 Dx_1 + v_2 Dx_2 + v_3 Dx_3 + x_1 Dv_1 + x_2 Dv_2 + x_3 Dv_3 \\ = a_1(v_1 x_1 + v_2 x_2 + v_3 x_3) + b_1(v_1 y_1 + v_2 y_2 + v_3 y_3) \\ + c_1(v_1 z_1 + v_2 z_2 + v_3 z_3) + f_1(t). \end{aligned} \tag{7–32}$$

However, since the triple x_1, y_1, z_1 is a solution of the homogeneous system (7–29), we have the relation

$$v_1 Dx_1 = v_1(a_1 x_1 + b_1 y_1 + c_1 z_1).$$

We obtain similar expressions for $v_2 Dx_2$, $v_3 Dx_3$. Hence (7–32) reduces to the equation

$$x_1 Dv_1 + x_2 Dv_2 + x_3 Dv_3 = f_1(t).$$

Similar reasoning applies to the remaining equations (7–28); hence the new equations for v_1, v_2, v_3 are

$$\begin{aligned} x_1 Dv_1 + x_2 Dv_2 + x_3 Dv_3 &= f_1(t), \\ y_1 Dv_1 + y_2 Dv_2 + y_3 Dv_3 &= f_2(t), \\ z_1 Dv_1 + z_2 Dv_2 + z_3 Dv_3 &= f_3(t). \end{aligned} \tag{7–33}$$

In (7–33), $x_1, \ldots, y_1, \ldots, z_1, \ldots$ represent known functions of t, and v_1, v_2, v_3 are sought as functions of t. Since (7–33) is a set of simultaneous linear equations for Dv_1, Dv_2, Dv_3, we can solve by elimination or by determinants to obtain the expressions

$$Dv_1 = g_1(t), \qquad Dv_2 = g_2(t), \qquad Dv_3 = g_3(t).$$

Then v_1, v_2, v_3 are obtained by integration:

$$v_1 = \int g_1(t)\,dt, \qquad v_2 = \int g_2(t)\,dt, \qquad v_3 = \int g_3(t)\,dt.$$

Only one choice of the indefinite integrals is needed; this choice yields one particular solution

$$x^*(t) = v_1 x_1 + v_2 x_2 + v_3 x_3, \qquad y^*(t) = \ldots, \qquad z^*(t) = \ldots,$$

in accordance with (7–31). The general solution is then given by

$$\begin{aligned} x &= x^*(t) + C_1 x_1(t) + C_2 x_2(t) + C_3 x_3(t), \\ y &= y^*(t) + \cdots, \qquad z = z^*(t) + \cdots, \end{aligned}$$

by Theorem 1 of Section 7–1.

EXAMPLE. The system is

$$Dx = 4x - 9y + 5z + 1 + 13t, \qquad Dy = x - 10y + 7z + 3 + 15t,$$
$$Dz = x - 17y + 12z + 2 + 26t.$$

It is the same as Example 2 of Section 7–1. The solution of the related homogeneous system is given by (7–9):

$$\begin{aligned} x &= C_1e^t + C_2e^{2t} + C_3e^{3t}, \\ y &= 2C_1e^t + 3C_2e^{2t} - C_3e^{3t}, \\ z &= 3C_1e^t + 5C_2e^{2t} - 2C_3e^{3t}. \end{aligned}$$

We now write

$$\begin{aligned} x &= v_1e^t + v_2e^{2t} + v_3e^{3t}, \\ y &= 2v_1e^t + 3v_2e^{2t} - v_3e^{3t}, \\ z &= 3v_1e^t + 5v_2e^{2t} - 2v_3e^{3t}, \end{aligned}$$

and we try to determine v_1, v_2, v_3 as functions of t, so that the corresponding functions x, y, z satisfy the given nonhomogeneous system. The equations (7–33) become

$$\begin{aligned} e^tDv_1 + e^{2t}Dv_2 + e^{3t}Dv_3 &= 1 + 13t, \\ 2e^tDv_1 + 3e^{2t}Dv_2 - e^{3t}Dv_3 &= 3 + 15t, \\ 3e^tDv_1 + 5e^{2t}Dv_2 - 2e^{3t}Dv_3 &= 2 + 26t. \end{aligned}$$

Elimination of v_3 leads to the equations

$$3e^tDv_1 + 4e^{2t}Dv_2 = 4 + 28t, \qquad 5e^tDv_1 + 7e^{2t}Dv_2 = 4 + 52t,$$

from which we find

$$\begin{aligned} Dv_1 &= (12 - 12t)e^{-t}, &\qquad Dv_2 &= (-8 + 16t)e^{-2t}, \\ v_1 &= 12te^{-t}, & v_2 &= -8te^{-2t}, \\ Dv_3 &= (-3 + 9t)e^{-3t}, & v_3 &= -3te^{-3t}, \end{aligned}$$

$$\begin{aligned} x &= 12t - 8t - 3t = t, \\ y &= 24t - 24t + 3t = 3t, \\ z &= 36t - 40t + 6t = 2t. \end{aligned}$$

The general solution is then as given in Section 7–1:

$$x = C_1e^t + C_2e^{2t} + C_3e^{3t} + t, \qquad y = \dots, \qquad z = \dots$$

Remark 1. Solution of Eqs. (7–33) for Dv_1, Dv_2, Dv_3 is possible, for arbitrary $f_1(t), f_2(t), f_3(t)$, only if the determinant of coefficients is never 0. As pointed out in Section 7–1, linear independence of the three solutions $x_j(t)$, $y_j(t)$, $z_j(t)$, $(j = 1, 2, 3)$, guarantees that the determinant cannot be zero. (See Prob. 6 following Section 7–1.)

Remark 2. As for the single linear equation of order n, the method of variation of parameters is applicable to equations with *variable* coefficients. However, when the coefficients are variable, solution of the related homogeneous system becomes much more difficult.

7–6 Nonhomogeneous systems. Operational methods. Differential operators can be used to carry out an elimination process resembling that for simultaneous linear equations in algebra. However, certain precautions should be followed if we are to avoid extraneous solutions, which can be rejected only after a time-consuming check in the original differential equations. The following principle is the basis of the process: *the two linear equations*

$$f_1(D)x + g_1(D)y + \cdots = F_1(t), \tag{7–34}$$

$$f_2(D)x + g_2(D)y + \cdots = F_2(t) \tag{7–35}$$

are equivalent to the two equations

$$f_1(D)x + g_1(D)y + \cdots = F_1(t), \tag{7–36}$$

$$[\phi(D)f_1(D) + kf_2(D)]x + [\phi(D)g_1(D) + kg_2(D)]y + \cdots = \phi(D)F_1(t) + kF_2(t); \tag{7–37}$$

that is, if $x = x(t)$, $y = y(t)$, ... satisfy the first pair of equations, then $x = x(t)$, $y = y(t)$, ... satisfy the second pair of equations, and conversely. The number k is a nonzero constant. The operators $f_1(D)$, $g_1(D)$, ..., $f_2(D)$, $g_2(D)$, ..., and $\phi(D)$ may have variable coefficients (depending on t), but we shall apply the principle only for operators with constant coefficients. We shall assume that $F_1(t)$, $F_2(t)$ have continuous derivatives of all orders required. To justify the principle, we remark that if $x(t)$, $y(t)$, ... satisfy (7–34) and (7–35), then (7–36) holds since it is the same as (7–34), and (7–37) holds since it is obtained from (7–34), (7–35) by applying $\phi(D)$ to the first equation, multiplying the second equation by k, and adding the results. Conversely, if (7–36), (7–37) hold, then (7–34) holds since it is the same as (7–36), and (7–35) holds since it is obtained from (7–36), (7–37) by multiplying (7–36) by $\phi(D)$, subtracting (7–37), and then dividing by $-k$ (assumed different from 0).

To illustrate the procedure, we consider the two equations

$$3x - (D - 1)y = 1, \tag{7-38}$$

$$(D - 1)x + (D - 2)y = e^t. \tag{7-39}$$

We multiply Eq. (7-38) by $\phi(D) = D - 1$, Eq. (7-39) by $k = -3$, and then add, thereby eliminating x:

$$(-D^2 - D + 5)y = -1 - 3e^t. \tag{7-39$'$}$$

The new equation and the old equation (7-38) are equivalent to (7-38), (7-39). The numbering (7-39′) indicates that the new equation replaces (7-39). Thus the *elimination process retains the equation which has been multiplied by* $\phi(D)$, *and replaces the one which has been multiplied by* k *by a new equation.* It can happen that $\phi(D)$ reduces to a nonzero constant; in that case, the elimination process is the same as in ordinary algebra, and we can use the new equation as a replacement for either one of the given equations.

We could eliminate y from Eqs. (7-38), (7-39) by multiplying the first by $(D - 2)$, the second by $(D - 1)$, and adding the results:

$$(D^2 + D - 5)x = -2. \tag{7-40}$$

However, although Eq. (7-40) is implied by (7-38), (7-39), we cannot combine it with either of the given equations to obtain the other. It is this sort of procedure which leads to extraneous solutions. Thus from the given equations we obtain (7-39′), (7-40) and, accordingly,

$$x = \tfrac{2}{5} + c_1e^{at} + c_2e^{bt}, \tag{7-41}$$

$$y = -\tfrac{1}{5} - e^t + c_3e^{at} + c_4e^{bt}, \tag{7-42}$$

where a, b are the numbers $\frac{1}{2}(-1 \pm \sqrt{21})$. However, (7-41), (7-42) contain too many arbitrary constants; if we substitute in (7-38), we find

$$[3c_1 - (a - 1)c_3]e^{at} + [3c_2 - (b - 1)c_4]e^{bt} = 0;$$

hence $c_1 = \frac{1}{3}(a - 1)c_3$, $c_2 = \frac{1}{3}(b - 1)c_4$, and

$$x = \tfrac{2}{5} + \tfrac{1}{3}[(a - 1)c_3e^{at} + (b - 1)c_4e^{bt}]. \tag{7-43}$$

With this expression for x, and with y as given in (7-42), we find that (7-39) is also satisfied; thus the general solution contains two arbitrary constants.

The same result could have been obtained without any possibility of extraneous solutions from (7–38), (7–39′); solving (7–39′) for y and substituting in (7–38) immediately gives (7–42), (7–43) as the general solution.

As a further illustration, we consider the system

$$(D - 14)x + 8y - 2z = t, \tag{I}$$

$$-41x + (D + 24)y - 7z = 0, \tag{II}$$

$$-73x + 44y + (D - 15)z = 0. \tag{III}$$

We have numbered the equations (I), (II), (III) to emphasize that at each stage there will be three equations; as primes are added, individual equations will be replaced by others. We first seek to eliminate z. Multiplication of Eq. (I) by 7, of Eq. (II) by -2, and addition yield the new equation

$$(7D - 16)x + (-2D + 8)y = 7t. \tag{II′}$$

Multiplication of Eq. (I) by $(D - 15)$, of Eq. (III) by 2, and addition yield

$$(D^2 - 29D + 64)x + (8D - 32)y = 1 - 15t. \tag{III′}$$

Multiplication of Eq. (II′) by 4, of Eq. (III′) by 1, and addition yield

$$(D^2 - D)x = 13t + 1. \tag{III″}$$

Thus our given system (I), (II), (III) has been replaced by the equivalent system (I), (II′), (III″). From (III″) we easily find x:

$$x = c_1 + c_2e^t - \tfrac{13}{2}t^2 - 14t; \tag{IV}$$

substitution in (II′) gives an equation for y:

$$\begin{aligned}(2D - 8)y &= (7D - 16)x - 7t\\ &= -16c_1 - 9c_2 + 104t^2 + 126t - 98.\end{aligned}$$

We find

$$y = 2c_1 + \tfrac{3}{2}c_2e^t + c_3e^{4t} - 13t^2 - \tfrac{89}{4}t + \tfrac{107}{16}. \tag{V}$$

Substitution of the expressions (IV), (V) in (I) gives z:

$$z = c_1 - \tfrac{1}{2}c_2e^t + 4c_3e^{4t} - \tfrac{13}{2}t^2 + 2t + \tfrac{79}{4}. \tag{VI}$$

Equations (IV), (V), (VI) give the general solution of the given system. We note that there are three arbitrary constants, but that the expression for x contains only two constants.

It is not difficult to show that the elimination process can always be applied to successively eliminate all but one unknown. For three unknowns we obtain an equivalent system of "triangular form":

$$\begin{aligned} f_1(D)x &= F_1(t), \\ f_2(D)x + g_2(D)y &= F_2(t), \\ f_3(D)x + g_3(D)y + h_3(D)z &= F_3(t). \end{aligned}$$

From these equations we obtain x, y, z, in turn. For further information see p. 160 of Reference 1, pp. 148–149 of Reference 5, and pp. 138–142 of Reference 7.

Remark. The operational procedure can also be applied to homogeneous equations, as an alternative to the method of Sections 7–2 through 7–4.

PROBLEMS

1. Find a particular solution for each of the following by variation of parameters; the general solution of the related homogeneous system is given by the answer to the corresponding problem following Section 7–3:

(a) $Dx = 7x + 6y - 10e^{3t}$, $Dy = 2x + 6y - 5e^{3t}$ (see Prob. 1 following Section 7–3);

(b) $Dx = -x + y + \cos t$, $Dy = -5x + 3y$ (see Prob. 2 following Section 7–3);

(c) $Dx = 16x + 4y + 38z - 2e^{-t}$, $Dy = -9x - 7y - 18z - 3e^{-t}$, $Dz = -4x - 4y - 11z + 2e^{-t}$ (see Prob. 3 following Section 7–3).

2. Apply the operational method to obtain the general solution of each of the following parts of Prob. 1:

(a) part (a), (b) part (b), (c) part (c).

3. Obtain the general solution by the operational method:

$$Dx = x + y, \qquad Dy = y + z, \qquad Dz = z + u, \qquad Du = u + x.$$

4. Let the following nonhomogeneous linear system be given for $t > 0$:

$$t^3 Dx + (-1 - 2t^2)x + ty = t^2, \qquad t^4 Dy + (t^2 - 1)x + (t - 2t^3)y = t^3.$$

(a) Verify that the following pairs are linearly independent solutions of the related homogeneous system:

$$x_1 = t^2, \qquad y_1 = t; \qquad x_2 = t, \qquad y_2 = t^2 + 1.$$

(b) Obtain the general solution of the related homogeneous system.

(c) Apply variation of parameters to obtain the general solution of the given nonhomogeneous system.

ANSWERS

1. (a) $x = e^{3t}$, $y = e^{3t}$; (b) $x = \sin t - \cos t$, $y = 2\sin t - \cos t$;
(c) $x = -2te^{-t}$, $y = -3te^{-t}$, $z = 2te^{-t}$.

2. (a) $x = 2c_1e^{10t} + e^{3t}(3c_2 + 1)$, $y = c_1e^{10t} + e^{3t}(-2c_2 + 1)$;
(b) $x = e^t(c_1 \cos t + c_2 \sin t) - \cos t + \sin t$,
$y = e^t[c_1(2\cos t - \sin t) + c_2(2\sin t + \cos t)] + 2\sin t - \cos t$;
(c) $x = c_1e^{2t} - 2e^{-t}(c_2 + t) - 2c_3e^{-3t}$, $y = -c_1e^{2t} - 3e^{-t}(c_2 + t)$,
$z = 2e^{-t}(c_2 + t) + c_3e^{-3t}$.

3. $x = c_1 + c_2e^{2t} + e^t(c_3 \cos t + c_4 \sin t)$,
$y = -c_1 + c_2e^{2t} + e^t(c_4 \cos t - c_3 \sin t)$,
$z = c_1 + c_2e^{2t} + e^t(-c_3 \cos t - c_4 \sin t)$,
$u = -c_1 + c_2e^{2t} + e^t(-c_4 \cos t + c_3 \sin t)$.

4. (b) $x = c_1t^2 + c_2t$, $y = c_1t + c_2(t^2 + 1)$;
(c) $x = c_1t^2 + c_2t + (-6 - 2t^{-1} + t^{-2})/12$,
$y = c_1t + c_2(t^2 + 1) + (-6 - 2t^{-1} - 2t^{-2} + t^{-3})/12$.

7–7 Linear systems in general form. As remarked in Section 7–1, there are more general systems of simultaneous linear differential equations which are reducible to the basic form of (7–1), (7–2), or (7–3). For example, the equations

$$(D^2 - 1)x + (D + 2)y = t^2, \qquad (D^2 + D)y + 2Dx = 1 - t \tag{7–44}$$

are reducible to basic form by the introduction of the auxiliary variables $z = Dx$, $u = Dy$; Eqs. (7–44) are then equivalent to the four equations

$$Dx = z, \qquad Dy = u, \qquad Dz - x + u + 2y = t^2,$$
$$Du + u + 2z = 1 - t. \tag{7–45}$$

The most general case to be considered here is that of n linear equations in n unknowns, with coefficients which are polynomials in D:

$$\begin{aligned} \phi_{11}(D)x_1 + \cdots + \phi_{1n}(D)x_n &= f_1(t), \\ \phi_{21}(D)x_1 + \cdots + \phi_{2n}(D)x_n &= f_2(t), \\ &\vdots \\ \phi_{n1}(D)x_1 + \cdots + \phi_{nn}(D)x_n &= f_n(t). \end{aligned} \tag{7–46}$$

When the $f_j(t)$ are all 0, the system is called *homogeneous*. For the sake of simplicity, we assume the ϕ_{ij} to have constant coefficients; in general, the coefficients would be permitted to depend on t. Equations (7–44) provide an example with two unknown functions x, y; the following is an example with three unknowns:

$$\begin{aligned} (D^2 - 2D + 1)x + (D - 3)y + Dz &= 1, \\ (D^2 + 1)x + (2D + 1)y + (D - 2)z &= t, \\ (4D^2 - 4)x + (26D + 20)y - (19D + 4)z &= t^2. \end{aligned} \tag{7–47}$$

For each unknown a derivative of highest order will appear. For example, in (7–47) the derivatives of highest order are D^2x, Dy, Dz. If the determinant of coefficients of the highest derivatives is zero, we call the system *degenerate;* if the determinant is not zero, we call the system *nondegenerate.* For (7–47) the determinant is

$$\begin{vmatrix} 1 & 1 & 1 \\ 1 & 2 & 1 \\ 4 & 26 & -19 \end{vmatrix} = -23;$$

hence the system is nondegenerate.

A nondegenerate system can always be reduced to the basic form of Section 7–1. For since the determinant of coefficients is nonzero, we can solve the equations for the highest derivatives in terms of the remaining quantities. Introduction of new unknowns equal to the derivatives of lower order leads at once to the basic form. Thus, for example, (7–47) can be solved for D^2x, Dy, Dz. We write the equations as follows:

$$\begin{aligned} D^2x + Dy + Dz &= (2D - 1)x + 3y + 1, \\ D^2x + 2Dy + Dz &= -x - y + 2z + t, \\ 4D^2x + 26Dy - 19Dz &= 4x - 26y + 4z + t^2. \end{aligned}$$

Then either by elimination or by determinants we find

$$\begin{aligned} D^2x &= \tfrac{1}{23}(128Dx - 15x + 211y - 86z + t^2 - 45t + 64), \\ Dy &= -2Dx - 4y + 2z + t - 1, \\ Dz &= \tfrac{1}{23}(-36Dx - 8x - 50y + 40z - t^2 + 22t - 18). \end{aligned}$$

If we then set $u = Dx$, we obtain the system

$$\begin{aligned} Dx &= u, \qquad Dy = -2u - 4y + 2z + t - 1, \\ Dz &= \tfrac{1}{23}(-8x - 36u - 50y + 40z - t^2 + 22t - 18), \\ Du &= \tfrac{1}{23}(128u - 15x + 211y - 86z + t^2 - 45t + 64). \end{aligned} \tag{7–48}$$

We note that if (7–47) is replaced by the related homogeneous system, then so also is (7–48).

Since a nondegenerate system can be reduced to basic form, the existence theorem of Section 7–1 is applicable. For example, we can conclude that Eqs. (7–47) have a unique solution with given initial values of x, y, z and $u = Dx$. The general solution will be formed from four linearly independent solutions of the related homogeneous system and one particular solution of the nonhomogeneous system. (The related homogeneous system is first defined with reference to the equations in basic form; however, as the above example shows, it is equivalent to the system obtained by replacing the right-hand sides of (7–46) by 0.)

If the system is degenerate, the reduction to basic form is in general impossible. The equations may in fact be contradictory, as the following example shows:

$$Dx + 2Dy = 1, \qquad Dx + 2Dy = 2.$$

The variety of other possibilities is shown by Prob. 4 following Section 7–9. For a full discussion see pp. 138–142 of Reference 7.

7–8 Homogeneous linear systems in general form. We can rewrite a nondegenerate homogeneous linear system in basic form and then follow the procedures of Sections 7–2 through 7–4. However, we can achieve the same results by substituting directly in the given equations.

We illustrate the procedure by considering the homogeneous system related to (7–47):

$$\begin{aligned}(D^2 - 2D + 1)x + (D - 3)y + Dz &= 0,\\ (D^2 + 1)x + (2D + 1)y + (D - 2)z &= 0,\\ (4D^2 - 4)x + (26D + 26)y - (19D + 4)z &= 0.\end{aligned} \tag{7–49}$$

We set $x = \alpha e^{\lambda t}$, $y = \beta e^{\lambda t}$, $z = \gamma e^{\lambda t}$ and obtain

$$\begin{aligned}(\lambda^2 - 2\gamma + 1)\alpha + (\lambda - 3)\beta + \lambda\gamma &= 0,\\ (\lambda^2 + 1)\alpha + (2\lambda + 1)\beta + (\lambda - 2)\gamma &= 0,\\ (4\lambda^2 - 4)\alpha + (26\lambda + 20)\beta - (19\lambda + 4)\gamma &= 0.\end{aligned} \tag{7–50}$$

These equations have a nontrivial solution α, β, γ when

$$\begin{vmatrix} \lambda^2 - 2\lambda + 1 & \lambda - 3 & \lambda \\ \lambda^2 + 1 & 2\lambda + 1 & \lambda - 2 \\ 4\lambda^2 - 4 & 26\lambda + 20 & -19\lambda - 4 \end{vmatrix} = 0; \tag{7–51}$$

this is indeed the *characteristic equation* of the given system (or of the equivalent system in basic form). When expanded, (7-51) is a *fourth* degree equation in λ:

$$-23\lambda^4 + 76\lambda^3 + 23\lambda^2 - 76\lambda = 0.$$

The roots are found to be 0, ± 1, 76/23, and since they are simple, we obtain four linearly independent solutions of form $\alpha e^{\lambda t}$, $\beta e^{\lambda t}$, $\gamma e^{\lambda t}$. For example, when $\lambda = 0$, Eqs. (7-50) become

$$\begin{aligned} \alpha - 3\beta &= 0, \\ \alpha + \beta - 2\gamma &= 0, \\ -4\alpha + 20\beta - 4\gamma &= 0; \end{aligned}$$

thus $\alpha = 3\beta$, $\gamma = 2\beta$. We can choose $\alpha = 3$, $\beta = 1$, $\gamma = 2$ and obtain the solution $x = 3$, $y = 1$, $z = 2$. Similarly, $\lambda = 1$, $\lambda = -1$, $\lambda = 76/23$ lead to solutions of the form sought, and the general solution is

$$\begin{aligned} x &= 3c_1 + c_2e^t + 11c_3e^{-t} - 301{,}070c_4e^{76t/23}, \\ y &= c_1 - 2c_2e^t + 10c_3e^{-t} + 394{,}910c_4e^{76t/23}, \\ z &= 2c_1 - 4c_2e^t + 4c_3e^{-t} + 447{,}440c_4e^{76t/23}. \end{aligned} \tag{7-52}$$

If we adjoin the relation

$$u = Dx = c_2e^t - 11c_3e^{-t} - 13{,}090c_4e^{76t/23}, \tag{7-53}$$

then we have the general solution of the equations in basic form.

If λ_1 is a multiple root of the characteristic equation, then we proceed as in Section 7-4. Complex roots are also handled as in the previous case.

7-9 Nonhomogeneous linear systems in general form. Both the method of variation of parameters and the operational method can be adapted to nonhomogeneous equations in general form. We apply both methods to the following example:

$$\begin{aligned} (3D^2 + 1)x + (D^2 + 3)y &= f(t), \\ (2D^2 + 1)x + (D^2 + 2)y &= g(t). \end{aligned} \tag{7-54}$$

Variation of parameters. The substitution $x = \alpha e^{\lambda t}$, $y = \beta e^{\lambda t}$ in the related homogeneous system leads to the characteristic equation $\lambda^4 - 1 = 0$. The roots are ± 1, $\pm i$. The general solution of the homogeneous system is

$$\begin{aligned} x &= c_1e^t + c_2e^{-t} + c_3 \cos t + c_4 \sin t, \\ y &= -c_1e^t - c_2e^{-t} + c_3 \cos t + c_4 \sin t. \end{aligned} \tag{7-55}$$

We introduce the variables $z = Dx$, $u = Dy$, so that

$$\begin{aligned} z &= c_1e^t - c_2e^{-t} - c_3 \sin t + c_4 \cos t, \\ u &= -c_1e^t + c_2e^{-t} - c_3 \sin t + c_4 \cos t. \end{aligned} \tag{7–56}$$

Thus (7–55), (7–56) together give the general solution of the homogeneous system in basic form.

We now replace the constants c_1, c_2, c_3, c_4 by variables v_1, v_2, v_3, v_4. Equations (7–55), (7–56) thus become equations that describe a change of variables:

$$\begin{aligned} x &= v_1e^t + v_2e^{-t} + v_3 \cos t + v_4 \sin t, \\ y &= -v_1e^t - v_2e^{-t} + v_3 \cos t + v_4 \sin t, \\ z &= v_1e^t - v_2e^{-t} - v_3 \sin t + v_4 \cos t, \\ u &= -v_1e^t + v_2e^{-t} - v_3 \sin t + v_4 \cos t. \end{aligned} \tag{7–57}$$

To obtain differential equations for $v_1, \ldots, v_4$ as functions of t, we substitute in the relations

$$\begin{aligned} 3Dz + x + Du + 3y = f, \qquad 2Dz + x + Du + 2y = g, \\ Dx = z, \qquad Dy = u. \end{aligned} \tag{7–58}$$

[The first two equations in (7–58) are simply the given differential equations (7–55).] After substitution we obtain the equations

$$\begin{aligned} 2v_1'e^t - 2v_2'e^{-t} - 4v_3' \sin t + 4v_4' \cos t &= f, \\ v_1'e^t - v_2'e^{-t} - 3v_3' \sin t + 3v_4' \cos t &= g, \\ v_1'e^t + v_2'e^{-t} + v_3' \cos t + v_4' \sin t &= 0, \\ -v_1'e^t - v_2'e^{-t} + v_3' \cos t + v_4' \sin t &= 0. \end{aligned} \tag{7–59}$$

The terms in $v_1, \ldots, v_4$ drop out, simply because (7–55) and (7–56) are the general solution of the homogeneous system related to (7–58). From (7–59) we easily find

$$\begin{aligned} v_1' &= \frac{e^t}{4}(3f - 4g), \qquad & v_2' &= \frac{e^t}{4}(4f - 3g), \\ v_3' &= \tfrac{1}{2}(f \sin t - 2g \sin t), \qquad & v_4' &= \tfrac{1}{2}(2g \cos t - f \cos t). \end{aligned} \tag{7–60}$$

If $f(t)$, $g(t)$ are given, $v_1, \ldots, v_4$ are easily found by integration. Substitution in (7–57) then yields a particular solution, which can be combined with (7–55) to give the general solution.

Operational method. We proceed as in Section 7–6. We obtain a system equivalent to (7–54) by replacing the second equation by the first minus the second:

$$(3D^2 + 1)x + (D^2 + 3)y = f(t), \tag{I}$$

$$D^2x + y = f(t) - g(t). \tag{II$'$}$$

Multiplication of Eq. (I) by -1, of Eq. (II$'$) by $(D^2 + 3)$, and addition give

$$(D^4 - 1)x = (D^2 - 4)f - 3g. \tag{I$'$}$$

We solve (I$'$) for x and then obtain y from Eq. (II$'$):

$$x = c_1e^t + c_2e^{-t} + c_3 \cos t + c_4 \sin t + x^*(t), \tag{7–61}$$

$$y = -c_1e^t - c_2e^{-t} + c_3 \cos t + c_4 \sin t + f(t) - g(t) - D^2x^*(t). \tag{7–62}$$

Equations (7–61) and (7–62) provide the general solution sought.

PROBLEMS

1. Verify that each of the following systems is nondegenerate, and obtain the general solution:

(a) $(D + 1)x + (D + 2)y = 0$, $(7D - 5)x + (8D - 4)y = 0$;

(b) $(2D - 3)x + (3D - 6)y + (D^2 + D + 5)z = 0$,
$(7D - 12)x + (11D - 24)y + (3D^2 + 4D + 12)z = 0$,
$(D - 3)x + (2D - 6)y + (D^2 + 3D - 1)z = 0$;

(c) $(D - 8)x - 4y + (D - 12)z = 0$,
$(D + 1)x + Dy + (2D + 1)z = 0$,
$(3D - 6)x + (2D - 4)y + (D^2 + 5D - 11)z = 0$.

2. Write each of the systems of Prob. 1 in basic form.

3. Obtain the general solution of each of the following systems. The related homogeneous systems are considered in Prob. 1.

(a) $(D + 1)x + (D + 2)y = 5$, $(7D - 5)x + (8D - 4)y = 2$.

(b) $(2D - 3)x + (3D - 6)y + (D^2 + D + 5)z = 0$,
$(7D - 12)x + (11D - 24)y + (3D^2 + 4D + 12)z = 0$,
$(D - 3)x + (2D - 6)y + (D^2 + 3D - 1)z = e^{3t}$.

(c) $(D - 8)x - 4y + (D - 12)z = \cos 3t$,
$(D + 1)x + Dy + (2D + 1)z = 0$,
$(3D - 6)x + (2D - 4)y + (D^2 + 5D - 11)z = 0$.

4. Verify that each of the following systems is degenerate, and obtain all solutions (if there are any):

(a) $(D - 1)x + (2D + 1)y = 0$, $(D + 1)x + (2D + 3)y = 0$;

(b) $(D - 1)x + (2D + 1)y = 2,\ (D + 1)x + (2D + 3)y = 0;$
(c) $(D - 1)x + Dy + 2Dz = 1,\ Dx - Dy + (D + 1)z = t,$
$(D - 3)x + 5Dy + (4D - 2)z = 4 - 2t;$
(d) $(D^2 - 1)x + (D^2 + 1)y = 0,\ (D + 2)x + (D + 2)y = 0;$
(e) $(D - 1)x + Dy = 0,\ x - y = 1.$

ANSWERS

1. (a) $x = 5c_1e^{3t} + 4c_2e^{2t},\ y = -4c_1e^{3t} - 3c_2e^{2t};$
(b) $x = 2c_1 + c_2e^{3t} + e^{-t}[c_3(17 \cos t + 5 \sin t) + c_4(17 \sin t - 5 \cos t)],$
$y = -c_1 - c_2e^{3t} + e^{-t}[c_3(-9 \cos t - 3 \sin t) + c_4(-9 \sin t + 3 \cos t)],$
$z = e^{-t}[c_3(\cos t + \sin t) + c_4(\sin t - \cos t)];$
(c) $x = c_1e^t + c_2e^{-t} + 2c_3e^{2t} + c_4e^{2t}(2t - 1),$
$y = c_1e^t + c_2e^{-t} - 3c_3e^{2t} + c_4e^{2t}(-3t + 2),\ z = -c_1e^t - c_2e^{-t}.$

2. (a) $Dx = -13x - 20y,\ Dy = 12x + 18y;$
(b) $Dx = -3x - 6y + 5u - 15z,\ Dy = 3x + 6y - 3u + 9z,\ Dz = u,$
$Du = -2z - 2u;$
(c) $Dx = 8x + 4y + 12z - u,\ Dy = -9x - 4y - 13z - u,\ Dz = u,$
$Du = z.$

3. (a) $x = -4 + 5c_1e^{3t} + 4c_2e^{2t},\ y = \frac{9}{2} - 4c_1e^{3t} - 3c_2e^{2t};$
(b) $x = -\frac{1}{3}e^{3t} + 2c_1 + c_2e^{3t} + e^{-t}[c_3(17 \cos t + 5 \sin t) + c_4(17 \sin t - 5 \cos t)],$
$y = -c_1 - c_2e^{3t} + e^{-t}[c_3(-9 \cos t - 3 \sin t) + c_4(3 \cos t - 9 \sin t)],$
$z = \frac{1}{17}e^{3t} + e^{-t}[c_3(\cos t + \sin t) + c_4(\sin t - \cos t)];$
(c) $x = c_1e^t + c_2e^{-t} + 2c_3e^{2t} + c_4e^{2t}(2t - 1) - (529 \cos 3t - 150 \sin 3t)/1690,$
$y = c_1e^t + c_2e^{-t} - 3c_3e^{2t} + c_4e^{2t}(2 - 3t) + (241 \cos 3t - 30 \sin 3t)/1690,$
$z = -c_1e^t - c_2e^{-t} + (\cos 3t)/10.$

4. (a) $x = ce^{-2t},\ y = -ce^{-2t};$ (b) $x = ce^{-2t} - \frac{3}{2},\ y = -ce^{-2t} + \frac{1}{2};$
(c) no solution; (d) $x = 5ce^{-2t},\ y = -3ce^{-2t};$ (e) $x = ce^{t/2},\ y = -1 + ce^{t/2}.$

7–10 Application of Laplace transforms. The solution of a linear system, with constant coefficients, which satisfies prescribed initial conditions can be obtained efficiently with the aid of the Laplace transform. The procedures parallel those of Section 5–5. We illustrate them for the system

$$\begin{aligned}(3D^2 + 1)x + (D^2 + 3)y &= f(t),\\ (2D^2 + 1)x + (D^2 + 2)y &= g(t)\end{aligned} \tag{7–63}$$

discussed in Section 7-9. The system is nondegenerate; hence we can prescribe initial values x_0 of x, y_0 of y, x_0' of $x' = Dx$, y_0' of $y' = Dy$, at time $t_0 = 0$. We take Laplace transforms on both sides of Eqs. (7-64) and apply the rule

$$\mathfrak{L}[D^2u] = s^2\mathfrak{L}[u] - [u'(0) + su(0)] \tag{7-64}$$

established in Section 5-5. We obtain the equations

$$\begin{aligned}(3s^2 + 1)\mathfrak{L}[x] + (s^2 + 3)\mathfrak{L}[y] &= \mathfrak{L}[f] + 3x_0' + 3sx_0 + y_0' + sy_0,\\ (2s^2 + 1)\mathfrak{L}[x] + (s^2 + 2)\mathfrak{L}[y] &= \mathfrak{L}[g] + 2x_0' + 2sx_0 + y_0' + sy_0.\end{aligned} \tag{7-65}$$

These can be solved for $\mathfrak{L}[x]$, $\mathfrak{L}[y]$:

$$\mathfrak{L}[x] = \frac{(s^2 + 2)\mathfrak{L}[f] - (s^2 + 3)\mathfrak{L}[g] + x_0s^3 + x_0's^2 - y_0s - y_0'}{s^4 - 1},$$

$$\mathfrak{L}[y] = \frac{(3s^2 + 1)\mathfrak{L}[g] - (2s^2 + 1)\mathfrak{L}[f] + y_0s^3 + y_0's^2 - x_0s - x_0'}{s^4 - 1}.$$

If $f(t)$ and $g(t)$ are given for $t \geqq 0$ (and satisfy appropriate conditions), $\mathfrak{L}[f]$ and $\mathfrak{L}[g]$ can be found; hence $\mathfrak{L}[x]$, $\mathfrak{L}[y]$ are known and x, y can be found. If a good set of tables of Laplace transforms is available, these steps usually cause little difficulty.

For example, if $f(t) = e^t$, $g(t) = e^{-t}$, $x_0 = 1$, $y_0 = 1$, $x_0' = 0$, $y_0' = 0$, we find (see Eq. 5-20)

$$\mathfrak{L}[f] = \frac{1}{s - 1},$$

$$\mathfrak{L}[g] = \frac{1}{s + 1},$$

$$\begin{aligned}\mathfrak{L}[x] &= \frac{s^5 - 2s^3 + 2s^2 + 5}{(s + 1)^2(s - 1)^2(s^2 + 1)}\\ &= \frac{-7/8}{(s - 1)^2} + \frac{1/4}{s - 1} + \frac{1}{(s + 1)^2} + \frac{9/8}{s + 1} + \frac{(3s + 3)/4}{s^2 + 1}.\end{aligned}$$

$$\begin{aligned}\mathfrak{L}[y] &= \frac{s^3 - 5s^2 - 2}{(s + 1)^2(s - 1)^2(s^2 + 1)}\\ &= \frac{-3/4}{(s - 1)^2} + \frac{5/8}{s - 1} + \frac{-1}{(s + 1)^2} + \frac{-3/8}{s + 1} + \frac{(3s + 3)/4}{s^2 + 1},\end{aligned}$$

with the aid of partial-fraction expansions. From Eqs. (5-20), (5-24),

(5–25) we now conclude that

$$x = -\tfrac{7}{8}e^t + \tfrac{1}{4}te^t + \tfrac{9}{8}e^{-t} + te^{-t} + \tfrac{3}{4}(\cos t + \sin t),$$
$$y = \tfrac{5}{8}e^t - \tfrac{3}{4}te^t - \tfrac{3}{8}e^{-t} - te^{-t} + \tfrac{3}{4}(\cos t + \sin t).$$

Remark. If we do not give numerical values for the initial values but denote them as above by x_0, x_0', y_0, y_0', then we obtain the general solution, with $x_0, x_0', \ldots$ as the arbitrary constants.

PROBLEMS

1. Find the solution for each of the following, with given initial values:

(a) $Dx = 7x + 6y,\ Dy = 2x + 6y;\ x = 1,\ y = 2$ for $t = 0$;

(b) $Dx = y,\ \ Dy = 4x + 3y - 4z,\ \ Dz = x + 2y - z;\ \ \ x = 0,\ y = 0,\ z = 1$ for $t = 0$;

(c) the system of Prob. 1(b) following Section 7–9, with initial conditions $x = 0,\ y = 0,\ z = 0,\ Dz = 1$ for $t = 0$.

2. Find the general solution for each of the following, with initial values as arbitrary constants:

(a) the system of Prob. 1(a) following Section 7–9;

(b) the system of Prob. 1(c) following Section 7–9.

ANSWERS

1. (a) $x = (16e^{10t} - 9e^{3t})/7,\ y = (8e^{10t} + 6e^{3t})/7$;

(b) $x = -4 + 4e^t(1 - t),\ y = -4te^t,\ z = e^t(5 - 6t) - 4$;

(c) $x = -6 + e^{(-1+i)t}[3 - (11/2)i] + e^{(-1-i)t}[3 + (11/2)i]$,
$y = -3 + 3e^{(-1+i)t}(-\tfrac{1}{2} + i) + 3e^{(-1-i)t}(-\tfrac{1}{2} - i)$,
$z = -\tfrac{1}{2}ie^{(-1+i)t} + \tfrac{1}{2}ie^{(-1-i)t}$.

2. (a) $x = x_0(16e^{2t} - 15e^{3t}) + 20y_0(e^{2t} - e^{3t})$,
$y = 12x_0(e^{3t} - e^{2t}) + y_0(16e^{3t} - 15e^{2t})$;

(b) $x = x_0e^{2t}(1 + 6t) + 4y_0te^{2t} + \tfrac{1}{2}z_0(-e^t - e^{-t} + 2e^{2t} + 20te^{2t}) + \tfrac{1}{2}u_0(e^{-t} - e^t)$,
$y = -9x_0te^{2t} + y_0(e^{2t} - 6te^{2t}) + \tfrac{1}{2}z_0(-e^t - e^{-t} + 2e^{2t} - 30te^{2t}) + \tfrac{1}{2}u_0(e^{-t} - e^t)$,
$z = \tfrac{1}{2}z_0(e^t + e^{-t}) + \tfrac{1}{2}u_0(e^t - e^{-t})$, where $Dz = u_0$ for $t = 0$.

7–11 Applications in mechanics. The majority of applications of simultaneous linear differential equations in mechanics arise in the analysis of oscillations about equilibrium. The linear nature of the equations generally results from an approximation, which is accurate only near the equilibrium position; accordingly, the theory is often described as that of "small vibrations."

One example, that of two coupled springs (Example B), is given in Section 6–7. The differential equations are

$$\begin{aligned}(m_1D^2 + b_1D + 2k^2)x_1 - k^2x_2 &= F_1(t),\\ (m_2D^2 + b_2D + 2k^2)x_2 - k^2x_1 &= F_2(t),\end{aligned} \tag{7–66}$$

where x_1, x_2 are coordinates measuring displacements from equilibrium, $F_1(t)$, $F_2(t)$ are applied forces, and m_1, m_2, b_1, b_2, and k^2 are positive constants.

The solution of (7–66) by elimination is carried out in Section 6–7. Here we consider the exponential substitution and certain physical concepts to which it leads.

We assume that $F_1(t)$ and $F_2(t)$ are 0 and that $b_1 = b_2 = 0$, so that there is no friction. Our equations then become

$$\begin{aligned}(m_1D^2 + 2k^2)x_1 - k^2x_2 &= 0,\\ (m_2D^2 + 2k^2)x_2 - k^2x_1 &= 0.\end{aligned} \tag{7–67}$$

The substitution $x_1 = \alpha e^{\lambda t}$, $x_2 = \beta e^{\lambda t}$ leads to the characteristic equation

$$0 = \begin{vmatrix} m_1\lambda^2 + 2k^2 & -k^2 \\ -k^2 & m_2\lambda^2 + 2k^2 \end{vmatrix} = m_1m_2\lambda^4 + 2k^2\lambda^2(m_1 + m_2) + 3k^4, \tag{7–68}$$

which is a quadratic equation for λ^2, both of whose roots are negative:

$$\lambda^2 = \frac{k^2}{m_1m_2}\left(-m_1 - m_2 \pm \sqrt{m_1^2 + m_2^2 - m_1m_2}\right); \tag{7–69}$$

since the quantity under the radical can be written as $(m_1 - m_2)^2 + m_1m_2$, it must be positive and, in any case, it cannot be as large as $(m_1 + m_2)^2$, so that λ^2 must be negative. It follows that the four values for λ can be given as

$$\lambda = \pm\gamma i, \qquad \lambda = \pm\delta i, \tag{7–70}$$

where γ and δ are positive and unequal.

When $\lambda = \gamma i$, we obtain the equations

$$\begin{aligned}(-m_1\gamma^2 + 2k^2)\alpha - k^2\beta &= 0,\\ -k^2\alpha + (-m_2\gamma^2 + 2k^2)\beta &= 0;\end{aligned}$$

these are satisfied if $\alpha = k^2$, $\beta = -m_1\gamma^2 + 2k^2$. Corresponding complex solutions are given by

$$x_1 = k^2 e^{i\gamma t}, \qquad x_2 = (2k^2 - m_1\gamma^2)e^{i\gamma t}; \tag{7-71}$$

real solutions are obtained by taking real and imaginary parts:

$$\begin{aligned} x_1 &= k^2 \cos \gamma t, \qquad x_2 = (2k^2 - m_1\gamma^2) \cos \gamma t; \\ x_1 &= k^2 \sin \gamma t, \qquad x_2 = (2k^2 - m_1\gamma^2) \sin \gamma t. \end{aligned} \tag{7-72}$$

Similar expressions can be obtained for the other two solutions, with γ replaced by δ. The general solution can be written

$$\begin{aligned} x_1 &= A_1k^2 \sin (\gamma t + \phi_1) + A_2k^2 \sin (\delta t + \phi_2), \\ x_2 &= A_1(2k^2 - m_1\gamma^2) \sin (\gamma t + \phi_1) \\ &\quad + A_2(2k^2 - m_1\delta^2) \sin (\delta t + \phi_2), \end{aligned} \tag{7-73}$$

where A_1, A_2, ϕ_1, ϕ_2 are arbitrary constants.

The solutions for which $A_2 = 0$ describe a sinusoidal oscillation:

$$\begin{aligned} x_1 &= A_1k^2 \sin (\gamma t + \phi), \\ x_2 &= A_1(2k^2 - m_1\gamma^2) \sin (\gamma t + \phi_1). \end{aligned} \tag{7-74}$$

The two masses oscillate with the same frequency γ, with the same phase (perfect synchronization), and with amplitudes in a fixed ratio (possibly negative; see Prob. 1 below, following Section 7–12). A similar synchronous oscillation is obtained with frequency δ. The two types of sinusoidal motion are called *normal modes* of the physical system. The general motion is a linear combination of the two types; it will in general not even be periodic, unless δ and γ are commensurable.

The absence of friction in this example leads to the conclusion that there is no dissipation of energy or that the system is *conservative* (Prob. 2 below). Many other examples of conservative systems described by a pair of simultaneous equations such as (7–66) can be given. Such systems have two degrees of freedom; that is, two coordinates can vary.

For a more thorough discussion of applications of simultaneous linear differential equations to mechanics, one is referred to Section 6–13 of ODE and to Reference 2 at the end of this chapter.

7–12 Applications to electric networks. The analysis of a general electric network is based on Kirchhoff's laws:

I. The total voltage drop about each closed circuit (mesh) is zero.
II. The total current entering each junction (node) is zero.

A general network has a scheme such as that of Fig. 7-1. The nodes are represented by large dots, the branches by lines (possibly curved), each of which connects two nodes. Each branch has a positive direction selected, with respect to which currents and voltage drops are measured.

If there are N branches, then the N currents $I_1, \ldots, I_N$ can be taken as unknowns. By virtue of the second law, some of these can be eliminated, and n currents remain, in terms of which all others can be expressed.

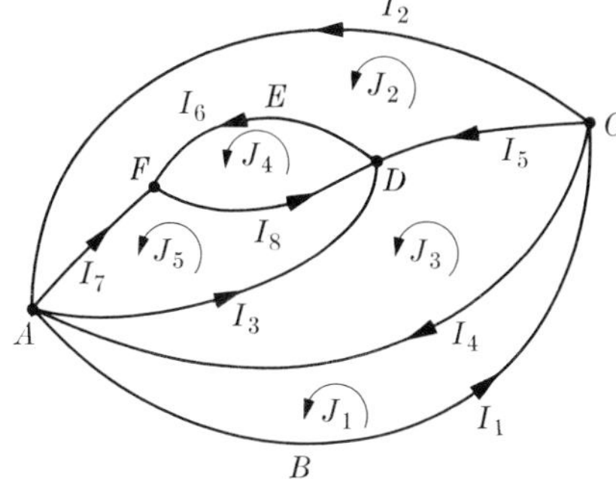

FIG. 7-1. Mesh currents in a planar network.

An alternative procedure is to introduce n *mesh currents* $J_1, \ldots, J_n$. These are certain linear combinations of $I_1, \ldots, I_N$, in terms of which $I_1, \ldots, I_N$ can all be expressed. The term *mesh* refers to a closed circuit in the network. For simplicity restrict attention to planar networks (i.e., those that can be placed in a plane without forcing two branches to cross). For a network in a plane the boundaries of the regions into which the interior of the network is subdivided form n meshes with which $J_1, \ldots, J_n$ can be associated; each is assumed to flow in the counterclockwise direction. If the kth mesh contains a branch on the outermost boundary, we can choose the current J_k as the current I through that branch. (We can assume the positive direction on the outermost boundary to be counterclockwise, as in Fig. 7-1.) The other mesh currents are then defined by systematically applying the rule that *if the lth branch is common to two meshes, say the pth and the qth, then* $I = \pm(J_p - J_q)$, *with a plus sign when the chosen direction on the branch is the same as the counterclockwise direction in the pth mesh, and a minus sign otherwise.*

For the network of Fig. 7-1 we choose $J_1 = I_1$, $J_2 = I_2$, then

$$\begin{aligned} I_4 &= J_1 - J_3, & I_5 &= J_3 - J_2, \\ I_6 &= J_4 - J_2, & I_8 &= J_4 - J_5, \\ I_7 &= J_2 - J_5, & I_3 &= J_5 - J_3. \end{aligned} \tag{7-75}$$

Hence

$$\begin{aligned} J_3 = J_1 - I_4 = I_1 - I_4, \qquad J_4 = J_2 + I_6 = I_2 + I_6, \\ J_5 = J_4 - I_8 = I_2 + I_6 - I_8. \end{aligned} \tag{7-76}$$

We can verify that by virtue of Kirchhoff's second law, all the equations (7-75) are satisfied. Thus $I_1, \ldots, I_8$ can be expressed in terms of $J_1 \ldots,$

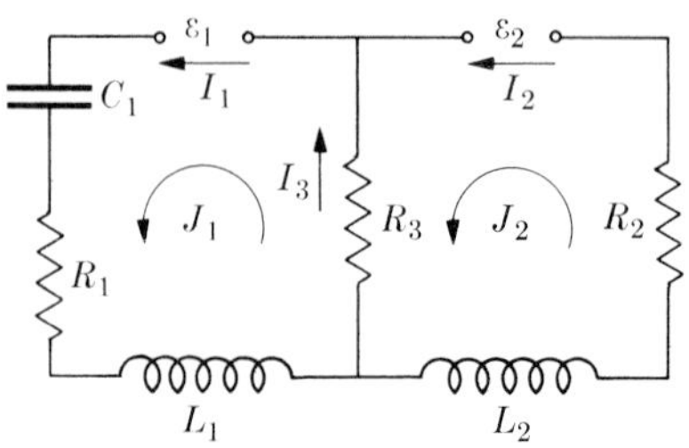

FIGURE 7–2

J_5, and conversely. For the network of Fig. 7–2 we have

$$J_1 = I_1, \qquad J_2 = I_2,$$
$$I_3 = J_1 - J_2, \tag{7–77}$$

in agreement with Kirchhoff's second law.

To obtain the differential equations for the network, we now apply Kirchhoff's first law to each mesh separately, and express the results in terms of the mesh currents. We illustrate this for the network of Fig. 7–2. For the first mesh,

$$L_1 \frac{dI_1}{dt} + R_1 I_1 + \frac{q_1}{C_1} + R_3 I_3 = \mathcal{E}_1,$$

where

$$q_1 = \int I_1 \, dt$$

is the charge on the capacitor. By (7–77) this can be rewritten

$$L_1 \frac{dJ_1}{dt} + R_1 J_1 + \frac{1}{C_1} \int J_1 \, dt + R_3(J_1 - J_2) = \mathcal{E}_1. \tag{7–78}$$

Similarly, for the second mesh,

$$L_2 \frac{dJ_2}{dt} + R_2 J_2 + \frac{1}{C_2} \int J_2 \, dt + R_3(J_2 - J_1) = \mathcal{E}_2. \tag{7–79}$$

By differentiating (7–78), (7–79), we eliminate the integral signs:

$$L_1 \frac{d^2 J_1}{dt^2} + R_1 \frac{dJ_1}{dt} + \frac{J_1}{C_1} + R_3 \left(\frac{dJ_1}{dt} - \frac{dJ_2}{dt} \right) = \frac{d\mathcal{E}_1}{dt},$$
$$L_2 \frac{d^2 J_2}{dt^2} + R_2 \frac{dJ_2}{dt} + \frac{J_2}{C_2} + R_3 \left(\frac{dJ_2}{dt} - \frac{dJ_1}{dt} \right) = \frac{d\mathcal{E}_2}{dt}. \tag{7–80}$$

We can also introduce the *mesh charges* Q_1, Q_2:

$$Q_1 = \int J_1 \, dt, \qquad Q_2 = \int J_2 \, dt, \tag{7–81}$$

for appropriate choices of the indefinite integrals. The equations (7–80) then become

$$L_1 \frac{d^2Q_1}{dt^2} + R_1 \frac{dQ_1}{dt} + \frac{Q_1}{C_1} + R_3 \left(\frac{dQ_1}{dt} - \frac{dQ_2}{dt}\right) = \mathcal{E}_1,$$
$$L_2 \frac{d^2Q_2}{dt^2} + R_2 \frac{dQ_2}{dt} + \frac{Q_2}{C_2} + R_3 \left(\frac{dQ_2}{dt} - \frac{dQ_1}{dt}\right) = \mathcal{E}_2. \tag{7–82}$$

For a general planar network containing inductance, resistance, capacitance, and driving emf's, we obtain a system of equations of second order

$$\sum_{\beta=1}^{n} (L_{\alpha\beta}D^2 + R_{\alpha\beta}D + \gamma_{\alpha\beta})J_\beta = \frac{d\mathcal{E}_\alpha}{dt}, \tag{7–83}$$

for $\alpha = 1, \ldots, n$. In terms of mesh charges $Q_\alpha = \int J_\alpha \, dt$, the system becomes

$$\sum_{\beta=1}^{n} (L_{\alpha\beta}D^2 + R_{\alpha\beta}D + \gamma_{\alpha\beta})Q_\beta = \mathcal{E}_\alpha. \tag{7–84}$$

The $\mathcal{E}_\alpha$ on the right-hand side is the total driving emf in the α'th mesh. From the way in which the mesh currents are defined, we can verify the *reciprocity law:*

$$L_{\alpha\beta} = L_{\beta\alpha}, \qquad R_{\alpha\beta} = R_{\beta\alpha}, \qquad \gamma_{\alpha\beta} = \gamma_{\beta\alpha}. \tag{7–85}$$

These equations follow from the fact that $L_{\alpha\beta}$ corresponds to the inductance contributed to the α'th mesh along the branch shared by the α'th mesh and β'th mesh; by the above definitions, interchanging α and β describes exactly the same inductance. A similar argument holds for the other terms.

For further information on applications of simultaneous differential equations to electrical networks one is referred to Section 6–14 of ODE and to References 3 and 4 below.

PROBLEMS

1. Let the characteristic roots $\pm\gamma i$, $\pm\delta i$ in Eqs. (7–70) be labeled so that γ corresponds to the plus sign in Eq. (7–69), δ to the minus sign, so that $0 < \gamma < \delta$.

(a) Show that

$$2k^2 - m_1\gamma^2 > 0, \quad 2k^2 - m_1\delta^2 < 0.$$

(b) Show that this implies that in the normal mode (7–74) the masses oscillate in phase, but in the other normal mode ($A_1 = 0$) the masses are 180° out of phase.

2. The kinetic energy T and potential energy V associated with Eqs. (7–67) are defined as follows:

$$T = \tfrac{1}{2}m_1(Dx_1)^2 + \tfrac{1}{2}m_2(Dx_2)^2, \qquad V = k^2(x_1^2 - x_1x_2 + x_2^2).$$

(a) Show that for each solution of the differential equations, $T + V = \text{const}$ (*conservation of energy*). [*Hint:* Show that, by virtue of the differential equations, $D(T + V) \equiv 0$.]

(b) Show that V has only one minimum point, namely $x_1 = 0$, $x_2 = 0$.

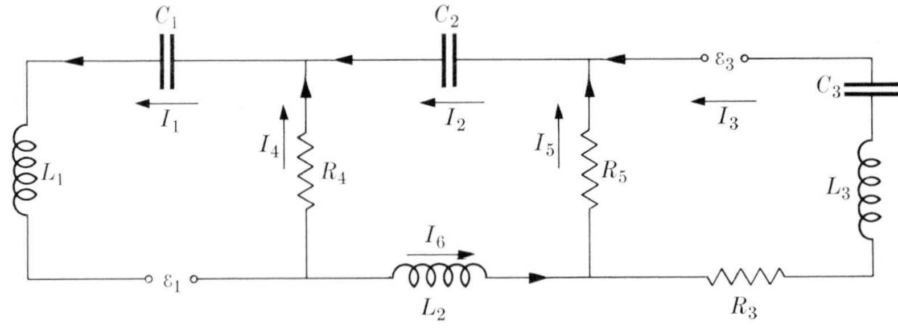

FIGURE 7–3

3. (a) For the network of Fig. 7–3 define mesh currents in terms of branch currents, and express all branch currents in terms of mesh currents. (Note that $I_2 = I_6$ by Kirchhoff's second law.)

(b) Obtain the differential equations satisfied by the mesh charges associated with the mesh currents of part (a).

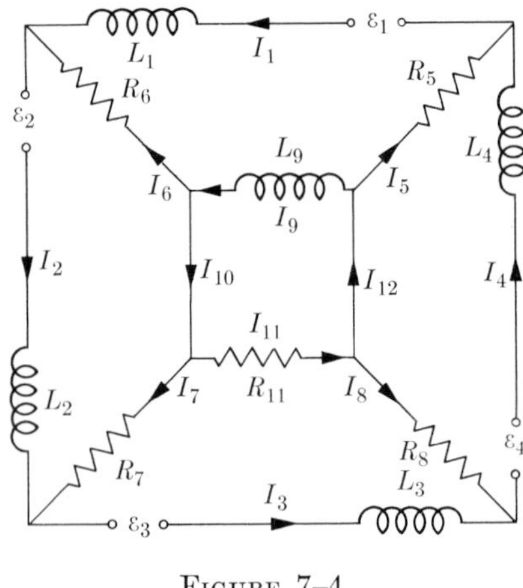

FIGURE 7–4

4. (a) Proceed as in Prob. 3(a) for the network of Fig. 7–4.

(b) Obtain the differential equations for the mesh currents of part (a).

ANSWERS

3. (a) $J_1 = I_1$, $J_2 = I_2 = I_6$, $J_3 = I_3$, $I_4 = J_1 - J_2$, $I_5 = J_2 - J_3$;
(b) $[L_1D^2 + R_4D + (1/C_1)]Q_1 - R_4DQ_2 = \mathcal{E}_1$,
$-R_4DQ_1 + [L_2D^2 + (R_4 + R_5)D + (1/C_2)]Q_2 - R_5DQ_3 = 0$,
$-R_5DQ_2 + [L_3D^2 + (R_3 + R_5)D + (1/C_3)]Q_3 = \mathcal{E}_3$.

4. (a) $J_1 = I_1$, $J_2 = I_2$, $J_3 = I_3$, $J_4 = I_4$, $J_5 = I_1 + I_9 = I_2 + I_{10} = \cdots$, $I_5 = J_1 - J_4$, $I_6 = J_2 - J_1$, $I_7 = J_3 - J_2$, $I_8 = J_4 - J_3$, $I_9 = J_5 - J_1$, $I_{10} = J_5 - J_2$, $I_{11} = J_5 - J_3$, $I_{12} = J_5 - J_4$;
(b) $[(L_1 + L_9)D + (R_5 + R_6)]J_1 - R_6J_2 - R_5J_4 - L_9DJ_5 = \mathcal{E}_1$,
$-R_6J_1 + [L_2D + (R_6 + R_7)]J_2 - R_7J_3 = \mathcal{E}_2$,
$-R_7J_2 + [L_3D + (R_7 + R_{11} + R_8)J_3] - R_8J_4 - R_{11}J_5 = \mathcal{E}_3$,
$-R_5J_1 - R_8J_3 + [L_4D + (R_5 + R_8)J_4] = \mathcal{E}_4$,
$-L_9DJ_1 - R_{11}J_3 + [L_9D + R_{11}]J_5 = 0$.

SUGGESTED REFERENCES

1. Frazer, R. A., Duncan, W. J., and Collar, A. R., *Elementary Matrices.* Cambridge, Eng.: Cambridge University Press, 1938.

2. Goldstein, Herbert, *Classical Mechanics.* Reading, Mass.: Addison-Wesley, 1950.

3. Guillemin, E. H., *Communication Networks,* Vol. 1. New York: John Wiley and Sons, Inc., 1931.

4. Guillemin, E. H., *Mathematics of Circuit Analysis.* New York: John Wiley and Sons, Inc., 1949.

5. Ince, E. L., *Ordinary Differential Equations.* New York: Dover, 1956.

6. Kaplan, Wilfred, *Operational Methods for Linear Systems.* Reading, Mass.: Addison-Wesley, 1962.

7. Perlis, Sam, *Theory of Matrices.* Reading, Mass.: Addison-Wesley, 1952.

CHAPTER 8

EQUATIONS NOT OF FIRST DEGREE

8–1 Reduction to first degree equation. A differential equation of nth order has the general form

$$F(x, y, y', \ldots, y^{(n)}) = 0. \tag{8-1}$$

The equation is said to be of first degree (Section 1–2) when it has the form

$$f(x, y, \ldots, y^{(n-1)})y^{(n)} + g(x, y, \ldots, y^{(n-1)}) = 0. \tag{8-2}$$

Thus the differential equation is in the form of a first degree equation for the highest derivative; hence we can solve for the highest derivative:

$$y^{(n)} = -g/f = G(x, y, \ldots, y^{(n-1)}), \tag{8-3}$$

except where f is 0.

The differential equation is said to be of kth degree if it is of degree k in the highest derivative. For example,

$$y'^2 + 2x^2y^3y' + x^4 + y^4 = 0 \tag{8-4}$$

is a quadratic equation for y', and hence has degree two. We can replace Eq. (8–4) by two first degree equations by solving for y':

$$y' = -x^2y^3 \pm (x^4y^6 - x^4 - y^4)^{1/2}. \tag{8-5}$$

Each of the two first degree equations

$$\begin{aligned} y' &= -x^2y^3 + (x^4y^6 - x^4 - y^4)^{1/2}, \\ y' &= -x^2y^3 - (x^4y^6 - x^4 - y^4)^{1/2} \end{aligned} \tag{8-6}$$

can be analyzed as in Chapter 2. The solutions form two families of curves in the xy-plane. In general, there will be *two* solution curves through each point (one with each of the slopes 8–6). Similarly, an equation of degree k can (in principle) be replaced by k first order equations.

The general equation (8–1) need not have the form of an algebraic equation in $y^{(n)}$; for example, the equation

$$e^{y''} - y'^2 + xy = 0 \tag{8-7}$$

is not algebraic in y''. However, we can solve for y'':

$$y'' = \log(y'^2 - xy), \tag{8-8}$$

and obtain one equivalent first degree equation. Other nonalgebraic equations may be very difficult to solve for the highest derivative and may have infinitely many solutions.

Equation (8-4) illustrates another complication. The equation was replaced by the two first order equations (8-6). These are meaningful, however, only when the quantity under the radical is positive; thus for some points (x, y) the equation may prescribe imaginary slopes, for others two equal slopes, and for still others unequal slopes. For the equation of degree k there is a corresponding variety of possibilities; for given values of $x, y, \ldots, y^{(n-1)}$ some roots may be real and others imaginary.

EXAMPLE 1.

$$y'^2 + y'(x^2y - xy) - x^3y^2 = 0.$$

We can solve for y' by factoring:

$$(y' - xy)(y' + x^2y) = 0;$$

$$y' = xy, \qquad y' = -x^2y.$$

The two first degree equations can then be solved by separation of variables. We find the solutions to be

$$y = c_1e^{x^2/2}, \qquad y = c_2e^{-x^3/3}.$$

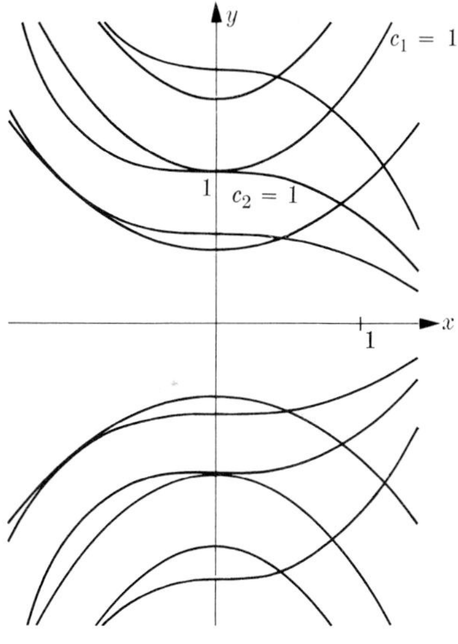

FIG. 8-1. Solutions of a second degree equation.

They are graphed in Fig. 8-1. As the figure shows, there are, in general, two solutions through each point. The x-axis is an exception; along this line both slopes are zero, and hence there is just one solution through each point, the axis itself. Along the y-axis both slopes are zero, and along the line $x = -1$ both slopes equal $-y$; however there are still two (tangent) solutions through each point. These comprise all the exceptional points, for equality of the two slopes occurs where

$$xy = -x^2y,$$

and hence where $x = 0$, $y = 0$, or $x = -1$.

EXAMPLE 2. $y'^2 - 4y = 0$. We find at once

$$y' = 2\sqrt{y}, \quad y' = -2\sqrt{y} \qquad (y \geqq 0);$$

$$\sqrt{y} = x + c_1, \qquad \sqrt{y} = -x + c_2.$$

The solutions are shown in Fig. 8–2. The slopes are imaginary when $y < 0$; hence there are no solutions in the lower half-plane. The slopes are equal and both are zero along the x-axis; the line $y = 0$ is a solution common to both families. Through each point of the upper half-plane pass two solutions. Each solution is half of a parabola. For example, $\sqrt{y} = x$ is half of the parabola $y = x^2$; it contains only the points for which $x \geqq 0$. The missing half of the parabola is contained in the other family; it is the curve $\sqrt{y} = -x$. In general, we can combine the two families into one by squaring:

$$y = (x + c)^2;$$

the solutions now appear as complete parabolas.

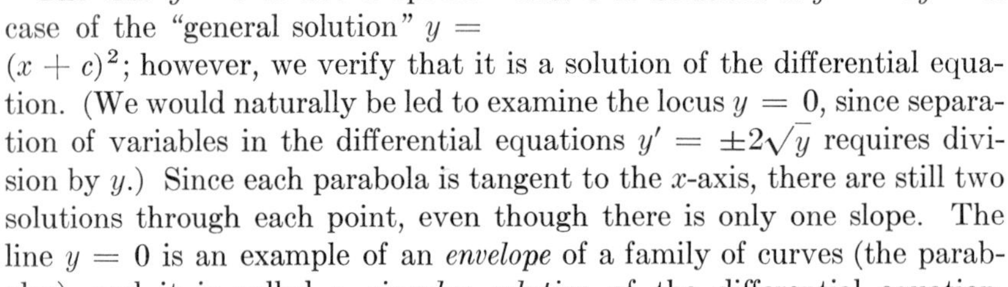

FIG. 8–2. Solutions of $y'^2 - 4y = 0$.

The line $y = 0$ is not a special case of the "general solution" $y = (x + c)^2$; however, we verify that it is a solution of the differential equation. (We would naturally be led to examine the locus $y = 0$, since separation of variables in the differential equations $y' = \pm 2\sqrt{y}$ requires division by y.) Since each parabola is tangent to the x-axis, there are still two solutions through each point, even though there is only one slope. The line $y = 0$ is an example of an *envelope* of a family of curves (the parabolas), and it is called a *singular solution* of the differential equation. (See Section 8–2 below.)

Remark. When the family of solutions has an envelope, as in the example, we can construct further solutions by piecing together parts of solutions. For example, the curve formed of the three portions

$$y = x^2, x \leqq 0, \qquad y = 0, 0 \leqq x \leqq 1, \qquad y = (x - 1)^2, x \geqq 1,$$

defines a function $y = f(x)$ having a continuous derivative and satisfying the differential equation for all x.

EXAMPLE 3. $y'^4 - 2y'^2 + 1 - y^4 = 0$. We find four slopes:

$$y' = \pm\sqrt{1 \pm y^2}.$$

Two are imaginary when $y^2 > 1$; two are equal (both zero) when $y^2 = 1$; there are two equal pairs ($+1$ and -1) when $y = 0$; otherwise all four slopes are real and distinct. The solutions are found to be (Prob. 1(k) below)

$$y = \sin(x + c_1), \qquad y = \pm\sinh(x + c_2), \qquad y = \pm 1.$$

They are graphed in Fig. 8–3. The solutions $y = \pm 1$ are envelopes of the solutions $y = \sin(x + c_1)$ and are singular solutions (Section 8–2). The line $y = 0$ (along which there are two equal pairs of slopes) is not a solution.

EXAMPLE 4. $y''^2 - y^2 = 0$. There are two first degree equations: $y'' = \pm y$, for which the solutions are

$$y = c_1 \cos x + c_2 \sin x, \qquad y = c_3 e^x + c_4 e^{-x}.$$

Since the two equations are of second order, a solution of each passes through each point (x, y) with prescribed slope y' (that is, a unique solution passes through each point (x, y, y') of the *three*-dimensional space of these variables; see Section 1–7). The two solutions have different values of y'' (hence different *curvatures*) except where $y = 0$. The points $y = 0$ form a solution which is included in both families of general solutions (whether or not it is a singular solution is a matter of terminology; Section 8–2).

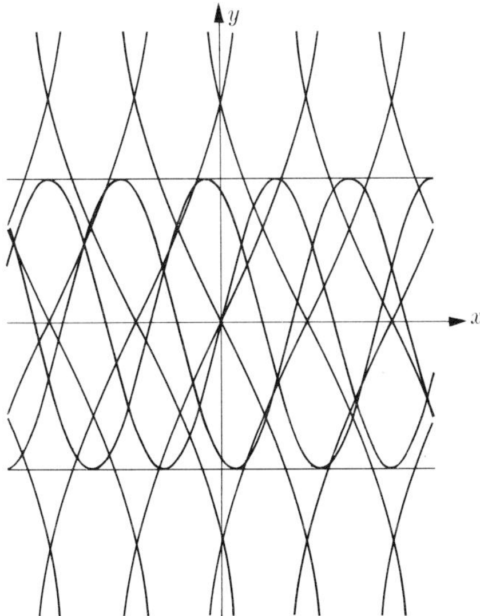

FIG. 8–3. Solutions of a fourth degree equation.

PROBLEMS

1. Reduce to first degree equations and find all solutions for the following:
(a) $y'^2 + xy' - 2x^2 = 0$, (b) $y'^2 - y^2 + 2e^x y - e^{2x} = 0$,
(c) $y'^2 - xy = 0$, (d) $xy'^2 - 2yy' + x = 0$,
(e) $x^2y'^2 + 2xyy' + x^2 + y^2 - 1 = 0$,
(f) $x^2y'^2 + 2xyy' + y^2 - y^4 - x^2y^4 = 0$,
(g) $y''^2 + (x^2 - x)y'' - x^3 = 0$,
(h) $y''^2 + y''(y' + 2y) + 4yy' - 8y^2 = 0$,
(i) $y'^3 + yy'^2 - x^2y^2y' - x^2y^3 = 0$,
(j) $xy'^3 - (2y + xy)y'^2 + (2y^2 + 4x)y' - 4xy = 0$,
(k) $y'^4 - 2y'^2 + 1 - y^4 = 0$ (Example 3 above),
(l) $\sin y' - x = 0$.

ANSWERS

1. (a) $y = c_1 - x^2$, $y = c_2 + \frac{1}{2}x^2$; (b) $y = e^x(c_1 - x)$, $y = \frac{1}{2}e^x + c_2e^{-x}$;
(c) $9y = (x^{3/2} + c)^2$ for $x \geqq 0$, $-9y = [(-x)^{3/2} + c]^2$ for $x \leqq 0$ and the line $y = 0$; (d) $y = (1 + c^2x^2)/2c$, $y = \pm x$;
(e) $2xy = \pm [x\sqrt{1 - x^2} + \sin^{-1} x] + c$;
(f) $y = [cx \pm \sqrt{1 + x^2} \pm x \log (x + \sqrt{1 + x^2})]^{-1}$, $y = 0$;
(g) $y = c_1x + c_2 + \frac{1}{6}x^3$, $y = c_3x + c_4 - \frac{1}{12}x^4$;
(h) $y = c_1e^{-2x} + c_2e^x$, $y = c_3 \cos 2x + c_4 \sin 2x$;
(i) $y = c_1e^{-x}$, $y = c_2e^{x^2/2}$, $y = c_3e^{-x^2/2}$;
(j) $y = c_1e^x$, $y = (c_2^2x^2 + 4)/2c_2$;
(k) $y = \sin (x + c_1)$, $y = \pm\sinh (x + c_2)$, $y = \pm 1$;
(l) $y = x (\sin^{-1} x + 2n\pi) + \sqrt{1 - x^2} + c_1$,
$y = x[(2n + 1)\pi - \sin^{-1} x] - \sqrt{1 - x^2} + c_2$; $\sin^{-1} x$ is principal value, $n = 0, \pm 1, \pm 2, \ldots$

8–2 Singular solutions. In Section 8–1 it has been shown that an equation

$$F(x, y, y') = 0 \tag{8–9}$$

can be reduced to first degree form by *solving for* y'; in general, there are several solutions and, accordingly, several first degree equations.

It is not obvious that every equation (8–9) can be solved for y' in terms of x and y; indeed, we can easily give examples for which this is not possible:

$$x^2 + y^2 + y'^2 = 0; \qquad e^y + y'^2 = 0. \tag{8–10}$$

It is shown in advanced calculus (pp. 117–121 of Reference 1) that solution for y' is possible *except where* $\partial F/\partial y' = 0$. More precisely, let $F(x, y, y')$ be continuous and have continuous first partial derivatives with respect to x, y, and y' in some open region D of xyy'-space. If x_0, y_0, y'_0 is a triple in D such that $F(x_0, y_0, y'_0) = 0$, and $\partial F/\partial y' \neq 0$ for $x = x_0, y = y_0, y' = y'_0$, then there is a *unique* function $y' = f(x, y)$, defined for x and y close enough to x_0, y_0 (respectively) such that $y'_0 = f(x_0, y_0)$, and satisfying the equation $F(x, y, y') = 0$; that is,

$$F[x, y, f(x, y)] \equiv 0.$$

Moreover, $f(x, y)$ has continuous first partial derivatives, so that the existence theorem of Section 1–7 applies to the differential equation $y' = f(x, y)$.

The theorem just formulated is known as the *implicit function theorem* for the equation $F(x, y, y') = 0$. Its significance can be seen geometrically. The equation $F(x, y, y') = 0$ describes a *surface* in xyy'-space (Fig. 8–4). The tangent plane to this surface at (x_0, y_0, y'_0) has the equation

$$\frac{\partial F}{\partial x}(x - x_0) + \frac{\partial F}{\partial y}(y - y_0) + \frac{\partial F}{\partial y'}(y' - y'_0) = 0, \qquad (8\text{–}11)$$

where the partial derivatives are evaluated at (x_0, y_0, y'_0). If $\partial F/\partial y' \neq 0$ at that point, the tangent plane is *not* vertical, and y' is a well-defined function of x, y near (x_0, y_0). If $\partial F/\partial y' = 0$ at the point, the tangent plane is vertical and y' is in general not a "well-behaved" function of x, y near (x_0, y_0). The two cases are shown in Fig. 8–4.

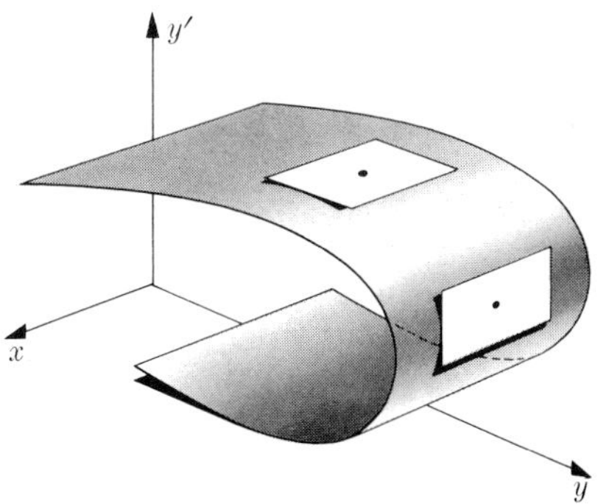

FIG. 8–4. Implicit function theorem.

In the first example in (8–10), the equation is satisfied at $x = 0$, $y = 0$, $y' = 0$; however, $\partial F/\partial y' = 2y' = 0$ at the point, and no function $y' = f(x, y)$ is obtained. In the second example the equation is not satisfied for any values of x, y, y'. These examples are extreme, in that no function $y' = f(x, y)$ is obtained. More typical is the following, which has some exceptional points:

$$x^2 + y^2 + y'^2 - 1 = 0. \qquad (8\text{–}12)$$

The surface in xyy'-space is a sphere, whose tangent plane is vertical where $x^2 + y^2 = 1$. For $x^2 + y^2 < 1$ we obtain two continuous functions:

$$y' = \pm\sqrt{1 - x^2 - y^2}. \tag{8-13}$$

The exceptional points $x^2 + y^2 = 1$ are precisely those at which $\partial F/\partial y' = 0$, for $\partial F/\partial y' = 2y' = 0$ when $y' = 0$, and hence, by (8–12), when $x^2 + y^2 = 1$.

We call the locus of all points (x, y) such that for some y',

$$F(x, y, y') = 0, \qquad \frac{\partial F}{\partial y'}(x, y, y') = 0 \tag{8-14}$$

the *singular locus* relative to the differential equation $F(x, y, y') = 0$. For given F it is in general possible to eliminate y' between the two equations (8–14) and to obtain a single equation

$$Q(x, y) = 0 \tag{8-15}$$

which describes the singular locus. [The singular locus is also termed the *p-discriminant* locus; the term arises as a result of the notation p for y'; the equations (8–14) become $F(x, y, p) = 0$, $F_p(x, y, p) = 0$.]

The singular locus may contain a solution of the given differential equation; that is, a solution curve $y = y(x)$, for which every point (x, y) lies in the singular locus. Such a solution is called a *singular solution* of the differential equation. A singular solution must thus be a function $y(x)$ such that, for each x, both equations (8–14) are satisfied when $y = y(x)$, $y' = y'(x)$. Not every curve $y = y(x)$ in the singular locus need be a singular solution.

EXAMPLE 1. $x^2 + y^2 + y'^2 - 1 = 0$. This is the Eq. (8–12) discussed above. The equations (8–14) become

$$x^2 + y^2 + y'^2 - 1 = 0, \qquad 2y' = 0,$$

and the singular locus (8–15) is the curve

$$x^2 + y^2 = 1,$$

which can be represented by two functions of x:

$$y = \pm\sqrt{1 - x^2}.$$

One or both of these may be singular solutions.

We find

$$y' = \frac{\pm x}{\sqrt{1 - x^2}},$$

$$x^2 + y^2 + y'^2 - 1 \equiv x^2 + 1 - x^2 + \frac{x^2}{1 - x^2} - 1 \equiv \frac{x^2}{1 - x^2} \not\equiv 0.$$

The differential equation is satisfied only at $x = 0$. Hence there are no singular solutions.

EXAMPLE 2. $y'^2 - 4y = 0$. This is Example 2 of Section 8–1 (Fig. 8–2). Here the equations (8–14) are

$$y'^2 - 4y = 0, \qquad 2y' = 0.$$

The singular locus (8–15) is the line $y = 0$. It is a solution of the differential equation; hence $y = 0$ is a singular solution.

EXAMPLE 3. $y'^4 - 2y'^2 + 1 - y^4 = 0$. This is Example 3 of Section 8–1 (Fig. 8–3). The equations (8–14) are

$$y'^4 - 2y'^2 + 1 - y^4 = 0, \qquad 4y'^3 - 4y' = 0.$$

Elimination of y' leads to the equations

$$y^4 = 0, \qquad y^4 = 1;$$

the singular locus is the combination of these two loci; we can represent both by one equation:

$$y^4(y^4 - 1) = 0,$$

but both parts must be examined separately. The line $y = 0$ does not satisfy the differential equation; the locus $y^4 = 1$ consists of two lines, $y = \pm 1$, both of which satisfy the differential equation. Hence the lines $y = \pm 1$ are singular solutions.

EXAMPLE 4. $e^{y'} - y' + xy - x - 1 = 0$. The equations (8–14) and the singular locus (8–15) are

$$e^{y'} - y' + xy - x - 1 = 0, \qquad e^{y'} - 1 = 0;$$

$$xy - x = 0.$$

The locus contains the lines $y = 1$, $x = 0$. Only the former has the form $y = g(x)$, and it does satisfy the differential equation. Hence $y = 1$ is the singular solution. In this example, finding the general solution would be very difficult, but the singular solution is found with ease.

Singular solutions of higher order equations. For a second order equation

$$F(x, y, y', y'') = 0 \tag{8–16}$$

we reduce to first degree form by solving for y''. This is possible (under appropriate continuity assumptions) except where $\partial F/\partial y'' = 0$. A solution $y = g(x)$ of Eq. (8–16) such that $\partial F/\partial y'' = 0$ at each point is called a singular solution.

Similarly, for an nth order equation

$$F(x, y, y', \ldots, y^{(n)}) = 0 \tag{8–17}$$

a singular solution is a solution $y = g(x)$ such that $\partial F/\partial y^{(n)} = 0$ at each point.

8–3 Envelopes. Let a family of curves be given in implicit form:

$$G(x, y, c) = 0; \tag{8–18}$$

for each constant value of c, Eq. (8–18) is to represent one or more curves in the xy-plane. For example,

$$(x - c)^2 - y = 0 \tag{8–19}$$

represents such a family; the curves are parabolas.

A curve C in the xy-plane is called an *envelope* of the family (8–18) if at each point of C at least one member of the family is tangent to C, different members being tangent at differing points of C. This is illustrated by the family (8–19); the curve C is the x-axis. As shown in Fig. 8–2, the x-axis has one tangent parabola at each point.

We note that for each point (x, y) of the upper half-plane there are *two* parabolas through the point; that is, Eq. (8–19) has two solutions for c in terms of x, y, when $y > 0$:

$$c = x + \sqrt{y}, \quad c = x - \sqrt{y} \qquad (y > 0). \tag{8–20}$$

These solutions are two continuous functions of x, y. As in Section 8–2, the implicit function theorem ensures that an equation (8–18) can be solved for c in this manner, except where $\partial G/\partial c = 0$. The locus in the xy-plane described by the equations

$$G(x, y, c) = 0, \qquad G_c(x, y, c) = 0 \tag{8–21}$$

is termed the *c-discriminant locus.* For Eq. (8–19) this is the locus

$$(x - c)^2 - y = 0, \qquad 2(x - c) = 0;$$

hence it is the line $y = 0$, which is precisely the locus of points where the two functions (8–20) become discontinuous (since there are no values at all for $y < 0$). Furthermore, in this example the c-discriminant locus is an envelope of the family.

It can be shown (see Prob. 5 below) that a curve C in the c-discriminant locus will represent such an envelope of the family (8–18), provided $\partial G/\partial x$ and $\partial G/\partial y$ are never both zero at a point of C, and provided C is representable in the form $x = x(c)$, $y = y(c)$ in terms of the parameter c.

Equation (8–19) can be considered as a family of solutions of a first order differential equation. Differentiation and elimination of c lead to the equation

$$y'^2 = 4y. \tag{8–22}$$

There are two slopes $\pm 2\sqrt{y}$ at each point (x, y) for $y > 0$. On the line $y = 0$ the two slopes coincide, and we verify that the line $y = 0$ is a singular solution of the differential equation. Thus, in this example, the singular solution and envelope are the same. This is normally the case; however, there are exceptions (see Prob. 4 below). For a full discussion the reader is referred to pp. 83–93 of Reference 2.

PROBLEMS

1. Find all singular solutions for each of the following:

(a) $y'^2 + 2xy' + x^2 - y^2 = 0$, (b) $y'^2 - 4xy' + 2x^2 + 2y = 0$,
(c) $y'^3 - 3x^2y' + 4xy = 0$,
(d) $3y'^5 + 5xy'^3 - 30x^2y' + 33xy = 0$.

2. For each of the following differential equations find all solutions; also graph and discuss the singular locus:

(a) $y'^2 = x$, (b) $(3y - 1)^2y'^2 - 4y = 0$,
(c) $(x^2 - 1)y'^2 + x^2 = 0$, (d) $y'^3 - y = 0$.

3. Graph each of the following families of curves; also, find the c-discriminant locus for each, and determine whether it is an envelope of the family:

(a) $y - 2cx + c^2 = 0$, (b) $y^3 = (x - c)^2$,
(c) $x^2 + y^2 = c^2$, (d) $(x - c)^2 + y^2 = 1$,
(e) $y(y - 1)^2 = (x - c)^2$, [cf. Prob. 2 (b)].

4. (a) Show that the line $y = 0$ is a singular solution of the equation $y'^3 - y^3 = 0$ but is not an envelope of the remaining solutions.

(b) Show that the line $y = 0$ is an envelope of the family of solutions of the equation $y' - y^{2/3} = 0$ but is not a singular solution of the equation. [*Remark.* In this example, $F \equiv y' - y^{2/3}$ does not have continuous first partial derivatives along the line $y = 0$, for $F_y = -\frac{2}{3}y^{-1/3}$. Hence the existence theorem of Section 1–7 does not apply and, in fact, there is not a *unique* solution through each point on the x-axis. When F has continuous partial derivatives along the envelope, then $F_{y'}$ must be 0, so that the curve is a singular solution. For otherwise we could solve for y', apply the existence theorem, and obtain a unique solution through each point; but this is impossible along an envelope.]

5. Prove: if $x = x(c)$, $y = y(c)$ represents a curve C in the c-discriminant locus (8–21) and G_x, G_y are not both zero along C, then the curve C is an envelope of the family $G(x, y, c) = 0$. [*Hint:* The slope of the tangent to each curve of the family is determined by the equation $G_x\,dx + G_y\,dy = 0$. Now

$$G[x(c), y(c), c] = 0.$$

Differentiate this equation with respect to c, and use the equation $G_c = 0$ to conclude that $G_x\,dx + G_y\,dy = 0$ along C also.]

6. Determine all singular solutions of the second order equation

$$y''^2 - 2y'y'' + y^2 = 0.$$

[*Hint:* By the definition each singular solution must satisfy both of the equations

$$y''^2 - 2y'y'' + y^2 = 0, \qquad 2y'' - 2y' = 0.$$

Find all solutions of the second equation and determine which of these satisfy the first equation.]

7. Show that a linear equation

$$p_0(x)y'' + p_1(x)y' + p_2(x)y = Q(x) \qquad [p_0(x) \not\equiv 0]$$

has no singular solution.

ANSWERS

1. (a) None, (b) $y = x^2$, (c) $y = \pm\frac{1}{2}x^2$, (d) $y = \pm\frac{2}{3}x^{3/2}$.

2. (a) $y = \pm\frac{2}{3}x^{3/2} + c$; singular locus $x = 0$, a locus of cusps, not a singular solution; (*b*) $y(y-1)^2 = (x-c)^2$, $y > 0$; singular locus $y = 0$ (envelope, a singular solution), line $y = \frac{1}{3}$ is a locus of vertical tangents; (c) $x^2 + (y-c)^2 = 1$; singular locus $x = 0$, a tac locus (or locus along which two solutions touch), not a singular solution; lines $x = \pm 1$ can also be considered as part of the singular locus; they are loci of vertical tangents and are envelopes; (d) $27y^2 = 8(x-c)^3$; singular locus $y = 0$, a locus of cusps, a singular solution.

3. (a) $y = x^2$, an envelope; (b) $y = 0$, not an envelope (locus of cusps); (c) point $(0, 0)$, not an envelope; (d) $y = \pm 1$, an envelope; (e) $y = 0$, an envelope; $y = 1$, not an envelope (locus of nodes, i.e., self-intersections).

6. $y = ce^x$.

8–4 First order equations solvable for y, or for x. If a first order equation is solvable for y in terms of x, y', or for x in terms of y, y', then it may be possible to obtain the solutions by *differentiating* the equation. We illustrate the method by examples and give a discussion below.

EXAMPLE 1. $y'^2 - 4y = 0$. This is Example 2 of Section 8–1. We write

$$p = y', \tag{8–23}$$

so that on solving for y, we obtain

$$y = \tfrac{1}{4}p^2. \tag{8–24}$$

Differentiation with respect to x gives, in view of Eq. (8–23),

$$p = \frac{1}{4}2p\frac{dp}{dx},$$

or

$$p\left(1 - \frac{1}{2}\frac{dp}{dx}\right) = 0.$$

Hence we obtain the two equations

$$p = 0 \qquad \text{or} \qquad \frac{dp}{dx} = 2.$$

The first, when combined with (8–24), gives

$$y = 0,$$

which we recognize as the *singular solution*. The second can be integrated:

$$p = 2(x + c);$$

when this relation is combined with Eq. (8–24), we find

$$y = (x + c)^2,$$

which we recognize as the remaining solutions.

The fact that the equation obtained by differentiation has a factor which, when equated to zero, leads to the singular solution is no accident. (An explanation is given below.) This factor may provide only a singular *locus*, and hence we must check in each case to see whether a solution is obtained.

EXAMPLE 2. $xy'^2 - 2yy' + x = 0$. We can solve for y:

$$y = \frac{xp}{2} + \frac{x}{2p} \qquad \left(p = \frac{dy}{dx}\right). \tag{8–25}$$

Differentiation gives

$$p = \left(\frac{x}{2} - \frac{x}{2p^2}\right)\frac{dp}{dx} + \frac{p}{2} + \frac{1}{2p},$$

$$p^3 - p = (xp^2 - x)\frac{dp}{dx},$$

$$(p^2 - 1)\left(x\frac{dp}{dx} - p\right) = 0.$$

Again we obtain two equations:

$$p^2 = 1, \qquad x\frac{dp}{dx} - p = 0.$$

The first, when combined with (8–25), gives

$$y = \pm x;$$

both functions are singular solutions. The second is a first order equation, whose general solution we find to be

$$p = cx;$$

this relation, when combined with (8–25), yields

$$y = \frac{cx^2}{2} + \frac{1}{2c} \qquad (c \neq 0),$$

which gives all other solutions of the given differential equation.

EXAMPLE 3. $y'^3 + xy' - y = 0$. We can solve either for y or for x. We solve for x and then differentiate *with respect to* y:

$$x = \frac{y}{p} - p^2,$$

$$\frac{dx}{dy} = \frac{1}{p} = \left(\frac{-y}{p^2} - 2p\right)\frac{dp}{dy} + \frac{1}{p},$$

$$(y + 2p^3)\frac{dp}{dy} = 0,$$

$$y + 2p^3 = 0, \qquad \frac{dp}{dy} = 0.$$

The first equation gives a singular solution

$$x = \frac{y}{-y^{1/3}2^{-1/3}} - \frac{y^{2/3}}{2^{2/3}}, \qquad 4x^3 = -27y^2;$$

the second equation can be integrated to give the other solutions:

$$p = c, \qquad x = \frac{y}{c} - c^2, \qquad y = cx + c^3.$$

Discussion. Here we indicate in a rough way what is the basis of the method. A more precise explanation, based on the concept of "integral" of a differential equation, is given in Section 8–4 of ODE.

We consider an equation

$$F(x, y, y') = 0. \tag{8–26}$$

Differentiation with respect to x leads to the second order equation

$$F_x + F_y y' + F_{y'} y'' = 0. \tag{8–27}$$

The general solution of this second order equation depends on *two* constants. It may be possible to find this general solution in the form of two equations relating x, y, y' and arbitrary constants c_1, c_2. In particular, since (8–27) was obtained from (8–26) by differentiation, we deduce that

$$F(x, y, y') = c_1 \tag{8–28}$$

on each solution of (8–27). If we can somehow find a second such relation (independent of (8–28)):

$$G(x, y, y') = c_2, \tag{8–29}$$

then we can (in theory) eliminate y' between (8–28), (8–29) to obtain $y = \phi(x, c_1, c_2)$, the general solution of (8–27). However, we want only the solutions of (8–26); thus we must require $c_1 = 0$. Accordingly, if we write $c_2 = c$, our solutions are obtained from the two equations

$$\begin{aligned} F(x, y, y') &= 0, \\ G(x, y, y') &= c. \end{aligned} \tag{8–30}$$

[Elimination of y' from these equations is in general impossible where $F_{y'} = 0$; that is, on the singular locus. It may happen that $F_{y'}$ appears as a factor of Eq. (8–27); in that case, equating the factor to 0 gives the singular locus and, possibly, the singular solutions.]

When Eq. (8–26) is solved for y:

$$y = f(x, p) \qquad (p = y'),$$

the differentiation process leads to the second order equation

$$p = f_x + f_p \frac{dp}{dx} \qquad \left(\frac{dp}{dx} = y''\right);$$

since only x and p appear, we can consider this as a first order equation. The methods of Chap. 2 may give us the general solution in the form $G(x, p) = c$. The two equations

$$y = f(x, p),$$
$$G(x, p) = c$$

then give the general solution.

Equations solvable for x can be analyzed in the same way. The differentiation with respect to y is the same as differentiation with respect to x followed by division by p:

$$\frac{du}{dy} = \frac{du}{dx}\frac{dx}{dy} = \frac{1}{p}\frac{du}{dx}.$$

Remark. Elimination of y' between the two equations (8–30) may not always be feasible. In that case, Eqs. (8–30) themselves define the solutions in implicit form. Occasionally, we can solve Eqs. (8–30) for x and y:

$$x = \phi(p, c), \qquad y = \psi(p, c);$$

this gives the solutions in parametric form, with p as parameter.

8–5 Clairaut equation. This name is given (after its discoverer) to the equation of form

$$y = xy' + f(y') \equiv xp + f(p). \tag{8–31}$$

Application of the procedure of differentiation (Section 8–4) leads to the equations

$$p = p + [x + f'(p)]\frac{dp}{dx},$$
$$x + f'(p) = 0, \qquad \frac{dp}{dx} = 0. \tag{8–32}$$

The first relation, when combined with Eq. (8–31), leads to the singular locus. It may not be possible to eliminate p, but the equations

$$\begin{aligned} x &= -f'(p), \\ y &= xp + f(p) = -pf'(p) + f(p) \end{aligned} \tag{8–33}$$

serve as a parametrization of the singular locus, in terms of the parameter p. It can be shown (Prob. 5(a) below) that (8–33) represents a singular solution, except where $f''(p) = 0$. The second part of (8–32) can be integrated and combined with (8–31) to yield the other solutions:

$$p = c,$$
$$y = cx + f(c); \qquad (8\text{–}34)$$

they are straight lines. It can be shown (Prob. 5(b) below) that they are tangent to the curve (8–33), which is thus an envelope of the family (8–34). Indeed, *the solutions of the Clairaut equation consist of a curve and the lines tangent to it* (Fig. 8–5).

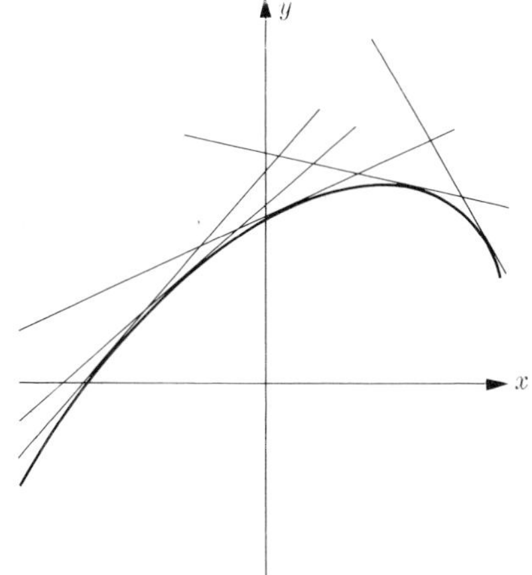

Fig. 8–5. Solutions of a Clairaut equation.

We have tacitly assumed continuity of $f(p)$, $f'(p)$, $f''(p)$ in some interval of p. It is noteworthy that, without any such hypothesis, the lines (8–34) are solutions of Eq. (8–31), wherever $f(c)$ is defined (Prob. 5(c) below).

PROBLEMS

1. Obtain all solutions of each of the following by solving for y and differentiating:

(a) $2y'^2 + x^3y' - 2x^2y = 0$, (b) $y'^2 + 2xy' - y = 0$,
(c) $(1 + y)y'^2 - 2xy' + 1 + y = 0$, (d) $xy'^2 - yy' - xy = 0$.

2. Obtain all solutions of the following by solving for x:

(a) $4yy'^2 + 2xy' - y = 0$,
(b) part (b) of Prob. 1,
(c) part (d) of Prob. 1.

3. Write the following as Clairaut equations, obtain all solutions, and graph:

(a) $y'^3 + 3xy' - 3y = 0$,
(b) $xy'^3 - yy'^2 + xy' - y = 1$,
(c) $e^{xy'}(y'^2 + 1) - e^y = 0$.

4. (a) Extend the result of Section 8–5 to the *Clairaut equation in implicit form:*

$$F(y - xy', y') = 0.$$

[*Hint:* Differentiate with respect to x and obtain the integral: $p = c$.]

(b) Find all solutions:

$$(xy' - y)^3 + xy' - y + y'^2 + 1 = 0.$$

5. (a) Show that Eqs. (8–33) represent the singular locus of Eq. (8–31) and that if $f''(p) \neq 0$, the locus is a singular solution. [*Hint:* For a curve given parametrically in terms of the parameter p: $x = x(p)$, $y = y(p)$, we have $dy/dx = (dy/dp)/(dx/dp)$. Show here that $dy/dx = p$.]

(b) Show that the line (8–34) is tangent to the curve (8–33) at the point for which $p = c$.

(c) Show that if $f(p)$ is defined for $p = p_0$ (and perhaps for no other value), then the line $y = p_0x + f(p_0)$ is a solution of Eq. (8–31).

6. Find the differential equation satisfied by each of the following curves and its tangent lines:

(a) the parabola $y = x^2$,
(b) the circle $x^2 + y^2 = 1$,
(c) the curve $y = e^x$,
(d) the curve $y = f(x)$.

ANSWERS

1. (a) $y = cx^2 + 4c^2$, $y = -x^4/6$; (b) $3xp^2 + 2p^3 = c$, where $p = -x \pm \sqrt{x^2 + y}$; (c) $(y + 1)^2 = 2cx - c^2$, $x - y - 1 = 0$, $x - y + 1 = 0$; (d) $xp^2 - yp - xy = 0$, $p + x = c(p - x)^3$ and $y = 0$.

2. (a) $y^2 = cx + c^2$, $y = -\frac{1}{4}x^2$.

3. (a) $c^3 + 3cx - 3y = 0$; $4x^3 + 9y^2 = 0$; (b) $xc^3 - yc^2 + xc - y = 1$; $x = -2p(1 + p^2)^{-2}$, $y = (-1 - 3p^2)(1 + p^2)^{-2}$; (c) $y = cx + \log(1 + c^2)$, $x = -2p(1 + p^2)^{-1}$, $y = \log(1 + p^2) - 2p^2(1 + p^2)^{-1}$.

4. (b) $(xc - y)^3 + xc - y + c^2 + 1 = 0$; singular solution: $3x(xp - y)^2 + x + 2p = 0$, $(xp - y)^3 + xp - y + p^2 + 1 = 0$.

6. (a) $y = xp - \frac{1}{4}p^2$, (b) $(y - xp)^2 = 1 + p^2$, (c) $y = xp + p(1 - \log p)$, (d) $y = xp - pg(p) + f[g(p)]$, where $g(p)$ is the solution of $p = f'(x)$ for x in terms of p.

MISCELLANEOUS EXERCISES

Find all solutions.

1. $y'^2 + y'(y - x^2y) - x^2y^2 = 0$.
2. $xy'^2 + 1 - y = 0$.
3. $xyy'^2 - y'(x^2 + y^2) + xy = 0$.
4. $y'^3 - xy' - 2y = 0$.
5. $xy'e^{y'} - ye^{y'} + y' = 0$.
6. $y'^3 + 2y'^2 - y' - 2 = 0$.
7. $y'^3 - y'^2(x + y + x^2) + y'(x^3 + xy + x^2y) - x^3y = 0$.
8. $y'^2(1 + 4x^2 + 8y) + 2xy' + x^2 = 0$.
9. $y'^2 + x^2 - 5y = 0$.
10. $x^2y'^2 - 2xyy' + y^2 - 1 = 0$.
11. $x^2y'^2 + 2x(x - y)y' + 2y^2 - 2xy = 0$.
12. $y''^2 - y''(x + y') + xy' = 0$.

ANSWERS

1. $y = c_1 e^{x^3/3}, y = c_2 e^{-x}$. 2. $(y - 1 - x - c)^2 = 4cx, y = 1$. 3. $y = c_1 x$, $y^2 - x^2 = c_2$. 4. $x = 2cp^{-1/3} + (3p^2/7), y = -cp^{2/3} + (2p^3/7)$, and $y = 0$. 5. $y = cx + ce^{-c}$ and $x = (p - 1)e^{-p}$, $y = p^2 e^{-p}$. 6. $y = x + c_1$, $y = -x + c_2, y = -2x + c_3$. 7. $y = \frac{1}{2}x^2 + c_1, y = \frac{1}{3}x^3 + c_2, y = c_3 e^x$. 8. $x^2 + 4(y - c)^2 + 2y = 0$, $y = -\frac{1}{2}x^2$. 9. $(p - 2x)^4 = c(2p - x)$, where $p^2 + x^2 - 5y = 0$. 10. $y = cx \pm 1$. 11. $x \pm \sqrt{x^2 - y^2} \pm y \sin^{-1}(y/x) = y \log |x| + c$, where $\pm$ signs agree for $x > 0$, are opposite for $x < 0$. 12. $y = c_1 + c_2 e^x$, $y = c_3 + c_4 x + (x^3/6)$.

SUGGESTED REFERENCES

1. Courant, Richard J., *Differential and Integral Calculus*, Vol. 2, transl. by E. J. McShane. New York: Interscience, 1947.

2. Ince, E. L., *Ordinary Differential Equations*. New York: Dover Publications, Inc., 1956.

CHAPTER 9

SOLUTIONS IN TERMS OF POWER SERIES

9–1 Application of Taylor's series. Let $f(x)$ be defined in some interval $a < x < b$ and let x_0 be a point of this interval. If all derivatives of $f(x)$ exist at x_0, we can form the Taylor series of $f(x)$:

$$f(x_0) + \frac{f'(x_0)}{1!}(x - x_0) + \frac{f''(x_0)}{2!}(x - x_0)^2 + \cdots + \frac{f^{(n)}(x_0)}{n!}(x - x_0)^n + \cdots \tag{9–1}$$

Under appropriate hypotheses, this power series will converge to $f(x)$ for all x or else in an interval with x_0 as midpoint (p. 359 of Reference 3). For example,

$$e^x = 1 + x + \frac{x^2}{2!} + \cdots + \frac{x^n}{n!} + \cdots \qquad (\text{all } x),$$

$$\tan x = x + \frac{x^3}{3} + \cdots \qquad \left(|x| < \frac{\pi}{2}\right).$$

We illustrate the application of the Taylor series to differential equations by an example.

EXAMPLE 1. $y' = x^2 - y^2, \qquad y = 1$ when $x = 1.$ (9–2)

If we assume that the solution $y = f(x)$ can be represented by its Taylor series, then we can obtain $f(x)$ in the form of a series as follows. We take $x_0 = 1$ in Eq. (9–1). Then $f(1)$ is given as 1. By Eq. (9–2) we obtain expressions for the higher derivatives:

$$y'' = 2x - 2yy', \qquad y''' = 2 - 2y'^2 - 2yy'', \qquad y^{(\mathrm{iv})} = -6y'y'' - 2yy''', \qquad \ldots \tag{9–3}$$

Since $y = 1$, $y' = 0$ when $x = 1$, we find successively $y'' = 2$, $y''' = -2$, $y^{(\mathrm{iv})} = 4$, ...; that is, $f''(1) = 2$, $f'''(1) = -2$, $f^{(\mathrm{iv})}(1) = 4$, ... Accordingly,

$$f(x) = 1 + \frac{2}{2!}(x - 1)^2 - \frac{2(x - 1)^3}{3!} + \frac{4(x - 1)^4}{4!} + \cdots \tag{9–4}$$

This is the desired solution in the form of a power series.

There are several important questions which now arise. Does the series (9–4) converge for some x? For which x? Does the sum $f(x)$ satisfy the differential equation? Can we find the general term of the series? How rapidly does the series converge? If we take only the first k terms of the series as an approximation to $f(x)$, how great can the error be?

A detailed discussion of convergence is given in Section 9–4 of ODE. Here we state merely that there is an interval $|x - 1| < a$ within which the series (9–4) converges to $f(x)$, that $f(x)$ is the desired solution of the differential equation, and that the rapidity of convergence can be estimated. Finding the general term of the series is a difficult problem; only for certain special equations can a simple expression be found for the general term. It should be noted that although it is convenient to have such an expression, the general term is well defined by the procedure described above, and that for each numerical application of the series, only a finite number of terms will be used.

The method described above applies equally well to equations of higher order, as in the following example.

EXAMPLE 2.

$$y'' = e^{-x}y' + e^{-x}y^2 - 1, \qquad y = 1, \quad y' = 1 \text{ when } x = 0. \tag{9–5}$$

We find

$$y''' = e^{-x}(y'' + 2yy' - y' - y^2),$$
$$y^{(\text{iv})} = e^{-x}(y''' + 2y'^2 + 2yy'' - 2y'' - 4yy' + y^2 + y').$$

Hence, when $x = 1$, $y'' = 1$, $y''' = 1$, $y^{(\text{iv})} = 1$, and

$$y = 1 + x + \frac{x^2}{2!} + \frac{x^3}{3!} + \frac{x^4}{4!} + \cdots$$

The form of the series suggests that $y = e^x$, and it can be easily verified that $y = e^x$ is indeed a solution of Eq. (9–5). In this example the series converges for all x and the solution is valid for all x.

The method can be applied in similar fashion to systems of equations (Prob. 4 below). If the initial values are left general, the method provides a general solution. It is more common to fix the initial value of x and leave the initial values of y, y', ... general; we then obtain a general solution only for an interval of x (an interval which may depend on the initial values of y, y', ...).

EXAMPLE 3. $\quad y' = x^2 - y^2, \qquad y = c$ for $x = 0$. (9–6)

The differential equation is the same as that of Example 1. Hence

Eqs. (9–3) apply and we find $y' = -c^2$, $y'' = 2c^3$, $y''' = 2 - 6c^4$, $y^{(iv)} = 24c^5 - 4c, \ldots$, for $x = 0$, so that the solution sought is

$$y = c - c^2x + c^3x^2 - (c^4 - \tfrac{1}{3})x^3 + \left(c^5 - \frac{c}{6}\right)x^4 + \cdots$$

It can be shown that this series is the general solution for $|x| < \tan^{-1}|c|^{-1}$.

PROBLEMS

1. Obtain the first four nonzero terms of the power series solution for each of the following differential equations with initial conditions:
   (a) $y' = x^2y^2 + 1$, $y = 1$ for $x = 1$;
   (b) $y' = \sin(xy) + x^2$, $y = 3$ for $x = 0$;
   (c) $y'' = x^2 - y^2$, $y = 1$ and $y' = 0$ for $x = 0$;
   (d) $y''' = xy + yy'$, $y = 0$, $y' = 1$, $y'' = 2$ for $x = 0$;
   (e) $y' = x + e^y$, $y = c$ for $x = 0$;
   (f) $y'' + y = 0$, $y = c_1$, $y' = c_2$ for $x = 0$.

2. Given the differential equation $3y^2y' = y^3 - x$,
   (a) find the first four terms of the power series solution such that $y = 1$ when $x = 0$;
   (b) graph the result of part (a) and compare with the graph of $y = (1 + x)^{1/3}$, which represents the same solution.

3. To obtain the power series solution of a general first order equation $y' = F(x, y)$, it is necessary to differentiate the equation successively to obtain y'', y''', ... Show that $y'' = F_x + F_y y'$ and find expressions for y''', $y^{(iv)}$.

4. Obtain a solution in series form for each of the following, up to terms in $(x - x_0)^3$:

   (a) $\dfrac{dy}{dx} = y + 2xz$, $\dfrac{dz}{dx} = xy - z$, $y = 0$ and $z = 1$ for $x = 1$;

   (b) $\dfrac{dy}{dx} = yz$, $\dfrac{dz}{dx} = xz + y$, $y = 1$ and $z = 0$ for $x = 0$.

[*Hint:* Differentiate both equations to obtain expressions for higher derivatives in terms of lower ones.]

5. Obtain a solution in series form for the following, up to terms in x^3:

$$y'^3 + 3xy'^2 + x - y = 0, \qquad y = 1 \text{ for } x = 0.$$

[*Hint:* Differentiate the equation as it stands to find the higher derivatives.]

ANSWERS

1. (a) $1 + 2(x-1) + 3(x-1)^2 + \frac{19}{3}(x-1)^3 + \cdots$, (b) $3 + \frac{3}{2}x^2 + \frac{1}{3}x^3 - \frac{3}{4}x^4 + \cdots$, (c) $1 - \frac{1}{2}x^2 + \frac{1}{6}x^4 - (7/360)x^6 + \cdots$, (d) $x + x^2 + \frac{1}{24}x^4 + \frac{1}{15}x^5 + \cdots$, (e) $c + e^c x + (1 + e^{2c})(x^2/2) + (2e^{3c} + e^c)(x^3/6) + \cdots$, (f) $c_1[1 - (x^2/2!) + \cdots] + c_2[x - (x^3/3!) + \cdots]$.

2. (a) $y = \frac{1}{81}(81 + 27x - 9x^2 + 5x^3 + \cdots)$.

3. $y''' = F_{xx} + 2F_{xy}y' + F_{yy}y'^2 + F_y y''$, $y^{(\text{iv})} = F_{xxx} + 3F_{xxy}y' + 3F_{xyy}y'^2 + F_{yyy}y'^3 + 3F_{xy}y'' + 3F_{yy}y'y'' + F_y y'''$.

4. (a) $y = 2(x-1) + (x-1)^2 + \frac{2}{3}(x-1)^3 + \cdots$,
$z = 1 - (x-1) + \frac{3}{2}(x-1)^2 + \frac{1}{2}(x-1)^3 + \cdots$;
(b) $y = 1 + 0 + \frac{1}{2}x^2 + 0 + \cdots$, $z = 0 + x + 0 + \frac{1}{2}x^3 + \cdots$

5. $1 + x - \frac{1}{2}x^2 + \frac{5}{18}x^3 + \cdots$

9–2 Method of undetermined coefficients. The method to be described resembles that of Section 4–9. We seek a solution of a differential equation in the form of a power series:

$$y = c_0 + c_1(x - x_0) + c_2(x - x_0)^2 + \cdots \tag{9–7}$$

Substitution in the differential equation then yields relations between the c's from which they can be determined (or expressed in terms of a certain set of c's which serve as arbitrary constants). The method is most effective for linear equations.

The steps depend on the basic rules for operation with convergent series and on the following two principles for power series:

A. if a power series (9–7) converges for $|x - x_0| < a$, then the series obtained by differentiating term-by-term also converges for $|x - x_0| < a$ and represents y';

B. if a power series (9–7) has a sum which is identically 0 for

$$|x - x_0| < a,$$

then each coefficient is 0.
(See pp. 353–355 of Reference 3.)

Example 1. $y'' + xy' + y = 0$. We seek a solution of form (9–7) with $x_0 = 0$. By principle A, the function and its derivatives are given as follows:

$$y = c_0 + c_1x + c_2x^2 + \cdots + c_nx^n + \cdots,$$

$$y' = c_1 + 2c_2x + \cdots + nc_nx^{n-1} + \cdots,$$

$$y'' = 2c_2 + 6c_3x + \cdots + n(n-1)c_nx^{n-2} + \cdots$$

If the three expressions are multiplied by 1, x, 1, and added, we obtain a series for $y'' + xy' + y$. If y satisfies the differential equation, we can equate this series to 0:

$$(c_0 + 2c_2) + x(2c_1 + 6c_3) + x^2(3c_2 + 12c_4) + \cdots + x^n[(n+1)c_n + (n+1)(n+2)c_{n+2}] + \cdots = 0.$$

By principle B, each coefficient must equal 0. Hence we obtain the equations

$$c_0 + 2c_2 = 0, \qquad 2c_1 + 6c_3 = 0, \qquad 3c_2 + 12c_4 = 0, \qquad \ldots, \qquad c_n + (n+2)c_{n+2} = 0, \qquad \ldots$$

Therefore there is a *recursion formula* for the coefficients:

$$c_{n+2} = -\frac{c_n}{n+2},$$

and we find

$$c_2 = -\frac{c_0}{2}, \qquad c_4 = -\frac{c_2}{4} = \frac{c_0}{2\cdot 4}, \qquad c_6 = -\frac{c_0}{2\cdot 4\cdot 6}, \qquad \ldots,$$

$$c_3 = -\frac{c_1}{3}, \qquad c_5 = \frac{c_1}{3\cdot 5}, \qquad c_7 = -\frac{c_1}{3\cdot 5\cdot 7}, \qquad \ldots$$

It appears that c_0, c_1 are arbitrary constants; they are, in fact, simply the initial values of y and y' at $x = 0$. The solutions can now be written in the form

$$y = c_0\left(1 - \frac{1}{2}x^2 + \frac{1}{2\cdot 4}x^4 - \frac{1}{2\cdot 4\cdot 6}x^6 + \cdots + \frac{(-1)^n}{2\cdot 4\cdot 6\cdots 2n}x^{2n} + \cdots\right) + c_1\left(x - \frac{1}{3}x^3 + \frac{1}{3\cdot 5}x^5 + \cdots + \frac{(-1)^{n+1}}{3\cdot 5\cdot 7\cdots(2n-1)}x^{2n-1} + \cdots\right). \tag{9–8}$$

Here an application of the ratio test (Prob. 7 below) shows that both series converge for all x. Furthermore, each series satisfies the differential equation for all x. Since the corresponding functions

$$y_1(x) = 1 + \sum_{n=1}^{\infty} \frac{(-1)^n x^{2n}}{2\cdot 4\cdots 2n}, \qquad y_2(x) = \sum_{n=1}^{\infty} \frac{(-1)^{n+1} x^{2n-1}}{1\cdot 3\cdots(2n-1)}$$

are linearly independent, the function

$$y = c_0 y_1(x) + c_1 y_2(x)$$

gives the general solution of the differential equation.

It can be verified that the method of undetermined coefficients is equivalent to the Taylor series method described in Section 9–1; that is, both yield the same series. For linear equations the method of undetermined coefficients is somewhat more convenient, but for nonlinear equations the method of undetermined coefficients becomes awkward (see Prob. 8 below).

In the linear equation of Example 1 the coefficients are powers of x and the equation is homogeneous. When more general coefficients appear or the right-hand side is not a polynomial, we are forced to expand the coefficients or right-hand side in Taylor's series.

EXAMPLE 2. $y'' + (\sin x)y = e^{x^2}$. If our solution is again to have form

$$y = \sum_{n=0}^{\infty} c_n x^n,$$

then we must expand $\sin x$ and e^{x^2} in their Taylor series about $x = 0$:

$$\sin x = x - \frac{x^3}{3!} + \frac{x^5}{5!} - \cdots, \qquad e^{x^2} = 1 + x^2 + \frac{x^4}{2!} + \frac{x^6}{3!} + \cdots$$

Accordingly,

$$\begin{aligned}(\sin x)y &= \left(x - \frac{x^3}{3!} + \frac{x^5}{5!} + \cdots\right)(c_0 + c_1 x + c_2 x^2 + \cdots)\\ &= c_0 x + c_1 x^2 + x^3\left(c_2 - \frac{c_0}{3!}\right) + \cdots\end{aligned}$$

Substitution in the differential equation leads to the relation

$$\begin{aligned}(2c_2 + 6c_3 x + 12c_4 x^2 + 20c_5 x^3 + \cdots) + c_0 x + c_1 x^2 + x^3\left(c_2 - \frac{c_0}{3!}\right)\\ + \cdots = 1 + x^2 + \frac{x^4}{2!} + \cdots\end{aligned}$$

By principle B, we can now compare coefficients of like powers of x:

$$2c_2 = 1, \qquad 6c_3 + c_0 = 0, \qquad 12c_4 + c_1 = 1,$$
$$20c_5 + c_2 - \frac{c_0}{3!} = 0, \qquad \cdots$$

Accordingly,

$$c_3 = -\frac{1}{6}c_0, \qquad c_2 = \frac{1}{2}, \qquad c_5 = \frac{1}{20}\left(\frac{c_0}{6} - c_2\right) = \frac{c_0}{120} - \frac{1}{40},$$

$$\ldots, \qquad c_4 = \frac{1}{12} - \frac{c_1}{12}, \qquad \ldots$$

Again c_0, c_1 are arbitrary:

$$\begin{aligned} y &= c_0 + c_1 x + \frac{1}{2}x^2 - \frac{1}{6}c_0 x^3 \\ &\qquad + \left(\frac{1}{12} - \frac{c_1}{12}\right)x^4 + \left(\frac{c_0}{120} - \frac{1}{40}\right)x^5 + \cdots \\ &= c_0\left(1 - \frac{1}{6}x^3 + \frac{1}{120}x^5 + \cdots\right) \\ &\qquad + c_1\left(x - \frac{x^4}{12} + \cdots\right) + \frac{1}{2}x^2 + \frac{1}{12}x^4 + \cdots \end{aligned}$$

The solution appears in the form

$$y = c_0 y_1(x) + c_1 y_2(x) + y^*(x),$$

where $y^*(x)$ is a particular solution. The general terms of the series can be found with some effort and the convergence of the series analyzed. However, a general convergence theorem (Section 9–6 of ODE) is applicable to show that the series converge for all x.

At first sight, the solutions in series form appear to be rather unsatisfactory. It is difficult to obtain the general term of the series, there are awkward questions of convergence, and the solutions are generally not related to familiar functions. However, we can take the point of view stressed in Chapter 1 that a differential equation is a way of describing new functions. A number of new functions (e.g., Bessel functions, hypergeometric functions) do arise naturally in this way. From the differential equations which define them, various properties of the functions can be deduced; the series expansion is simply one aspect of each function and it can be helpful in forming a table of function values. Once the new functions have been studied and tabulated, they become "familiar functions."

9–3 Techniques for forming series solutions. We can shorten the process of finding series solutions by judicious application of the $\sum$ notation. The following relation is important:

$$\sum_{n=k}^{\infty} a_n = \sum_{n=k-l}^{\infty} a_{n+l} = a_k + a_{k+1} + \cdots \tag{9–9}$$

We consider again the equation of Example 1 in Section 9–2:

$$y'' + xy' + y = 0.$$

We write our series solution as

$$y = \sum_{n=0}^{\infty} c_n x^n.$$

Then

$$y' = \sum_{n=1}^{\infty} nc_n x^{n-1}, \qquad xy' = \sum_{n=1}^{\infty} nc_n x^n,$$

$$y'' = \sum_{n=2}^{\infty} n(n-1)c_n x^{n-2}.$$

Hence substitution in the differential equation gives

$$\sum_{n=2}^{\infty} n(n-1)c_n x^{n-2} + \sum_{n=1}^{\infty} nc_n x^n + \sum_{n=0}^{\infty} c_n x^n = 0.$$

We apply the rule (9–9) to the first term, replacing n by $n + 2$:

$$\sum_{n=0}^{\infty} (n+2)(n+1)c_{n+2}x^n + \sum_{n=1}^{\infty} nc_n x^n + \sum_{n=0}^{\infty} c_n x^n = 0.$$

The general term in all three series now contains the same nth power of x, so that we can combine the series into one power series. However, since there is no term $n = 0$ in the middle series, we write out the terms $n = 0$ separately:

$$2c_2 + c_0 + \sum_{n=1}^{\infty} [(n+2)(n+1)c_{n+2} + nc_n + c_n]x^n = 0.$$

Hence, as before,

$$2c_2 + c_0 = 0, \quad (n+2)(n+1)c_{n+2} + (n+1)c_n = 0 \qquad (n = 1, 2, \ldots)$$

and we obtain the recursion formula

$$c_{n+2} = -\frac{c_n}{n+2}.$$

The general solution is then obtained as in Section 9–2.

As a second example, consider the equation

$$(x^3 + 1)y'' + x^2y' - 4xy = 0.$$

The work then proceeds as follows:

$$y = \sum_{n=0}^{\infty} c_n x^n, \qquad y' = \sum_{n=1}^{\infty} n c_n x^{n-1}, \qquad y'' = \sum_{n=2}^{\infty} n(n-1) c_n x^{n-2},$$

$$xy = \sum_{n=0}^{\infty} c_n x^{n+1}, \qquad x^2 y' = \sum_{n=1}^{\infty} n c_n x^{n+1},$$

$$x^3 y'' = \sum_{n=2}^{\infty} n(n-1) c_n x^{n+1},$$

$$\sum_{n=2}^{\infty} n(n-1) c_n x^{n+1} + \sum_{n=2}^{\infty} n(n-1) c_n x^{n-2} + \sum_{n=1}^{\infty} n c_n x^{n+1} - 4 \sum_{n=0}^{\infty} c_n x^{n+1} = 0,$$

$$\sum_{n=3}^{\infty} (n-1)(n-2) c_{n-1} x^n + \sum_{n=0}^{\infty} (n+2)(n+1) c_{n+2} x^n + \sum_{n=2}^{\infty} (n-1) c_{n-1} x^n - 4 \sum_{n=1}^{\infty} c_{n-1} x^n = 0,$$

$$2c_2 + (6c_3 - 4c_0)x + (12c_4 + c_1 - 4c_1)x^2 + \sum_{n=3}^{\infty} [(n-1)(n-2)c_{n-1} + (n+2)(n+1)c_{n+2} + (n-1)c_{n-1} - 4c_{n-1}]x^n = 0,$$

$$2c_2 = 0, \qquad 6c_3 - 4c_0 = 0, \qquad 12c_4 - 3c_1 = 0,$$

$$(n^2 - 2n - 3)c_{n-1} + (n+2)(n+1)c_{n+2} = 0 \qquad (n = 3, 4, \ldots),$$

$$c_2 = 0, \qquad c_3 = \tfrac{2}{3}c_0, \qquad c_4 = \tfrac{1}{4}c_1,$$

$$c_{n+2} = -\frac{n^2 - 2n - 3}{(n+2)(n+1)} c_{n-1} = -\frac{n-3}{n+2} c_{n-1},$$

$$c_5 = 0, \qquad c_8 = 0, \qquad c_{11} = 0, \qquad \ldots,$$

$$c_6 = -\tfrac{1}{6}c_3 = -\tfrac{1}{6} \cdot \tfrac{2}{3}c_0, \qquad c_9 = -\tfrac{4}{9}c_6 = \tfrac{4}{9} \cdot \tfrac{1}{6} \cdot \tfrac{2}{3}c_0,$$

$$c_{3k} = (-1)^k \frac{3k-5}{3k} \cdot \frac{3k-8}{3k-3} \cdots \frac{1}{6} \cdot \frac{-2}{3} c_0,$$

$$c_7 = -\tfrac{2}{7}c_4 = -\tfrac{2}{7} \cdot \tfrac{1}{4}c_1, \qquad c_{10} = -\tfrac{5}{10}c_7 = \tfrac{5}{10} \cdot \tfrac{2}{7} \cdot \tfrac{1}{4}c_1,$$

$$c_{3k+1} = (-1)^k \frac{3k-4}{3k+1} \cdot \frac{3k-7}{3k-2} \cdots \frac{2}{7} \cdot \frac{-1}{4} c_1,$$

$$y = c_0 \left(1 + \sum_{k=1}^{\infty} (-1)^k \frac{3k-5}{3k} \frac{3k-8}{3k-3} \cdots \frac{1}{6} \cdot \frac{-2}{3} x^{3k}\right)$$

$$+ c_1 \left(x + \sum_{k=1}^{\infty} (-1)^k \frac{3k-4}{3k+1} \frac{3k-7}{3k-2} \cdots \frac{2}{7} \cdot \frac{-1}{4} x^{3k+1}\right).$$

The procedures shown are applicable to linear equations with *polynomial* coefficients. Substitution of $y = \sum c_n x^n$ in the differential equation and equating the coefficient of x^n to zero leads to a recursion formula which connects the coefficients c_n. In each of the two examples above, the recursion formula relates *two* coefficients: c_n, c_{n+2} in the first; c_{n-1}, c_{n+2} in the second. Hence we say there is a *two-term recursion formula*. When only two coefficients are related, the general term of the solution can be found as in the example. When more than two terms are related, it becomes difficult to find the general term; in such cases the recursion formula defines c_n as a new function of n, just as the differential equation defines y as a new function of x.

The following example has a three-term recursion formula:

$$y'' + y' + xy = 0,$$

$$\sum_{n=2}^{\infty} n(n-1)c_n x^{n-2} + \sum_{n=1}^{\infty} nc_n x^{n-1} + \sum_{n=0}^{\infty} c_n x^{n+1} = 0,$$

$$\sum_{n=0}^{\infty} (n+2)(n+1)c_{n+2}x^n + \sum_{n=0}^{\infty} (n+1)c_{n+1}x^n + \sum_{n=1}^{\infty} c_{n-1}x^n = 0,$$

$$2c_2 + c_1 = 0, \qquad (n+2)(n+1)c_{n+2} + (n+1)c_{n+1} + c_{n-1} = 0,$$

$$c_{n+2} = -\frac{(n+1)c_{n+1} + c_{n-1}}{(n+2)(n+1)} \qquad (n = 1, 2, \ldots),$$

$$c_2 = -\tfrac{1}{2}c_1, \qquad c_3 = -\frac{2c_2 + c_0}{6} = \frac{c_1 - c_0}{6},$$

$$c_4 = -\frac{3c_3 + c_1}{12} = \frac{c_0 - 3c_1}{24}, \qquad \ldots,$$

$$y = c_0 + c_1 x - \frac{1}{2}c_1 x^2 + \frac{c_1 - c_0}{6} x^3 + \frac{c_0 - 3c_1}{24} x^4 + \cdots$$

$$= c_0 \left(1 - \frac{x^3}{6} + \frac{x^4}{24} + \cdots\right) + c_1 \left(x - \frac{x^2}{2} + \frac{x^3}{6} - \frac{x^4}{8} + \cdots\right).$$

We can consider the equations for the c_n as simultaneous linear equations, to be solved for $c_2, c_3, \ldots$ in terms of c_0, c_1. The first n equations involve only the n unknowns $c_2, c_3, \ldots, c_{n+2}$; hence they can be solved by determinants. We find $c_{n+2} = P_n/Q_n$, where Q_n is the determinant

$$\begin{vmatrix} 2 & 0 & 0 & 0 & 0 & \cdots & 0 & 0 & 0 & 0 \\ 2 & 6 & 0 & 0 & 0 & & 0 & 0 & 0 & 0 \\ 0 & 3 & 12 & 0 & 0 & & 0 & 0 & 0 & 0 \\ 1 & 0 & 4 & 20 & 0 & & 0 & 0 & 0 & 0 \\ 0 & 1 & 0 & & & & 0 & 0 & 0 & 0 \\ \vdots & & & & & & & & & \vdots \\ 0 & 0 & 0 & 0 & 0 & \cdots & 1 & 0 & n+1 & n^2+3n+2 \end{vmatrix}$$

and P_n is obtained from Q_n by replacing the elements of the last column by $-c_1, -c_0, 0, \ldots, 0$. It should also be noted that the recursion formula is a linear finite-difference equation and can be studied by special methods for such equations (Reference 2 at the end of this chapter).

In all the examples the power series have had the form $\sum c_n x^n$; that is, they are Taylor series about $x_0 = 0$. To obtain series solutions in powers of $x - x_0$ for $x_0 \neq 0$, it is simpler to make the substitution $u = x - x_0$ and obtain a differential equation for y in terms of u. A series solution $\sum c_n u^n$ then becomes the desired series $\sum c_n (x - x_0)^n$.

PROBLEMS

1. For each of the following obtain the general solution in the form of a power series $\sum c_n x^n$ and show that the series converges for all x:
(a) $y'' + 2xy' + 4y = 0$, (b) $y'' - x^2 y = 0$.

2. For each of the following obtain the general solution in the form of a power series $\sum c_n (x - a)^n$ and show that the series converges for all x:
(a) $y'' + (x-1)^2 y' + (x-1)y = 0, \quad a = 1$;
(b) $y'' + 2(x-2)y' + y = 0, \quad a = 2$.

3. (a) Find a particular solution of the equation $y'' + 2xy' + 4y = e^x$. [*Hint:* Assume $y = 0$, $y' = 0$ at $x = 0$, and hence take

$$y = \sum_{n=2}^{\infty} c_n x^n.]$$

(b) Find the general solution of the differential equation of part (a). [See Prob. 1(a).]

4. Find the general solution of the differential equation $y'' - x^2y = \sin x$. [*Hint:* Proceed as in Prob. 3(a) to find a particular solution. Then use the result of Prob. 1(b).]

5. Find a solution $y = \sum c_n x^n$ up to terms in x^6 for each of the following:
(a) $y'' + y' + xy = 0$, $y = 1$, $y' = 0$ for $x = 0$;
(b) $y''' + xy'' + y' + xy = 1 + x$, $y = 0$, $y' = 0$, $y'' = 0$ for $x = 0$.

6. Obtain solutions as series in powers of x, up to terms in x^3:

(a) $\dfrac{dy}{dx} = y + xz$, $\dfrac{dz}{dx} = y + (x - 1)z$, $y = 1$ and $z = 2$ for $x = 0$;

(b) $\dfrac{dy}{dx} = y - z$, $\dfrac{dz}{dx} = xz + y$, $y = 0$ and $z = 1$ for $x = 0$.

7. (a) Show that in Eq. (9–8) the series multiplied by c_0 is equal to $e^{-x^2/2}$.
(b) Show that both series in Eq. (9–8) converge for all x.

8. For each of the following find the solution as a power series by the method of undetermined coefficients:

(a) $y' = x^2 - y^2$, $y = 1$ when $x = 1$ (Example 1 of Section 9–1); obtain terms up to $(x - 1)^4$;

(b) $y' = x + e^y$, $y = c$ when $x = 0$ (Prob. 1(e) following Section 9–1); obtain terms up to x^3. [*Hint:* $y = c + c_1x + c_2x^2 + \cdots$,

$$\begin{aligned} e^y = e^c e^{y-c} &= e^c\{1 + (y - c) + \tfrac{1}{2}(y - c)^2 + \cdots\} \\ &= e^c\{1 + (c_1x + c_2x^2 + \cdots) + \tfrac{1}{2}(c_1x + c_2x^2 + \cdots)^2 + \cdots\} \\ &= e^c\{1 + c_1x + (c_2 + \tfrac{1}{2}c_1^2)x^2 + \cdots\}.] \end{aligned}$$

9. (a) Show that the equation $x^2y'' + xy' + y = 0$ has no solution of form $\sum_{n=0}^{\infty} c_n x^n$ except $y \equiv 0$. Show also that the existence theorem of Section 1–7 does not apply at $x = 0$.

(b) Show that the existence theorem of Section 1–7 does not apply at $x = 0$ to the equation $x^2y'' - 3xy' + 3y = 0$, but that solutions of form $\sum_{n=0}^{\infty} c_n x^n$ are obtainable.

10. Let the differential equation $a_0(x)y'' + a_1(x)y' + a_2(x)y = 0$ be given, where $a_0(x)$, $a_1(x)$, $a_2(x)$ are polynomials and $a_0(0) \neq 0$. Let L be the corresponding operator $a_0(x)D^2 + a_1(x)D + a_2(x)$. Assume that the substitution $y = \sum c_n x^n$ leads to a two-term recursion formula for the c's.

(a) Show that the differential equation must have the form

$$(\alpha x^k + \beta)y'' + \gamma x^{k-1}y' + \delta x^{k-2}y = 0,$$

where α, β, γ, δ are constants and $\beta \neq 0$, $k \geqq 2$. Show that we then have

$$L(x^n) = f(n)x^{n-2} + g(n)x^{n+k-2} \qquad (n = 0, 1, 2, \ldots),$$

and find $f(n)$, $g(n)$.

(b) Let $y(x) = x^m(\sum_{s=0}^{\infty} c_s x^{sk})$, where $c_0 = 1$. Show that

$$L(y) = x^{m-2}\left(f(m) + \sum_{s=1}^{\infty} \{c_s f(m + sk) + c_{s-1} g[m + (s - 1)k]\} x^{sk}\right).$$

(c) Conclude from the result of part (b) that $y(x)$ is a solution of the differential equation if and only if $f(m) = 0$, so that $m = 0$ or $m = 1$, and

$$c_s f(m + sk) + c_{s-1} g[m + (s - 1)k] = 0 \qquad (s = 1, 2, \ldots).$$

Take $c_0 = 1$ and obtain an expression for c_s, $(s = 1, 2, \ldots)$. Show that the choices $m = 0$, $m = 1$ lead to the two solutions

$$y_1 = 1 + \sum_{s=1}^{\infty} (-1)^s x^{sk} \frac{g(0)g(k) \cdots g[(s - 1)k]}{f(k)f(2k) \cdots f(sk)},$$

$$y_2 = x + x \sum_{s=1}^{\infty} (-1)^s x^{sk} \frac{g(1)g(k + 1) \cdots g[1 + (s - 1)k]}{f(1 + k)f(1 + 2k) \cdots f(1 + sk)}.$$

(d) With the aid of the expressions for $f(n)$, $g(n)$ obtained in part (a), apply the ratio test to show that the power series for y_1, y_2 of part (c) converge for $|x| < |\beta/\alpha|^{1/k}$ if $\alpha \neq 0$ and for all x if $\alpha = 0$.

ANSWERS

1. (a) $$c_0\left(1 + \sum_{n=1}^{\infty} \frac{(-1)^n 2^n x^{2n}}{1 \cdot 3 \cdots (2n - 1)}\right) + c_1 \sum_{n=1}^{\infty} \frac{(-1)^n x^{2n-1}}{(n - 1)!},$$

(b) $$c_0\left(1 + \sum_{n=1}^{\infty} \frac{x^{4n}}{3 \cdot 4 \cdot 7 \cdot 8 \cdots (4n - 1)(4n)}\right) + c_1\left(x + \sum_{n=1}^{\infty} \frac{x^{4n+1}}{4 \cdot 5 \cdot 8 \cdot 9 \cdots (4n)(4n + 1)}\right).$$

2. (a) $$c_0\left(1 + \sum_{n=1}^{\infty} \frac{1 \cdot 4 \cdots (3n - 2)\,(-1)^n (x - 1)^{3n}}{2 \cdot 3 \cdot 5 \cdot 6 \cdots (3n - 1)(3n)}\right) + c_1(x - 1)\left(1 + \sum_{n=1}^{\infty} \frac{2 \cdot 5 \cdots (3n - 1)\,(-1)^n (x - 1)^{3n}}{3 \cdot 4 \cdot 6 \cdot 7 \cdots (3n)(3n + 1)}\right),$$

(b) $$c_0\left(1 + \sum_{n=1}^{\infty} \frac{1 \cdot 5 \cdots (4n - 3)\,(-1)^n (x - 2)^{2n}}{(2n)!}\right) + c_1(x - 2)\left(1 + \sum_{n=1}^{\infty} \frac{3 \cdot 7 \cdots (4n - 1)\,(-1)^n (x - 2)^{2n}}{(2n + 1)!}\right).$$

3. (a) $\frac{1}{2}x^2 + \frac{1}{6}x^3 - \frac{7}{24}x^4 - \frac{3}{40}x^5 + (85/720)x^6 + \cdots = y^*$, (b) $y^* + y_c$, where y_c is the answer to Prob. 1(a).

4. $\frac{1}{3!}x^3 - \frac{1}{5!}x^5 + \frac{21}{7!}x^7 - \frac{43}{9!}x^9 + \cdots + y_c$, where y_c is the answer to Prob. 1(b).

5. (a) $1 - \frac{1}{6}x^3 + \frac{1}{24}x^4 - (1/120)x^5 + (1/144)x^6 + \cdots$,
(b) $\frac{1}{6}x^3 + \frac{1}{24}x^4 - \frac{1}{40}x^5 - (1/180)x^6 + \cdots$

6. (a) $y = 1 + x + \frac{3}{2}x^2 + \frac{1}{6}x^3 + \cdots$, $z = 2 - x + 2x^2 - \frac{1}{2}x^3 + \cdots$;
(b) $y = -x - \frac{1}{2}x^2 - \frac{1}{6}x^3 + \cdots$, $z = 1 - \frac{1}{6}x^3 + \cdots$

7. (c) $y = c_1e^{-x^2/2} + c_2e^{-x^2/2}\int e^{x^2/2}\,dx$.

9. (b) $c_1x + c_2x^3$ is the general solution.

10. (a) $f(n) = \beta n(n-1)$, $g(n) = \alpha n^2 + (\gamma - \alpha)n + \delta$;

(c) $c_s = (-1)^s \dfrac{g(m)g(m+k)\cdots g[m+(s-1)k]}{f(m+k)f(m+2k)\cdots f(m+sk)}$.

9–4 Series solutions for linear equations at a singular point. We now consider a homogeneous linear equation of second order:

$$a_0(x)y'' + a_1(x)y' + a_2(x)y = 0. \tag{9–10}$$

The results to be described can be extended to equations of higher order, to systems of linear differential equations, and to nonhomogeneous equations. For the general theory see References 1, 4, and 6 at the end of this chapter.

It will be assumed that the coefficients $a_0(x)$, $a_1(x)$, $a_2(x)$ in Eq. (9–10) are analytic in an interval $|x - x_0| < a$ and that $a_0(x)$ is not identically 0 for $|x - x_0| < a$. For simplicity, x_0 will be taken to be 0; a translation reduces the general case to this one. Thus it is assumed that

$$a_0(x) = \sum_{n=0}^{\infty} \alpha_n x^n, \qquad a_1(x) = \sum_{n=0}^{\infty} \beta_n x^n, \qquad a_2 = \sum_{n=0}^{\infty} \gamma_n x^n \tag{9–11}$$

for $|x| < a$. Finally it is assumed that $a_0(0) = 0$; that is, that the constant term α_0 is 0. We term $x = 0$ a singular point of the equation.

Under the assumptions made, the existence theorem of Section 1–7 is not applicable at the initial value $x_0 = 0$ and we cannot expect to obtain solutions with arbitrary initial values of y and y' at $x = 0$. Indeed, there may be no solution defined at $x = 0$ other than the trivial solution $y \equiv 0$.

Instead of seeking solutions which satisfy conditions at $x = 0$, we seek solutions represented by series for $0 < |x| < b$, that is, solutions defined *near* 0 but not at 0. Occasionally, the solutions turn out to be valid also at $x = 0$. It will be seen that under certain conditions solutions can be found having the form

$$x^m \sum_{n=0}^{\infty} c_n x^n \qquad (0 < |x| < b). \tag{9–12}$$

If $m = 1$, the solution continues to be valid for $x = 0$. But if $m = -3$, for example, the solution is meaningless at $x = 0$.

Regular singular points. An equation such as

$$xy'' + (x^2 - x)y = 0 \tag{9–13}$$

has a singular point at $x = 0$, according to the above definition. However, the singular point can be removed by dividing by x:

$$y'' + (x - 1)y = 0. \tag{9–14}$$

(Equation (9–13) is equivalent to the *differential* equation (9–14) and the *algebraic* relation $x = 0$.) Such a singular point is called *removable*. In the subsequent discussion only singular points which are *not* removable will be considered.

Equation (9–10) is said to have a *regular singular point* at $x = 0$ if, after cancellation of the highest power of x which is a common factor of the coefficients, the equation takes one of the two forms

$$(\alpha_1 x + \alpha_2 x^2 + \cdots)y'' + (\beta_0 + \cdots)y' + (\gamma_0 + \cdots)y = 0 \qquad (\alpha_1 \neq 0), \tag{9–15a}$$

$$(\alpha_2 x^2 + \alpha_3 x^3 + \cdots)y'' + (\beta_1 x + \cdots)y' + (\gamma_0 + \cdots)y = 0 \qquad (\alpha_2 \neq 0). \tag{9–15b}$$

An equation of form (9–15a) or (9–15b) has at least one solution and possibly two linearly independent solutions of form (9–12).

EXAMPLE. $x^2y'' + xy' + (x^3 - 1)y = 0$. Here $a_0 = x^2$, $a_1 = x$, so that (9–15b) applies and we have a regular singular point at $x = 0$. We set

$$y = x^m(c_0 + c_1 x + \cdots + c_n x^n + \cdots)$$

and try to choose m and the c's so that the differential equation is satisfied (with y not identically 0). On substituting in the equation and collecting terms, we find the relation

$$x^m[c_0(m^2 - 1) + c_1(m^2 + 2m)x + c_2(m^2 + 4m + 3)x^2 + x^3\{c_0 + c_3(m^2 + 6m + 5)\} + \cdots + x^n\{c_{n-3} + c_n(\overline{m + n}^2 - 1)\} + \cdots] = 0.$$

For $x \neq 0$ we can ignore the factor x^m. Equating the coefficient of each power of x to 0, we obtain the relations

$$c_0(m^2 - 1) = 0,$$
$$c_1(m^2 + 2m) = 0,$$
$$c_2(m^2 + 4m + 3) = 0,$$
$$c_0 + c_3(m^2 + 6m + 8) = 0,$$
$$\vdots$$
$$c_{n-3} + c_n(\overline{m + n}^2 - 1) = 0 \qquad (n = 4, 5, \ldots).$$

The first equation gives $c_0 = 0$ or $m^2 - 1 = 0$. We can always assume $c_0 \neq 0$, for any other case can be reduced to this one by factoring out a suitable power of x and hence modifying the value of m. If $c_0 \neq 0$, then $m^2 - 1 = 0$; hence $m = -1$ or $m = 1$. For $m = -1$ we have

$$-c_1 = 0, \qquad 0 \cdot c_2 = 0, \qquad c_0 + 3c_3 = 0,$$
$$c_{n-3} + (n^2 - 2n)c_n = 0,$$

for $n = 4, 5, \ldots$; hence we have the recursion formula

$$c_n = -\frac{c_{n-3}}{n^2 - 2n} = -\frac{c_{n-3}}{n(n-2)}.$$

From this we conclude that $c_1 = 0$, $c_4 = 0$, $c_7 = 0, \ldots$ If n is a multiple of 3, then

$$c_n = \frac{-1}{n(n-2)} \cdot \frac{-1}{(n-3)(n-5)} \cdots \frac{-1}{3 \cdot 1} \cdot c_0.$$

If n is of form $3s + 2$, then

$$c_n = \frac{-1}{n(n-2)} \frac{-1}{(n-3)(n-5)} \cdots \frac{-1}{5 \cdot 3} c_2.$$

Thus c_0 and c_2 are arbitrary and the solutions found can be written

$$y = x^{-1}\left[c_0\left(1 + \sum_{s=1}^{\infty} (-1)^s x^{3s} \frac{1}{(1 \cdot 3)(4 \cdot 6) \cdots (3s-2)(3s)}\right)\right.$$
$$\left. + c_2\left(x^2 + x^2 \sum_{s=1}^{\infty} (-1)^s x^{3s} \frac{1}{(3 \cdot 5)(6 \cdot 8) \cdots (3s)(3s+2)}\right)\right].$$

This equation is clearly of the form $y = c_0 y_1(x) + c_2 y_2(x)$, and we can verify that y_1, y_2 are linearly independent, so that y is the general solution.

It follows from the ratio test that the series converge for all x, so that the solutions are valid for all x except 0 (because of the factor x^{-1}). We note that

$$y_2(x) = x + x\sum_{s=1}^{\infty}(-1)^s x^{3s}\frac{1}{(3\cdot 5)\cdot(6\cdot 8)\cdots(3s)(3s+2)},$$

and this solution is valid for all x.

In our analysis we were led to the equation $m^2 - 1 = 0$ and we chose only the root $m = -1$. If we choose the other root, $m = 1$, we obtain a solution $x\sum c_n x^n$, which is found to be a constant times $y_2(x)$.

9–5 Indicial equation. Equations with a two-term recursion formula. The method of the example of Section 9–4 can be applied to an arbitrary equation (9–10) with a regular singular point at $x = 0$. The substitution $y = x^m\sum c_n x^n$ leads to relations between the c's, of which the first has form

$$c_0 f(m) = 0,$$

where $f(m)$ is a polynomial of *second* degree in m. The equation $f(m) = 0$ is called the *indicial* equation. If m_1, m_2 are the roots of this equation, then by choosing $m = m_1$ or $m = m_2$ we obtain two sets of constants c_n and hence two series solutions $y_1(x)$, $y_2(x)$. The later constants are determined from the earlier ones by a recursion formula, which may involve two or more of the c's.

If $m_2 = m_1$, the method provides only one solution (up to a constant factor); if $m_2 \neq m_1$, but $m_2 - m_1$ is a positive integer, then the constants c_n that correspond to $m = m_1$ may fail to be defined. Thus complications can arise in applying the method. It may also happen that m_1, m_2 are complex; we then obtain complex solutions, from which the real solutions can be obtained as in Section 4–7.

The difficulties mentioned all arise for the equations with polynomial coefficients and with a two-term recursion formula. These equations include many which are very important for applications. Hence we shall concentrate attention on these equations, for which we can formulate precise results.

THEOREM 1. *Let L be the differential operator*

$$a_0(x)D^2 + a_1(x)D + a_2(x),$$

where $a_0(x)$, $a_1(x)$, $a_2(x)$ are polynomials without common factor. Let the differential equation $Ly = 0$ have a regular singular point at $x = 0$. Let

$$L(x^n) = f(n)x^{n+h} + g(n)x^{n+h+k} \qquad (k>0), \tag{9–16}$$

where $f(n) \not\equiv 0$. Then $h = 0$ or -1, $f(n)$ is a polynomial in n of second degree, and $g(n)$ is a polynomial in n of degree at most 2. The substitution

$$y = x^m \sum_{n=0}^{\infty} c_n x^n \tag{9–17}$$

in the differential equation leads to the indicial equation $f(m) = 0$ and to a two-term recursion formula for the c_n. If m_1, m_2 are the roots of the indicial equation and $(m_1 - m_2)/k$ is not an integer or zero, then two linearly independent solutions $y_1(x)$, $y_2(x)$ are given by

$$y_1(x) = \phi(x, m_1), \qquad y_2(x) = \phi(x, m_2), \tag{9–18}$$

where

$$\phi(x, m) = x^m \left\{1 + \sum_{s=1}^{\infty} (-1)^s x^{ks} \frac{g(m)g(m+k) \cdots g[m+(s-1)k]}{f(m+k)f(m+2k) \cdots f(m+sk)}\right\}. \tag{9–19}$$

If $g(n)$ is of degree 0 or 1, the solutions are valid for all x except perhaps $x = 0$. If $g(n)$ is of degree 2, then the solutions are valid for $0 < |x| < a$, where

$$a = \left|\frac{f_0}{g_0}\right|^{1/k}, \qquad f(n) = f_0 n^2 + \cdots, \qquad g(n) = g_0 n^2 + \cdots$$

Proof. Since $x = 0$ is a regular singular point, either (9–15a) or (9–15b) holds. If the former holds, then

$$\begin{aligned} L(x^n) &= n(n-1)(\alpha_1 x + \alpha_2 x^2 + \cdots)x^{n-2} + n(\beta_0 + \cdots)x^{n-1} \\ &\qquad + (\gamma_0 + \cdots)x^n \\ &= x^{n-1}[\alpha_1 n^2 + (\beta_0 - \alpha_1)n] \\ &\qquad + x^n[\alpha_2 n^2 + (\beta_1 - \alpha_2)n + \gamma_0] + \cdots \end{aligned}$$

Since $\alpha_1 \neq 0$, the first bracket is $f(n)$, not identical with 0, a polynomial of second degree. By assumption only one other power of x appears. This must be x^{n-1+k}, where $k > 0$, and the corresponding term is

$$x^{n-1+k}[\alpha_{k+1} n^2 + (\beta_k - \alpha_{k+1})n + \gamma_{k-1}] = g(n)x^{n-1+k}.$$

Thus $g(n)$ has the form described and $h = -1$. When (9–15b) holds, we find in the same way that $h = 0$, and

$$f(n) = \alpha_2 n^2 + (\beta_1 - \alpha_2)n + \gamma_0,$$

$$g(n) = \alpha_{k+2} n^2 + (\beta_{k+1} - \alpha_{k+2})n + \gamma_k.$$

If y is given by (9–17), then

$$\begin{aligned} Ly &= L\left(\sum_{n=0}^{\infty} c_n x^{m+n}\right) = \sum_{n=0}^{\infty} c_n L(x^{m+n}) \\ &= \sum_{n=0}^{\infty} c_n [f(m+n)x^{m+n+h} + g(m+n)x^{m+n+h+k}] \\ &= x^{m+h}\left\{\sum_{n=0}^{\infty} c_n f(m+n)x^n + \sum_{n=0}^{\infty} c_n g(m+n)x^{n+k}\right\} \\ &= x^{m+h}\Bigg\{c_0 f(m) + c_1 f(m+1)x + \cdots + c_{k-1} f(m+k-1)x^{k-1} \\ &\qquad + \sum_{n=k}^{\infty} [c_n f(m+n) + c_{n-k} g(m+n-k)]x^n\Bigg\}. \end{aligned}$$

Hence $f(m) = 0$ is the indicial equation and there is a two-term recursion formula which relates c_n and c_{n-k}. From the form of the recursion formula it appears that we will obtain independent solutions containing only the powers x^{m+sk} $(s = 0, 1, 2, \ldots)$. It is simpler, however, to take y in a corresponding form to start with:

$$y = x^m \sum_{s=0}^{\infty} c_s x^{ks}. \tag{9–20}$$

We can also take $c_0 = 1$ and later insert an arbitrary constant as factor. We now find as before

$$\begin{aligned} Ly &= L\left(\sum_{s=0}^{\infty} c_s x^{ks+m}\right) \\ &= \sum_{s=0}^{\infty} c_s [f(m+ks)x^{m+ks+h} + g(m+ks)x^{m+k(s+1)+h}] \\ &= x^{m+h}\left(f(m) + \sum_{s=1}^{\infty} \{c_s f(m+ks) + c_{s-1} g[m+k(s-1)]\} x^{ks}\right). \end{aligned}$$

Now the recursion formula is

$$c_s = -\frac{g[m+k(s-1)]}{f(m+ks)} c_{s-1}. \tag{9–21}$$

From this relation and the condition $c_0 = 1$, we find

$$c_s = (-1)^s \frac{g[m+k(s-1)]\cdots g(m+k)g(m)}{f(m+sk)\cdots f(m+2k)f(m+k)} \qquad (s = 1, 2, \ldots). \tag{9–22}$$

If the c_s are so chosen, then y becomes the function $\phi(x, m)$ defined by

Eq. (9–19), and

$$Ly = x^{m+h} f(m). \tag{9-23}$$

Now if $m = m_1$, where $f(m_1) = 0$, then y becomes $y_1 = \phi(x, m_1)$:

$$y_1 = x^{m_1}\left\{1 + \sum_{s=1}^{\infty} (-1)^s x^{ks} \frac{g(m_1) \cdots g[m_1 + (s-1)k]}{f(m_1 + k) \cdots f(m_1 + sk)}\right\}.$$

Equation (9–23) shows that $L(y_1) = 0$. Similarly, if $m = m_2$, then y becomes $y_2 = \phi(x, m_2)$ and $L(y_2) = 0$.

We have tacitly assumed that the constants c_s are well defined by Eq. (9–22) when $m = m_1$ or $m = m_2$. Difficulty can arise only if there is a zero in the denominator, that is, if $f(m + sk) = 0$ for some choice of s and $m = m_1$ or $m = m_2$. But $f(m_1 + sk) = 0$ can only mean $m_1 + sk = m_2$, that is, that $(m_2 - m_1)/k$ is an integer s. This is ruled out by assumption; similarly, $f(m_2 + sk) = 0$ is ruled out. Hence $\phi(x, m_1)$ and $\phi(x, m_2)$ are well defined.

Application of the ratio test shows that the series converge as stated in Theorem 1, so that $y_1(x)$ and $y_2(x)$ are solutions in the intervals given. The two solutions are linearly independent, for otherwise one would be a constant times the other; this is impossible since $m_1 \neq m_2$ (Prob. 13 below). Hence $c_1 y_1(x) + c_2 y_2(x)$ provides the general solution in the interval stated.

Example. $2x^2y'' + (x^2 - x)y' + y = 0$. There is a regular singular point at $x = 0$. We find $L(x^n) = x^n(2n^2 - 3n + 1) + nx^{n+1}$. Hence $f(n) = 2n^2 - 3n + 1 = (2n - 1)(n - 1)$, $g(n) = n$, $k = 1$, $h = 0$,

$$\phi(x, m) = x^m\left[1 + \sum_{s=1}^{\infty} (-1)^s x^s \frac{m(m+1)\cdots(m+s-1)}{(2m+1)(m)\cdots(2m+2s-1)(m+s-1)}\right].$$

The indicial equation has roots $\frac{1}{2}$, 1; their difference is not an integral multiple of k. Hence we obtain two solutions:

$$y_1 = \phi(x, \tfrac{1}{2}) = x^{1/2}\left[1 + \sum_{s=1}^{\infty} (-1)^s x^s \frac{\frac{1}{2}\cdot\frac{3}{2}\cdots[(2s-1)/2]}{(2\cdot\frac{1}{2})(4\cdot\frac{3}{2})\cdots(2s)[(2s-1)/2]}\right]$$

$$= x^{1/2}\left[1 + \sum_{s=1}^{\infty} (-1)^s x^s \frac{1}{2^s s!}\right],$$

$$y_2 = \phi(x, 1) = x\left[1 + \sum_{s=1}^{\infty} (-1)^s x^s \frac{1\cdot 2\cdots s}{(3\cdot 1)(5\cdot 2)\cdots(2s+1)s}\right]$$

$$= x\left[1 + \sum_{s=1}^{\infty} (-1)^s x^s \frac{1}{3\cdot 5\cdots(2s+1)}\right].$$

Since $g(n)$ is of degree 1, the series converge for all x and the general solution is

$$y = c_1 y_1(x) + c_2 y_2(x)$$

for all x except 0. We note that $y_2(x)$ is also valid as a solution at $x = 0$, and that $y_1(x)$ is imaginary for $x < 0$, because of the square root. A corresponding real solution for $x < 0$ is a constant multiple of $y_1(x)$,

$$\begin{aligned} y(x) &= i y_1(x) = i x^{1/2}(1 + \cdots) \\ &= \sqrt{-1}\,\sqrt{x}\,(1 + \cdots) = \sqrt{-x}\,(1 + \cdots). \end{aligned}$$

Remark 1. If $L(x^n)$ involves more than two powers of x, then the reasoning of the above proof shows that the recursion formula will relate more than two of the c's. Hence the assumption of a two-term recursion formula forces $L(x^n)$ to have the form shown. This in turn implies that the coefficients $a_0(x)$, $a_1(x)$, $a_2(x)$ are of special form (Prob. 6 below). It can happen that $L(x^n)$ involves only *one* power of x. In this case, the result of Prob. 6 implies that the differential equation can be written

$$\alpha_2 x^2 y'' + \beta_1 x y + \gamma_0 y = 0,$$

where α_2, β_1, γ_0 are constants. This is a Cauchy equation, discussed in Prob. 5 following Section 5–2. As shown there, $L(x^n) = f(n)x^n$ and, if $f(n)$ has distinct roots m_1, m_2, $y_1 = x^{m_1}$ and $y_2 = x^{m_2}$ are linearly independent solutions.

Remark 2. If $a_0(0) \neq 0$, so that $x = 0$ is an ordinary point (not singular) and $L(x^n)$ involves only two powers of x, then the results of Theorem 1 are still applicable. Since $a_0(0) \neq 0$, we find that $f(n)$ is $\alpha_0 n(n - 1)$, so that the indicial equation has roots 0, 1. A detailed analysis is given in Prob. 10 following Section 9–3.

Remark 3. If $m_1 = m_2$ or $m_2 = m_1 + sk$, where s is a positive integer, then Theorem 1 is not applicable. One can verify that, in these exceptional cases, $\phi(x, m_2)$ is still well defined and does provide one solution of the differential equation. Methods for obtaining a second solution, linearly independent of $\phi(x, m_2)$, are described in Sections 9–9 to 9–11 of ODE.

PROBLEMS

1. For each of the following differential equations determine all singular points and determine whether each is removable, regular, or irregular:
   (a) $x^2y'' + y' + x^2y = 0$,
   (b) $x^2y'' + x^3y' + (x^4 - x^2)y = 0$,
   (c) $(x^2 - x)y'' + (x + 1)y' + y = 0$,
   (d) $(x^2 - 2x - 3)^2y'' + (x - 3)y' + y = 0$.

2. Verify that each of the following equations has a regular singular point at $x = 0$, show that the conditions of Theorem 1 are satisfied, and find two linearly independent solutions near $x = 0$:

(a) $xy'' + (x^3 - 1)y' + 3x^2y = 0$,
(b) $x^2y'' + x^3y' - 2y = 0$,
(c) $xy'' - y' + x^2y = 0$,
(d) $(3x^2 + 3x^3)y'' - (x + 6x^2)y' + y = 0$,
(e) $2xy'' + (3 + 2x)y' - 2y = 0$.

3. Let $a + bi$ be a complex constant. We define the function $y = x^{a+bi}$ for $x > 0$ as follows:

$$y = x^{a+bi} = x^a x^{bi} = x^a e^{bi \log x} = x^a [\cos (b \log x) + i \sin (b \log x)].$$

Show that $y' = (a + bi)x^{a+bi-1}$ (see Section 4–7). The definition and conclusion can be extended to negative x by the rule

$$y = x^{a+bi} = (-|x|)^{a+bi} = (-1)^{a+bi}|x|^{a+bi} = \text{const} \cdot |x|^{a+bi}$$

$$= \text{const} \cdot |x|^a [\cos (b \log |x| + i \sin (b \log |x|)] \qquad (x < 0).$$

The constant has, in general, one of an infinite set of values (Reference 3, pp. 529–530), but we can choose the particular value

$$(-1)^{a+bi} = e^{-b\pi} (\cos a\pi + i \sin a\pi).$$

4. Let the following differential equation be given:

$$x^2y'' + (x + x^2)y' + y = 0.$$

(a) Show that there is a regular singular point at $x = 0$ and that the roots of the indicial equation are $\pm i$.
(b) Use the result of Prob. 3 to obtain complex solutions valid for $|x| > 0$.
(c) Write out the series for $m = i$ of part (b), as far as the term in x^3. Then take real and imaginary parts to obtain linearly independent real solutions for $|x| > 0$.

5. Show that each of the following equations has an irregular singular point at $x = 0$. Attempt to find a solution of form $x^m\sum_{n=0}^{\infty} c_n x^n$ and explain the difficulties which arise.

(a) $x^3y'' + (x + 2x^2)y' - (1 + x)y = 0$.
(b) $x^3y'' + x^2y' + (1 + x)y = 0$.

6. Let the equation $L(y) = (\alpha_0 + \alpha_1 x + \cdots)y'' + (\beta_0 + \beta_1 x + \cdots)y' + (\gamma_0 + \gamma_1 x + \cdots)y = 0$ be given. Let $L(x^n) = f(n)x^{n+h} + g(n)x^{n+k+h}$, $k \geqq 0$. Show that $\alpha_{j+2}, \beta_{j+1}, \gamma_j$ are 0 for $j \neq h, j \neq k + h$.

7. An equation $a_0(x)y'' + a_1(x)y' + a_2(x)y = 0$, with polynomial coefficients, is said to have a *regular singular point at* $x = \infty$ if the substitution

$t = 1/x$ leads to an equation with a regular singular point at $t = 0$. Show that each of the following differential equations has a regular singular point at $x = \infty$:

(a) $x^5y'' + x^4y' + (1 - x^3)y = 0$, (b) $2x^3y'' + (2x + x^2)y' + 2y = 0$.

8. For an equation $L(y) = 0$ with a regular singular point at infinity (Prob. 7), we can obtain series solutions by setting $t = 1/x$ and obtaining series in terms of t. We can also proceed directly as follows (in case of a two-term recursion formula). Let

$$L(x^n) = f(n)x^{n+h-k} + g(n)x^{n+h} \qquad (k > 0).$$

The fact that the singular point at infinity is regular forces $g(n)$ to be of second degree, and the equation $g(m) = 0$ becomes the indicial equation, with roots m_1, m_2. We then seek solutions

$$y = x^m\left[1 + \sum_{s=1}^{\infty}(-1)^s c_s x^{-ks}\right].$$

If $(m_2 - m_1)/k$ is not an integer or 0, show that two linearly independent solutions for $|x| > a$ are given by

$$y_1 = \Phi(x, m_1), \qquad y_2 = \Phi(x, m_2),$$

where

$$\Phi(x, m) = x^m\left\{1 + \sum_{s=1}^{\infty}(-1)^s x^{-ks}\frac{f(m)\cdots f[m - (s - 1)k]}{g(m - k)\cdots g(m - sk)}\right\}.$$

9. Apply the method of Prob. 8 to obtain linearly independent solutions for large $|x|$ of the equations (a) and (b) of Prob. 7.

10. *The Legendre equation* is given by

$$(1 - x^2)y'' - 2xy' + N(N + 1)y = 0,$$

where N is a constant.

(a) Show that $x = 0$ is an ordinary point, so that the indicial equation has roots 0, 1. Apply the method of Theorem 1 to obtain the solutions for $|x| < 1$:

$$y_1 = 1 + \sum_{s=1}^{\infty}(-1)^s x^{2s} \times \frac{\{N(N - 2)\cdots(N - 2s + 2)\}\{(N + 1)(N + 3)\cdots(N + 2s - 1)\}}{(2s)!},$$

$$y_2 = x\left(1 + \sum_{s=1}^{\infty}(-1)^s x^{2s} \times \frac{\{(N - 1)(N - 3)\cdots(N - 2s + 1)\}\{(N + 2)(N + 4)\cdots(N + 2s)\}}{(2s + 1)!}\right).$$

(b) Show that when N is a positive even integer or 0, the solution y_1 of part (a) reduces to a polynomial of degree N. [For $N > 0$ this polynomial is

$$(-1)^{N/2}\frac{2\cdot 4\cdots N}{1\cdot 3\cdots (N-1)}P_N(x),$$

where $P_N(x)$ is the *Legendre polynomial* of even degree N. For $N = 0$, $y_1(x) \equiv P_0(x) \equiv 1$.]

(c) Show that when N is a positive odd integer, the solution y_2 of part (a) reduces to a polynomial of degree N. [For $N > 0$ this polynomial is

$$(-1)^{(N-1)/2}\frac{2\cdot 4\cdots (N-1)}{1\cdot 3\cdots N}P_N(x),$$

where $P_N(x)$ is the *Legendre polynomial* of odd degree N. For $N = 1$, $y_1(x) \equiv P_1(x) \equiv x$.]

(d) Show that the differential equation has a regular singular point at infinity (Probs. 7, 8, 9) and that the indicial equation has roots N, $-N-1$. Assume that $N + \frac{1}{2}$ is not an integer and obtain the linearly independent solutions for $|x| > 1$:

$$y_1 = x^N\left(1+\sum_{s=1}^{\infty}(-1)^s x^{-2s}\frac{N(N-1)\cdots(N-2s+2)(N-2s+1)}{2^s s!(2N-1)\cdots(2N+1-2s)}\right),$$

$$y_2 = x^{-N-1}\left(1+\sum_{s=1}^{\infty}x^{-2s}\frac{(N+1)(N+2)\cdots(N+2s-1)(N+2s)}{2^s s!(2N+3)\cdots(2N+2s+1)}\right).$$

(e) Show that when N is a positive integer or 0, the solution $y_1(x)$ of part (d) remains valid and is a polynomial. [For $N > 0$ this polynomial is

$$\frac{N!}{1\cdot 3\cdots(2N-1)}P_N(x),$$

where $P_N(x)$ is the Legendre polynomial of degree N. For $N = 0$, $y_1(x) \equiv P_0(x) \equiv 1$.]

11. *The hypergeometric equation* is given by

$$x(1-x)y'' + [c-(a+b+1)x]y' - aby = 0,$$

where a, b, c are constants.

(a) Show that the equation has a regular singular point at $x = 0$ and that the indicial equation has roots 0, $1-c$.

(b) Show that if c is not a negative integer or 0, then one solution is given by

$$y_1(x) = 1 + \frac{a\cdot b}{1\cdot c}x + \frac{a(a+1)}{2!}\frac{b(b+1)}{c(c+1)}x^2 + \cdots \qquad (|x| < 1).$$

This function is denoted by $F(a, b, c; x)$ and its series is termed the *hypergeometric series*. (When $a = 1$ and $b = c$, the series reduces to the *geometric* series $\sum x^n$).

(c) Show that if c is not an integer, then two linearly independent solutions or $0 < |x| < 1$ are given by $y_1 = F(a, b, c; x)$ and

$$y_2 = x^{1-c}F(a - c + 1, b - c + 1, 2 - c; x).$$

12. *The Bessel equation* is given by

$$x^2y'' + xy' + (x^2 - N^2)y = 0,$$

where N is a constant.

(a) Show that there is a regular singular point at $x = 0$ and, for N not an integer, obtain the linearly independent solutions which are valid for $|x| > 0$,

$$y_1(x) = x^N\left(1 + \sum_{s=1}^{\infty} (-1)^s \frac{x^{2s}}{2^{2s}s!(N + 1)\cdots(N + s)}\right),$$

$$y_2(x) = x^{-N}\left(1 + \sum_{s=1}^{\infty} (-1)^s \frac{x^{2s}}{2^{2s}s!(1 - N)\cdots(s - N)}\right).$$

(b) Show that the solution $y_1(x)$ of part (a) is valid for $|x| > 0$ provided N is not a negative integer. [This function is

$$2^N\Gamma(N + 1)J_N(x),$$

where $J_N(x)$ is the *Bessel function of first kind* of order N and $\Gamma(x)$ is the Gamma function (p. 381 of Reference 3). When N is a positive integer or 0, $y_1(x)$ is $2^N N!J_N(x)$.]

(c) Show that the Bessel equation has an irregular singular point at $x = \infty$.

13. Prove that the two solutions $y_1(x)$, $y_2(x)$ of Theorem 1 are linearly independent. [*Hint:* If they were linearly dependent, we would have an identity of form

$$x^{m_1}[1 + p(x)] = cx^{m_2}[1 + q(x)],$$

where $p(x)$ and $q(x)$ are continuous at $x = 0$ and $c \neq 0$. Divide by the function on the right-hand side and let $x \to 0$ to conclude that $x^{m_1-m_2} \to c$ as $x \to 0$; show that this implies $m_1 = m_2$.]

ANSWERS

1. (a) $x = 0$, irregular; (b) $x = 0$, removable; (c) $x = 0$, regular and $x = 1$, regular; (d) $x = 3$, regular, $x = -1$, irregular.

2. (All summations, except in part (e), are with respect to s, from 1 to ∞).
   (a) $1 + \sum[(-1)^s x^{3s}/\{1 \cdot 4 \cdots (3s - 2)\}]$,
   $x^2(1 + \sum[(-1)^s x^{3s}/\{3^s s!\}])$, all x;

(b) for $x \neq 0$, $x^{-1}(1 + \sum[(-1)^s x^{2s}/\{2^s s!\}])$;
for all x, $x^2(1 + \sum[(-1)^s x^{2s}/\{5 \cdot 7 \cdots (2s+3)\}])$;

(c) $1 + \sum[(-1)^s x^{3s}/\{3^s s! 1 \cdot 4 \cdots (3s-2)\}]$, all x,
and $x^2(1 + \sum[(-1)^s x^{3s}/\{3^s s! 5 \cdot 8 \cdots (3s+2)\}])$, all x;

(d) $x + \frac{6}{5}x^2 + \frac{9}{20}x^3$, all x, and $x^{1/3}(1 + \sum[(-1)^s x^s (-8)(-5) \cdots (3s-11)/\{3^s s!\}])$, $0 < |x| < 1$;

(e) $1 + \frac{2}{3}x$, all x, and $x^{-1/2}(1 + 3x + \frac{1}{2}x^2 + 3\sum_{s=3}^{\infty}[(-1)^s x^s/\{s!(2s-3)(2s-1)\}])$, $|x| > 0$.

4. (b) $(\cos \log |x| \pm i \sin \log |x|)(1 + \sum_{s=1}^{\infty} (-1)^s x^s (\pm i)(1 \pm i) \cdots (s - 1 \pm i)]/\{(1 \pm 2i) \cdots (s^2 \pm 2is)\}])$, $x \neq 0$;

(c) $\cos(\log|x|)[1 - \frac{2}{5}x + \frac{1}{10}x^2 - (17/780)x^3 + \cdots] + \sin(\log|x|)[\frac{1}{5}x - \frac{1}{20}x^2 + (6/780)x^3 + \cdots]$,
$\sin(\log|x|)[1 - \frac{2}{5}x + \frac{1}{10}x^2 - (17/780)x^3 + \cdots] - \cos(\log|x|)[\frac{1}{5}x - \frac{1}{20}x^2 + (6/780)x^3 + \cdots]$.

5. (a) Indicial equation has only one root and series diverges for $x \neq 0$, (b) indicial equation has no roots.

9. (Summations are over s, from 1 to ∞).

(a) $x(1 + \sum[(-1)^s x^{-3s}/\{3^s s! 1 \cdot 4 \cdots (3s-2)\}])$,
$x^{-1}(1 + \sum[(-1)^s x^{-3s}/\{3^s s! 5 \cdot 8 \cdots (3s+2)\}])$, $x \neq 0$;

(b) $1 - [2/(3x)]$, $x^{1/2}(1 + \sum[(-1)^s x^{-s} 3 \cdot 1 \cdots (5-2s)/\{s! 1 \cdot 3 \cdots (2s-1)\}])$, $x \neq 0$.

SUGGESTED REFERENCES

1. Coddington, Earl A., and Levinson, Norman, *Theory of Ordinary Differential Equations*. New York: McGraw-Hill, 1955.

2. Jordan, Károly, *Calculus of Finite Differences*. New York: Chelsea, 1947.

3. Kaplan, Wilfred, *Advanced Calculus*. Reading, Mass.: Addison-Wesley, 1952.

4. Picard, Emile, *Traité d'Analyse* (3 vols.), 3rd ed. Paris: Gauthier-Villars, 1922, 1925, 1928.

5. Rainville, Earl D., *Intermediate Differential Equations*. New York: John Wiley and Sons, Inc., 1943.

6. Whittaker, E. T., and Watson, G. N., *A Course of Modern Analysis*, 4th ed. Cambridge, Eng.: Cambridge University Press, 1940.

CHAPTER 10

NUMERICAL METHODS

10–1 General remarks. In particular applications we are often required to tabulate a solution of a differential equation over a given interval. If an explicit formula for the solution has been found, we can use the formula, with tables of sines, cosines, logarithms, etc., to carry out the tabulation. If the solution is known in series form, the series itself becomes an explicit formula from which the solution can be computed to any desired accuracy (Chapter 9).

If no explicit formula has been found, we can consider the differential equation itself as a formula that enables us to evaluate the solution. One way of carrying this out is the method of *step-by-step integration* described in Section 1–5. In this chapter several alternative procedures are described. It will be seen that all the methods are closely related to the method of power series. Even when a series solution is available, the new methods may turn out to provide the desired accuracy with considerably less effort; indeed, they may be easier to use than an explicit formula for the solution.

With the development of digital computers of extreme rapidity, the interest in numerical methods has become very great. We have almost reached a stage where we can consider all solutions of all differential equations as tabulated and available for use. The table is "stored" in the computer. To get the table out for examination, we need only feed the correct program to the computer. From this point of view, finding solutions to differential equations is no more challenging than finding a square root or logarithm. We do of course need to learn how to prepare a program for the computer; that is one of the goals of the present chapter. Furthermore, the tabulated or graphed solution may appear to be very complicated, and a deeper mathematical study of the differential equation may provide better answers to questions about the nature of the solutions.

10–2 Step-by-step integration. Let us review briefly the method of step-by-step integration. For the equation

$$y' = F(x, y) \tag{10–1}$$

we consider the corresponding *difference equation*

$$\Delta y = F(x, y)\,\Delta x. \tag{10–2}$$

If (x_0, y_0) is the given initial point, we then compute successively the values $y_1, y_2, \ldots$, at $x_0 + \Delta x, x_0 + 2\Delta x, \ldots$, by the formulas

$$y_1 = y_0 + F(x_0, y_0)\,\Delta x, \qquad y_2 = y_1 + F(x_1, y_1)\,\Delta x, \qquad \ldots \tag{10–3}$$

The increment Δx can also be varied from step to step.

The step-by-step procedure corresponds to a series method that uses only terms up to degree 1. For if $y = f(x)$ is the solution sought, then

$$f(x_0) = y_0, \qquad f(x_0 + \Delta x) = f(x_0) + f'(x_0)\,\Delta x + f''(x_0)\,\frac{\overline{\Delta x}^2}{2} + \cdots,$$

$$\Delta y = f(x_0 + \Delta x) - f(x_0) = f'(x_0)\,\Delta x + \cdots = F(x_0, y_0)\,\Delta x + \cdots$$

Unless the series is very rapidly convergent, the error made by omitting terms of second and higher degree will be large; however, if Δx is very small, the error in turn will be small. Making Δx smaller requires more steps if y is to be found over a given interval. However, this is the only way to ensure accuracy. As $\Delta x \to 0$, the errors all approach 0 over the interval. By an elaboration of the reasoning of Section 9–4 to 9–6 of ODE, we can determine how small Δx must be in order to ensure that all errors are less than a given amount. In practice we usually settle this question by experiment. We compute with a given value of Δx over a given interval; then we recompute with a smaller value of Δx, say one-half of the first. If the values of y are changed to a negligible extent, we consider the solution to have been found to desired accuracy.

The method of step-by-step integration can be extended to systems of first order equations:

$$\frac{dy_i}{dx} = F_i(x, y_1, \ldots, y_n) \qquad (i = 1, \ldots, n). \tag{10–4}$$

The corresponding difference equations are

$$\Delta y_i = F_i(x, y_1, \ldots, y_n)\,\Delta x \qquad (i = 1, \ldots, n). \tag{10–5}$$

The method also extends to equations of higher order. For example, the equation

$$y'' = F(x, y, y')$$

is replaced by the system

$$\frac{dy_1}{dx} = y_2, \qquad \frac{dy_2}{dx} = F(x, y_1, y_2),$$

which is then analyzed as a special case of (10–4).

10–3 Series solution. For purposes of comparison we give here the series solution of Eq. (10–1) through terms of degree 4, as computed by the method of Section 9–1. With $h = \Delta x$, we find (Prob. 7 below)

$$\begin{aligned} y_1 = f(x_0 + h) &= y_0 + Fh + (F_x + F_yF)\,\frac{h^2}{2} \\ &+ (F_{xx} + 2FF_{xy} + F^2F_{yy} + F_xF_y + FF_y^2)\,\frac{h^3}{6} \\ &+ [F_{xxx} + 3F_xF_{xy} + F_yF_{xx} + F_xF_y^2 + F(3F_{xxy} + 5F_yF_{xy} \\ &+ 3F_xF_{yy} + F_y^3) + F^2(3F_{xyy} + 4F_yF_{yy}) + F_{yyy}F^3]\,\frac{h^4}{24} + \cdots, \end{aligned} \tag{10–6}$$

where F, $F_x = \partial F/\partial x$, . . . are all evaluated at (x_0, y_0).

10–4 Heun's method. For the equation

$$y' = F(x), \tag{10–7}$$

finding the solution $f(x)$ over the interval $x_0 \leqq x \leqq b$, with $y_0 = f(x_0)$ given, is equivalent to evaluating a definite integral:

$$f(x) = y_0 + \int_{x_0}^{x} F(t)\,dt \qquad (x_0 \leqq x \leqq b). \tag{10–8}$$

The definite integral can in turn be evaluated by the *trapezoidal rule*. For example, at $x_1 = x_0 + \Delta x$,

$$f(x_1) = y_0 + \Delta x\,\frac{F(x_0) + F(x_1)}{2} = y_0 + \Delta x\,\frac{y_0' + y_1'}{2}. \tag{10–9}$$

For the more general equation $y' = F(x, y)$ we cannot apply (10–9) because the slope y_1' at (x_1, y_1) is unknown. A reasonable estimate for y_1 is provided by step-by-step integration:

$$y_1 = y_0 + F(x_0, y_0)\,\Delta x.$$

Hence a reasonable estimate for y_1' is

$$y_1' = F[x_1, y_0 + F(x_0, y_0)\,\Delta x].$$

With this expression for y_1', (10–9) gives a new value for y_1:

$$y_1 = f(x_1) = y_0 + \frac{\Delta x}{2}\,\{F(x_0, y_0) + F[x_1, y_0 + F(x_0, y_0)\,\Delta x]\}. \tag{10–10}$$

Equation (10–10) is the basis of *Heun's method*. If we write $\Delta x = h$, $x_1 = x_0 + h$, then

$$
\begin{aligned}
F[x_1, y_0 + F(x_0, y_0)h] &= F[x_0 + h, y_0 + F(x_0, y_0)h] \\
&= F + h(F_x + FF_y) \\
&\quad + \frac{h^2}{2}(F_{xx} + 2F_{xy}F + F_{yy}F^2) + \cdots,
\end{aligned}
\tag{10–11}
$$

by a Taylor series expansion (Prob. 8 below), where F, F_x, . . . are evaluated at (x_0, y_0). Hence Eq. (10–10) gives

$$
\begin{aligned}
f(x_0 + h) &= f(x_0) + \frac{h}{2}[2F + h(F_x + FF_y) + \cdots] \\
&= f(x_0) + hF + \frac{h^2}{2}(F_x + FF_y) \\
&\quad + \frac{h^3}{4}(F_{xx} + 2F_{xy}F + F_{yy}F^2) + \cdots
\end{aligned}
\tag{10–12}
$$

A comparison of Eqs. (10–12) and (10–6) shows agreement through the term of *second* degree in h. Accordingly, Heun's method can be considered an alternative to computing a series solution through terms of second degree.

The steps in application of Heun's method are summarized in the following formulas:

$$
\begin{aligned}
m_0 &= F(x_0, y_0), \\
x_1 &= x_0 + \Delta x, \\
y_1^* &= y_0 + m_0\,\Delta x, \\
m_1 &= F(x_1, y_1^*), \\
m &= \tfrac{1}{2}(m_0 + m_1), \\
\Delta y &= m\,\Delta x, \\
y_1 &= y_0 + \Delta y.
\end{aligned}
\tag{10–13}
$$

Example. The equation chosen is

$$y' = xy^2 - y,$$

with $y = 1$ for $x = 0$. Trying to obtain an accuracy of two significant figures, we seek the solution for $0 \leqq x \leqq 1$.

TABLE 10–1

x_0	y_0	x_1	m_0	y_1^*	m_1	m	Δy
0	1.000	0.5	−1.000	0.500	−0.375	−0.688	−0.344
0.5	0.656	1.0	−0.441	0.435	−0.246	−0.344	−0.172
1.0	0.484						

TABLE 10–2

x_0	y_0	x_1	m_0	y_1^*	m_1	m	Δy
0	1.000	0.25	−1.000	0.75	−0.609	−0.805	−0.201
0.25	0.799	0.50	−0.639	0.639	−0.435	−0.537	−0.134
0.50	0.665	0.75	−0.444	0.554	−0.324	−0.384	−0.096
0.75	0.569	1.00	−0.326	0.487	−0.250	−0.0288	−0.072
1.00	0.497						

In Table 10–1 Δx is chosen as 0.5; in Table 10–2 Δx is reduced to 0.25. Since there is a change in the second significant figure, we should try to reduce Δx further, say to 0.125. If this is done, we find that the results of Table 10–2 are unchanged, up to the first two significant figures; hence Table 10–2 gives satisfactory results.

If we solve the problem by a Taylor series, we find

$$y = 1 - x + x^2 - x^3 + x^4 - \cdots \tag{10–14}$$

This suggests that the solution is given exactly by

$$y = \frac{1}{1+x},$$

and substitution in the differential equation proves the surmise to be correct. Accordingly, the exact values of y at $x = 0, 0.25, \ldots$ are 1, 0.800, 0.6666 . . . , 0.5714 . . . , 0.500, in very close agreement with Table 10–2. It should be noted that the series converges only for $|x| < 1$, and hence cannot be used for the whole interval. Even for $x = 0.5$, as many as nine terms of the series are needed to give an accuracy as good as that of Table 10–2. Heun's method is equivalent to recomputation of the series, through terms of degree 2, at each successive value of x.

Heun's method can be extended to equations of higher order and to systems (Prob. 4 below).

PROBLEMS

1. For the differential equation, with initial conditions,

$$y' = x - y \qquad (y = 1 \text{ for } x = 0),$$

carry out the following steps:

(a) obtain the solution for $x = 0, 0.1, 0.2, 0.3, 0.4$ by step-by-step integration;

(b) obtain the solution for $x = 0, 0.2, 0.4$ by Heun's method;

(c) obtain the solution for $x = 0, 0.1, 0.2, 0.3, 0.4$ by Heun's method; discuss the number of significant figures in the result;

(d) obtain the Taylor series solution up to terms of degree 4 and evaluate for $x = 0, 0.1, 0.2, 0.3, 0.4$;

(e) verify that the exact solution is $y = 2e^{-x} + x - 1$ and evaluate at $x = 0, 0.1, 0.2, 0.3, 0.4$.

2. Carry out the program of Prob. 1 for the following differential equation with initial conditions:

$$y' = 1 + (x + x^2)e^{-y} \qquad (y = 0 \text{ for } x = 0).$$

In part (e) show that $y = \log(4e^x - 3 - 3x - x^2)$ is the exact solution.

3. Carry out the program of Prob. 1 for the following differential equation with initial conditions:

$$y' = y^2e^{-x} + \tfrac{1}{2}y \qquad (y = \tfrac{1}{2} \text{ for } x = 0).$$

In part (e) show that $y = \frac{1}{2}e^x$ is the exact solution.

4. Show that the reasoning which leads to Heun's method can be extended to a system

$$\frac{dy}{dx} = F(x, y, z), \qquad \frac{dz}{dx} = G(x, y, z)$$

to yield the following rule. Given (x_0, y_0, z_0) and Δx, we evaluate Δy, Δz by the rules

$$\Delta y = \tfrac{1}{2}\,\Delta x[m_0 + F(x_0 + \Delta x, y_0 + m_0\,\Delta x, z_0 + n_0\,\Delta x)],$$

$$\Delta z = \tfrac{1}{2}\,\Delta x[n_0 + G(x_0 + \Delta x, y_0 + m_0\,\Delta x, z_0 + n_0\,\Delta x)],$$

where $m_0 = F(x_0, y_0, z_0)$, $n_0 = G(x_0, y_0, z_0)$.

5. Apply the method of Prob. 4 to evaluate the solution of the problem

$$\frac{dy}{dx} = y - 4z, \quad \frac{dz}{dx} = y - 3z \qquad (y = 2, z = 1 \text{ for } x = 0)$$

for $x = 0, 0.5, 1$. Compare the results with the exact solution $y = 2e^{-x}$, $z = e^{-x}$.

6. Given the second order equation, with initial conditions,

$$y'' + x^2 y = 0 \qquad (y = 1, y' = 1 \text{ for } x = 0),$$

(a) replace by the system $y' = z$, $z' = -x^2 y$ and obtain the solution as in Prob. 4 for $x = 0, 0.5, 1$.

(b) Obtain the Taylor series solution through terms of degree 5 and compare with the result of part (a).

7. Obtain the series expansion (10–6) for the solution of the equation $y' = F(x, y)$ with given initial values. [*Hint:* As in Prob. 3 following Section 9–1, we have

$$y' = F, \qquad y'' = F_x + F_y y' = F_x + FF_y, \qquad \ldots]$$

8. Obtain the series expansion (10–11). [*Hint:* As in Reference 4, page 370,

$$F(x_0 + h, y_0 + k) = F + hF_x + kF_y + \frac{1}{2!}(h^2 F_{xx} + 2hkF_{xy} + k^2 F_{yy})$$
$$+ \frac{1}{3!}(h^3 F_{xxx} + 3h^2 k F_{xxy} + 3hk^2 F_{xyy} + k^3 F_{yyy}) + \cdots,$$

where $F, F_x, F_y, \ldots$ are evaluated at (x_0, y_0).]

ANSWERS

1. (a) 1, 0.9, 0.82, 0.758, 0.712; (b) 1, 0.840, 0.745; (c) 1, 0.910, 0.8381, 0.7825, 0.7417; (d) 1, 0.9097, 0.8375, 0.7817, 0.7408; (e) 1, 0.9097, 0.8375, 0.7817, 0.7406.

2. (a) 0, 0.1, 0.210, 0.329, 0.457; (b) 0, 0.220. 0.474; (c) 0, 0.105, 0.220, 0.343, 0.474; (d) and (e) same as (c).

3. (a) 0.5, 0.55, 0.605, 0.665, 0.731; (b) 0.5, 0.609, 0.742; (c) 0.5, 0.553, 0.611, 0.675, 0.746; (d) and (e) same as (c).

5. $y = 2, 1.25, 0.781$, $z = 1, 0.625, 0.391$. Exact solution: $y = 2, 1.213, 0.736$, $z = 1, 0.607, 0.368$.

6. (a) $y = 1, 1.50, 1.91$, $z = 1, 0.91, 0.32$. (b) $y = 1 + x - (x^4/12) - (x^5/20)$, $y = 1, 1.49, 1.87$, $z = 1, 0.94, 0.42$.

10–5 Runge's method. Following the reasoning which led to Heun's method, we can try to attain greater accuracy by using *Simpson's rule.* For the area under the curve $y = F(x)$ from x_0 to $x_0 + h$, the rule gives the expression

$$\frac{h}{6}\left[F(x_0) + 4F\left(x_0 + \frac{h}{2}\right) + F(x_0 + h)\right].$$

Hence for the differential equation

$$y' = F(x, y),$$

we are led to the formula

$$\Delta y = \frac{\Delta x}{6}\left[y_0' + 4y_1' + y_2'\right],$$

where $y_0' = F(x_0, y_0)$ is the slope of the solution at $x = x_0$, y_1' is an estimate for the slope at $x_0 + \frac{1}{2}\Delta x$, and y_2' is an estimate for the slope at $x_0 + \Delta x$.

To obtain y_1', y_2', the Runge method uses the formulas

$$\begin{aligned} m_0 &= F(x_0, y_0), \\ m_1 &= F(x_0 + \tfrac{1}{2}\Delta x,\ y_0 + \tfrac{1}{2}m_0\,\Delta x), \\ m_2 &= F(x_0 + \Delta x,\ y_0 + m_0\,\Delta x), \\ m_3 &= F(x_0 + \Delta x,\ y_0 + m_2\,\Delta x). \end{aligned} \tag{10–15}$$

Then $y_0' = m_0$ and y_1' is chosen as m_1, y_2' as m_3 (*not* as m_2). Finally,

$$\Delta y = \frac{\Delta x}{6}(m_0 + 4m_1 + m_3) = m\,\Delta x. \tag{10–16}$$

The geometric meaning of the slopes $m_0, \ldots, m_3$ is shown in Fig. 10–1.

Taylor series expansions can be used to show that Runge's method is in agreement with the series solution through terms of degree 3 (Prob. 4 below). Hence it should give greater accuracy than Heun's method.

As an example we choose the equation, with initial condition,

$$y' = x - y \qquad (y = 1 \text{ for } x = 0). \tag{10–17}$$

This is the same as Prob. 1 following Section 10–3, so that we can compare the results obtained there with those given by the Runge method. The numerical work is shown in Table 10–3, with $\Delta x = 0.2$. The value obtained at $x = 0.2$ is 0.83733. Heun's method with $\Delta x = 0.2$ gives 0.840, and with $\Delta x = 0.1$ gives 0.8381. The exact solution gives 0.83746.

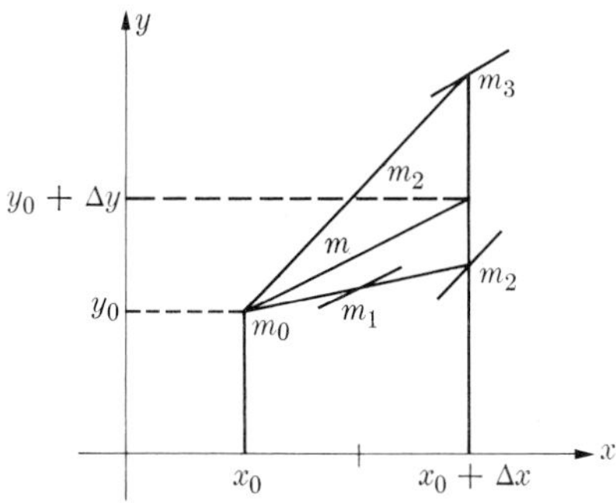

FIG. 10–1. Slopes used in Runge's method.

TABLE 10–3

x_0	0	0.2
y_0	1	0.83733
m_0	-1	-0.63733
$x_0 + \frac{1}{2}\,\Delta x$	0.1	0.3
$y_0 + \frac{1}{2}m_0\,\Delta x$	0.9	etc.
m_1	-0.8	
$x_0 + \Delta x$	0.2	
$y_0 + m_0\,\Delta x$	0.8	
m_2	-0.6	
$y_0 + m_2\,\Delta x$	0.88	
m_3	-0.68	
m	-0.81333	
Δy	-0.16267	

Runge's method can also be extended to systems and to equations of higher order (Prob. 5 below). The method has been modified by Kutta and others to give several procedures which are called *Runge-Kutta methods.* For descriptions of these see, for example, Chapter 5 of Reference 6 and Chapter 6 of Reference 10.

10–6 Milne's method. The methods of Heun and Runge have the defect that certain slopes are first estimated by extrapolation and then recomputed. Since computation of slopes is generally the most time-consuming part of the work, it is desirable to find a method which computes each slope only once. Milne's method has this advantage; instead of extrapolating, we use slopes already found in order to find the best estimate for Δy.

Let the differential equation $y' = F(x, y)$ be given, with initial point (x_0, y_0). Let us suppose that the successive points (x_1, y_1), (x_2, y_2), (x_3, y_3) have already been found, where $x_1 = x_0 + \Delta x$, $x_2 = x_0 + 2\,\Delta x$, $x_3 = x_0 + 3\,\Delta x$. The values y_1, y_2, y_3 can be found, for example, by Runge's method, or by infinite series; Milne's formula cannot be used to find these three values. It does give the succeeding values $y_4, y_5, \ldots$ In each case, four successive values are used to compute the fifth.

Given y_0, y_1, y_2, y_3, we now find y_4 as follows. We write

$$m_1 = F(x_1, y_1), \qquad m_2 = F(x_2, y_2), \qquad m_3 = F(x_3, y_3); \tag{10–18}$$

then

$$y_4 = y_0 + \frac{4\,\Delta x}{3}\,(2m_1 - m_2 + 2m_3). \tag{10–19}$$

It can be verified that this formula gives a result in agreement with the series solution, up to terms of degree 3. Indeed, if we seek a formula of the type

$$y_4 = y_0 + \Delta x(Am_1 + Bm_2 + Cm_3),$$

the requirement that the solution agree with the series solution up to terms of degree 3 leads to three conditions on A, B, C, from which we find $A = \frac{8}{3}$, $B = -\frac{4}{3}$, $C = \frac{8}{3}$, so that (10–19) is obtained (Prob. 6 below). This suggests generalizations of Milne's formula to achieve greater accuracy.

EXAMPLE. We consider again the problem of Eq. (10–17). The values of y for $x = 0.1, 0.2, 0.3$ are taken as the exact values (assumed to have been found to four significant figures by Runge's method). The values of y at $x = 0.4$ and 0.5 are computed by the Milne formula. Thus, for $x = 0.4$, $y_0 = 1$ and $m_1 = -0.8097$, $m_2 = -0.6375$, $m_3 = -0.4816$; for $x = 0.5$, $m_1 = -0.6375$, $m_2 = -0.4816$, $m_3 = -0.3407$, and $y_0 = 0.9097$. The results are shown in Table 10–4. The exact values for $x = 0.4$ and 0.5 are 0.740640 and 0.713062, respectively.

TABLE 10–4

x	0	0.1	0.2	0.3	0.4	0.5
y	1	0.9097	0.8375	0.7816	0.7407	0.7131
$F(x, y)$		−0.8097	−0.6375	−0.4816	−0.3407	

10–7 Accuracy of results. The problem of evaluating the accuracy of the tabulated solution is not particularly simple. The simplest test is to reduce the size of the Δx and determine whether the values of y are changed to the number of significant figures we wish to have. There are other check formulas, based on recalculation of the solution by the trapezoidal or Simpson's rule (or some generalization of these). We can return to the series solution and use the estimates of Sections 9–4 to 9–6 of ODE; these give reasonable bounds for methods which agree with the series solution up to terms of kth degree.

One basic difficulty is the accumulation of errors. If the solution is to be computed over a long interval of x, the errors at each stage influence those at the next, so that there is considerably less accuracy at the end than at the beginning. Under some favorable circumstances the computation is stable and errors introduced at each stage have little effect after a few stages have been passed. This can be shown graphically for the case of step-by-step integration (Fig. 10–2). If all solutions approach a given one as x increases, so that there is essentially a unique output, as in Section 6–2, then the step-by-step solution will also remain close to the output, so that errors will not accumulate.

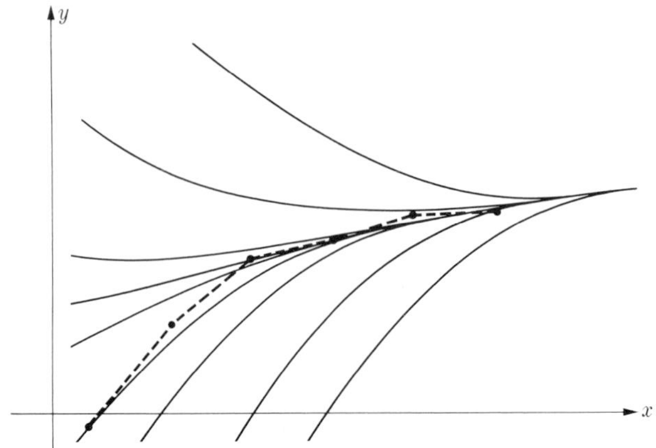

FIG. 10–2. Stability of numerical method.

When accuracy is very important, we must pay considerable attention to errors that arise from rounding off numbers in decimal form. We must compute to at least one and perhaps several decimal places beyond the one at which accuracy is desired. In a long computation, errors due to rounding off can accumulate to a disastrous extent.

10–8 Use of analog computers. The methods described in this chapter are ideally suited to digital computers (Reference 9). For some problems the relevant information can be obtained much more easily by means of differential analyzers or their most modern form, analog computers (see References 3 and 8). These are physical mechanisms which are built to obey given differential equations. Their accuracy is limited by the physical nature of the components used; however, in skilled hands they can give very accurate results. The computers are very flexible, so that we can modify coefficients in a differential equation or change initial conditions with great ease. Families of solution curves can be rapidly produced and qualitative features of the solutions noted visually.

PROBLEMS

1. Given the differential equation $y' = x + y$, with initial condition $y = 1$ for $x = 0$, determine the values of y for $x = 0.1, 0.2, 0.3, 0.4, 0.5$
   (a) by step-by-step integration, $\Delta x = 0.1$;
   (b) by infinite series, using terms up to degree 5;
   (c) by Runge's method;
   (d) from the exact solution.

2. The following values of y on the exact solution of Prob. 1 are found from tables: 1.11034, 1.24281, 1.39972, for $x = 0.1, 0.2, 0.3$. Use Milne's method to obtain the values of y for $x = 0.4, 0.5$ and compare with the results of Prob. 1.

3. Let the differential equation

$$y' = xy + xy^3$$

be given, with $y = 1$ for $x = 0$. Let it be known that the values of y for $x = 0.1, 0.2, 0.3$ are 1.010, 1.043, 1.104.

(a) Find the value of y for $x = 0.4$ by Runge's method.
(b) Find the value of y for $x = 0.4$ by Milne's method.

4. Let $h = \Delta x$. Show from the definitions (10–15) that by series expansions (Prob. 8 following Section 10–4)

$$m_0 = F, \qquad m_1 = F + \frac{a}{2}h + \frac{b}{8}h^2 + \cdots, \qquad m_2 = F + ah + \frac{b}{2}h^2 + \cdots,$$

where $a = F_x + FF_y$, $b = F_{xx} + 2FF_{xy} + F_{yy}F^2$, $c = F_xF_y + FF_y^2$, and $F, F_x, \ldots$ are all evaluated at (x_0, y_0). Show further that

$$\begin{aligned} m_3 &= m_0 + h(F_x + m_2F_y) + \frac{h^2}{2}(F_{xx} + 2m_2F_{xy} + m_2^2F_{yy}) + \cdots \\ &= F + ah + \frac{b + 2c}{2}h^2 + \cdots \end{aligned}$$

Hence conclude that

$$m = F + \frac{a}{2}h + \frac{b + c}{6}h^2 + \cdots,$$

$$y = y_0 + Fh + \frac{a}{2}h^2 + \frac{b + c}{6}h^3 + \cdots$$

and verify that this is in agreement with the series solution (10–6) through terms of degree 3.

5. Runge's method for a system

$$\frac{dy}{dx} = F(x, y, z), \quad \frac{dz}{dx} = G(x, y, z) \qquad (y = y_0, z = z_0 \text{ for } x = x_0)$$

gives the increments Δy, Δz corresponding to the increment $\Delta x = h$ by the following formulas:

$$\begin{aligned} m_0 &= F(x_0, y_0, z_0), \qquad n_0 = G(x_0, y_0, z_0), \\ x_1^* &= x_0 + \tfrac{1}{2}h, \qquad y_1^* = y_0 + \tfrac{1}{2}m_0h, \qquad z_1^* = z_0 + \tfrac{1}{2}n_0h, \\ x_2^* &= x_0 + h, \qquad y_2^* = y_0 + m_0h, \qquad z_2^* = z_0 + n_0h, \\ m_i &= F(x_i^*, y_i^*, z_i^*), \qquad n_i = G(x_i^*, y_i^*, z_i^*) \qquad (i = 1, 2), \\ m_3 &= F(x_2^*, y_0 + m_2h, z_0 + n_2h), \qquad n_3 = G(x_2^*, y_0 + m_2h, z_0 + n_2h), \\ m &= \tfrac{1}{6}(m_0 + 4m_1 + m_3), \qquad n = \tfrac{1}{6}(n_0 + 4n_1 + n_3), \\ \Delta y &= mh, \qquad \Delta z = nh. \end{aligned}$$

It can be verified, as in Prob. 4, that these formulas give values that are in agreement with the series solution through terms of degree 3.

Apply Runge's method to obtain the values of y and z for $x = 0.2$ for the system

$$\frac{dy}{dx} = xy^2 + z, \quad \frac{dz}{dx} = xz^2 + y \qquad (y = 0,\ z = -1 \text{ for } x = 0).$$

6. To compare Milne's method with a series solution, we consider expansions about (x_2, y_2) and assume that the values y_0, y_1, y_2, y_3 are exact. Let $\Delta x = h$, and

$$a = F_x + F_yF, \qquad b = F_{xx} + 2FF_{xy} + F_{yy}F^2, \qquad c = F_xF_y + FF_y^2,$$

where $F, F_x, \ldots$ are all evaluated at (x_2, y_2). Show that by Eq. (10–6)

$$y_1 = y_2 - Fh + \frac{a}{2}h^2 - \frac{b+c}{6}h^3 + \cdots,$$

and hence

$$m_1 = F(x_1, y_1) = F(x_2 - h, y_2 - Fh + \frac{a}{2}h^2 + \cdots)$$
$$= F - ah + \frac{b+c}{2}h^2 + \cdots$$

Similarly show that $m_2 = F$,

$$m_3 = F + ah + \frac{b+c}{2}h^2 + \cdots,$$

and by Eq. (10–6) that

$$y_0 = y_2 - 2Fh + 2ah^2 - \tfrac{4}{3}(b + c)h^3 + \cdots$$

Let

$$y_4 = y_0 + h(Am_1 + Bm_2 + Cm_3).$$

Show that the requirement that y_4 agree with the series solution of Eq. (10–6):

$$y_4 = y_2 + 2Fh + 2ah^2 + \tfrac{4}{3}(b + c)h^3 + \cdots$$

through the term in h^3 leads to the equations

$$A + B + C = 4, \qquad A - C = 0, \qquad A + C = \tfrac{16}{3}$$

and that hence $A = C = \frac{8}{3}$, $B = -\frac{4}{3}$.

7. Milne's method can be extended to the system

$$\frac{dy}{dx} = F(x, y, z), \quad \frac{dz}{dx} = G(x, y, z) \qquad (y = y_0,\ z = z_0 \text{ for } x = x_0)$$

as follows. Let the solution points (x_i, y_i, z_i) be known for $i = 1, 2, 3$, where

$x_1 = x_0 + \Delta x, x_2 = x_0 + 2\,\Delta x, x_3 = x_0 + 3\,\Delta x$. Let

$$m_i = F(x_i, y_i, z_i), \quad n_i = G(x_i, y_i, z_i) \qquad (i = 1, 2, 3).$$

Then we choose

$$y_4 = y_0 + \tfrac{4}{3}\,\Delta x(2m_1 - m_2 + 2m_3),$$

$$z_4 = z_0 + \tfrac{4}{3}\,\Delta x(2n_1 - n_2 + 2n_3).$$

Apply Milne's method in order to tabulate $\sin x$ as solution of the equation $y'' + y = 0$. To this end we consider the system $y' = z, z' = -y$ and assume the values (0, 0, 1), (0.1, 0.0998, 0.9950), (0.2, 0.1987, 0.9801), (0.3, 0.2955, 0.9553) known. We then compute y and z for $x = 0.4, 0.5$, etc.

ANSWERS

1. (a) 1.1, 1.22, 1.362, 1.528, 1.721; (b) 1.11034, 1.24281, 1.39972, 1.58364, 1.79740; (c) 1.11033, 1.24279, 1.39969, 1.58361, 1.79739; (d) exact solution is $2e^x - x - 1$; values are 1.11034, 1.24281, 1.39972, 1.58364, 1.79744.

2. 1.58364, 1.79743.

3. (a) 1.198, (b) 1.192.

5. $y = -0.19994$. $z = -0.99995$.

7. $x = 0.4, y = 0.3894, z = 0.9211; x = 0.5, y = 0.4794, z = 0.8776$.

SUGGESTED REFERENCES

1. Buckingham, R. A., *Numerical Methods*. New York: Pitman, 1957.
2. Collatz, Lothar, *Numerische Behandlung von Differentialgleichungen*, 2nd ed. Berlin: Springer, 1955.
3. Johnson, Clarence L., *Analog Computer Techniques*. New York: McGraw-Hill, 1956.
4. Kaplan, Wilfred, *Advanced Calculus*. Reading, Mass.: Addison-Wesley, 1952.
5. Levy, H., and Baggott, E. A., *Numerical Studies in Differential Equations*, Vol. 1. London: Watts and Co., 1934.
6. Milne, W. E., *Numerical Solution of Differential Equations*. New York: John Wiley and Sons, Inc., 1953.
7. Scarborough, James B., *Numerical Mathematical Analysis*, 2nd ed. Baltimore: Johns Hopkins Press, 1950.
8. Soroka, Walter W., *Analog Methods in Computation and Simulation*. New York: McGraw-Hill, 1954.
9. Wilkes, M. V., Wheeler, D. J., and Gill, Stanley, *The Preparation of Programs for an Electronic Digital Computer*, 2nd ed. Reading, Mass.: Addison-Wesley, 1957.
10. Willers, F. A., *Practical Analysis*, transl. by R. T. Beyer. New York: Dover, 1948.

INDEX

INDEX